Plate 1 *A composite scene from* James and the Giant Peach. *Plates 2 (a)–(e) show the elements making up Plate 1.*

Plate 2 *(b) The giant mechanical shark.*

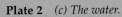

Plate 2 *(c) The water.*

Plates 1, 2b, and 2c from *James and the Giant Peach* © Disney Enterprises, Inc.

Plate 2 *(a) The peach.*

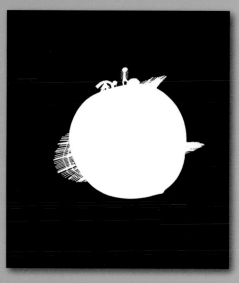

Plate 2 *(e) A matte of the peach.*

Plate 2 *(d) The sky.*

Plate 3 *The primary test image. Plates 4 (a)–(c) show the channels composing the primary test image.*

Plate 4 *(a) Red channel.*

Plate 4 *(b) Green channel.*

Plate 4 *(c) Blue channel.*

Plate 5 *The test image after being reduced to a color resolution of four bits per channel.*

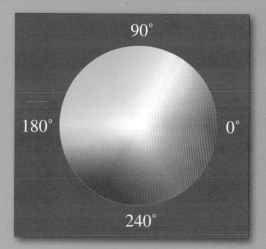

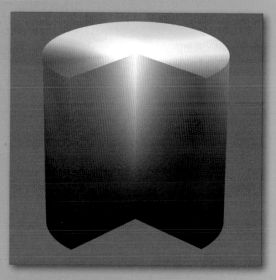

Plate 6 *HSV color representation. (a) Circular color palette representing hue and saturation.*

Plate 6 *(b) Three-dimensional color cylinder representing value along the third axis.*

Plate 7 *The test image with a brightness of 2.0 applied.*

Plate 8 *Result of RGB multiplication of (0.1, 1.25, 1.0) on test image.*

Plate 9 *Result of adding 0.2 to every pixel in the test image.*

Plate 10 *Result of gamma correction of 1.7 on the test image.*

Plate 11 *Test image showing result of (a) simple contrast operation.*

Plate 11 *(b) smoother contrast operation.*

Plate 12 *Test image with saturation reduced by approximately 50%.*

Plate 13 *Test image with hues rotated 180°.*

Plate 14 *Look-up table curves from Figure 3.9 applied to test image.*

Plate 15 *Saturation modified based on certain hues.*

Plate 16 *Result of applying a conditional arithmetic expression to the test image.*

Plate 17 *The effects of increased sharpening. (a) Original image.*

Plate 17 *(b) Image after some sharpening has been applied.*

Plate 17 *(c) Image with excessive sharpening. Note the ringing along transition areas.*

Plate 18 *Source images for illustrating multisource operators. (a) Foreground image.*

Plate 18 *(b) Background image.*

Plate 19 *Image resulting from adding Plates 18a and 18b.*

Plate 20 *Matte image.*

Plate 21 *Image resulting from placing Plate 18a over 18b using the matte image in Plate 20.*

Plate 22 *Premultiplied image, produced by multiplying Plate 18a by Plate 20.*

Plate 23 *Steps in the Over process. (a) An inverted matte image.*

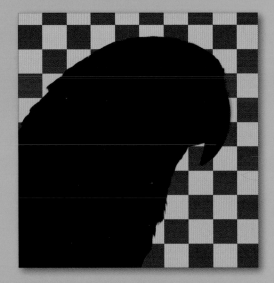

Plate 23 *(b) The image produced by multiplying the image from Plate 18b by Plate 23a.*

CHAPTER TWO

The Digital Representation of Visual Information

⌒

Digital compositing is, ultimately, about working with images. Before we can effectively discuss any of the basic tools of compositing, therefore, we need to build up a bit of background knowledge and vocabulary concerning how images are dealt with in the medium we are using. We initially cover, very briefly, some basic terms and concepts.

For the topic of **digital** compositing, an obvious issue is how the digital image data is stored and represented. Although this topic could conceivably be extended to include everything from binary data coding to disk formatting, we try to present information that will directly affect the decisions a typical compositing artist will need to make on a regular basis. There are dozens (or maybe hundreds) of different, reasonably well-defined ways to store an image digitally. But, in day to day usage, most of these methods have several things in common. Many of the concepts that are covered in the beginning of this chapter will be trivial and obvious to someone who has spent any time working with digital images, but it is suggested that you at least skim the sections because certain terms are introduced and defined that will then be used throughout the book.

IMAGE GENERATION

Before we can discuss how image data is stored, we need to cover where the images come from in the first place. Although the digital compositor will eventually be dealing with images that have all been converted to some specific digital format, the procedures that were used to initially create or capture those images may vary quite a bit. Elements that will be used for digital compositing generally come from one of the following three places:

1. Hand-painted or human-generated elements. These can range in complexity from a simple black-and-white matte to a photorealistic **matte painting** of a real or imaginary setting. Although in the past much of this type of artwork would have been generated outside the computer using more traditional painting methods, the advent of extremely powerful paint programs has made it far more common to hand-paint elements directly in the computer. An example of this is shown in Plate 60, a matte painting that was created for the film *Speed*, from 20th Century Fox.

2. Computer-generated images. Although no images are truly "computer generated," since their origin can eventually be traced back to a human being who defines a set of algorithms for the computer to use, this term is usually used to refer to elements that have been created or rendered using a specialized 2D or 3D computer animation package. In the *James and the Giant Peach* example from Chapter 1, the mechanical shark and the stylized water were both computer-generated images.

3. Images that have been **scanned** into the computer from some other source (typically film or video).

Breaking this topic up into three categories is extremely simplified—computer-generated elements may contain scanned or painted elements (used as texture maps, for instance), matte paintings often borrow heavily from other scanned sources, and live-action elements may be augmented with hand-painted **wire removals** or **effects animations**.

The first source of imagery, hand-painted elements, will be touched on throughout the body of this book as needed. We will not, however, spend a great deal of time detailing specific software or techniques. There are a number of popular software packages for hand-painting elements in the computer, some of whose manufacturers are listed in Appendix B.

The subject of how computer-generated (CG) images (our second potential source of imagery) are defined and rendered will not be covered in great detail, although there are a few sections of this book (notably in Chapter 15) that give some suggestions about how to ease the integration of 3D elements into composited scenes. Manufacturers of several popular software packages for producing CG images are also mentioned in Appendix B, and there are numerous others.

Some excellent reference works already exist on both of these topics, a few of which are mentioned in the bibliography at the end of this book. Not only are there a variety of books that cover digital painting, modeling, animation, and rendering from a generalized perspective, but there are also specific "how-to" guides for many of the more common software packages.

The third source of imagery—scanned/digitized "live-action" footage—is still probably the most common source with which we deal in digital compositing. There are a myriad of different formats that this source imagery can come from, some of them discussed in greater detail in Chapter 10 and Appendix D.

Understanding the methods that were used to generate a particular image sequence can be extremely important to a compositor. There are a number of distinguishing factors between CG elements and scanned live-action images in terms of how they are used in the compositing process. For instance, rendered CG elements can usually be generated with additional information that may be used to aid their placement into an existing scene. Information such as an additional matte channel (covered more in Chapter 4) or Z-depth information (Chapter 15) will allow the compositor to bypass or simplify several integration steps that are otherwise necessary when dealing with simple scanned images. More important, there needs to be a recognition that digital images that are created from live-action sources are actually just limited **samples** of the real-world scene. There is always a limit to the amount of detail and the range of color and brightness any given image capture technique can provide, a fact that should always be kept in mind as one is working with these images. This point is discussed a bit more in Chapter 11, and Chapter 15 has several sections that consider the relationship between captured images and the real world.

Pixels, Components, and Channels

Digital images are stored as an array of individual dots, or **pixels**. Each pixel will have a certain amount of information associated with it, and although it is still common to present a pixel as having a specific color, in reality there may be a great deal of additional information that is associated with each pixel in an image. But rather than taking the typical computer-graphics route of discussing all the possible characteristics of a pixel first and then looking at how these combine to make an image, we want to think of a color image as a layered collection of simpler images, or **channels**.

Digital images *are*, of course, a rectangular array of pixels. And each pixel does, of course, have a characteristic color associated with it. But the color of a pixel is actually a function of three specific **components** of that pixel: the red, green, and blue (usually simplified to R,G, and B) components.[1] By using a combination of

---

[1] There are any number of different ways to represent color, but because of its prevalence in the digital world we will primarily deal with the RGB model. A bit later we will talk about another model that represents color via hue, saturation, and value parameters.

these three primary colors at different intensities, we can represent the full range of the visible spectrum for each pixel.

If we look at a single component (red, let's say) of every pixel in an image and view *that* as a whole image, we have what is known as a specific **channel** of the complete color image. Thus, instead of referring to an image as a collection of colored pixels, we can think of it as a three-layer combination of primary-colored channels.

Consider an image such as that shown in Plate 3. The next three images, Plates 4a, 4b, and 4c, show the red channel, the green channel, and the blue channel of this sample image. In this case, we've tinted the individual channels to reflect the color they are associated with, and it is convenient to think of the channels as being transparent slides that can be layered (or projected) together to result in a full-color image. But these channels can also be thought of as monochrome images in their own right. Consider Figure 2.1, which is the same image as Plate 4a, the red channel, but without any colored tint applied. This monochrome representation is really more accurate, in the sense that a channel has no inherent color, and could conceivably be used for any channel in an image.

The reason for dealing with images in this fashion is twofold. First, single pixels are simply too small a unit to deal with individually; in general, compositing artists spend about as much time worrying about individual pixels as a painter might spend worrying about an individual bristle on her paintbrush. But more

Figure 2.1   *Monochrome equivalent of the test image's red channel (see Plate 4a).*

important, dealing with complete channels gives a great deal of additional control and allows for the use of techniques that were pioneered in the days when optical compositing was being developed. Color film actually consists of three different emulsion layers, each sensitive to either red, green, or blue light, and it became useful to photographically separate these three layers, or **records**, in order to manipulate them individually or in combination. A digital image (also known as a **bit-mapped image**) of this type will generally consist of these three color channels integrated into a single image, but it should be clear that these three channels can be thought of as separate entities that can be manipulated separately as well.

Looking at the individual channels for the image in question, we can see which areas contain large values of certain colors, and it is easy to find the correspondence in an individual channel. For instance, the background of the image—the area behind the parrot—is a fairly pure blue. If you look at the red channel of this image (Plate 4a), it should be obvious that there is essentially no red content in this area. On the other hand, the front of the head and the beak are areas with a good deal of red in them (yellow having heavy red *and* green values), which is also obvious when looking at the individual channels. Later we will see how manipulating and combining the individual channels of an image can be used for everything from color correction to matte extraction.

Spatial Resolution

A number of measurements are used to gauge the amount of information that is present in a digital image. The most obvious measurement is the number of pixels used to create the image. The larger the number of pixels that are used, the greater the **resolution** of the image. When we use the term "resolution" in this fashion, we are actually referring to the **spatial resolution** of the image. There are other types of resolutions, such as color or temporal (which will be discussed later), but the general convention is that the pixel count for an image is the primary measurement of the image's resolution.

A square image that is, for example, 500 pixels wide and 500 pixels tall has 250,000 pixels of resolution. Most images are not square, and thus it's generally more useful to speak of an image's resolution by giving the width and height in pixels. The above example would be referred to as an image that is 500 × 500, or "500 by 500." Greater spatial resolution will allow one to reproduce finer detail in the image, but it will also increase the resources needed to deal with the image.

Different media tend to work in widely different resolutions. At the low end, video games or Web pages may use images that are only 200 or 300 pixels wide. Broadcast video, depending on the standards of the country in question, is usually in the range of 700 × 500. Feature film work is generally done with an image that is approximately 2000 pixels wide, though this can vary a great deal. The process of working with various resolutions and formats will be discussed further in Chapter 10.

Some of the highest resolution requirements come from the print industry. Although the terminology is somewhat different and images are generally specified relative to their eventual output medium (i.e., using terms such as "dots per inch," or DPI), the data requirements for large images can be substantial. For instance, a full (two-page) spread in a magazine such as *The National Geographic* will require an image that was stored with a resolution of at least 4000 × 3000 pixels.

Bit Depth

Each component of a pixel can be represented by an arbitrary number of bits. A **bit** is the most basic representation of data within a digital system, and is capable of recording only two states. If we only have a single bit to represent a color, it would probably be used to specify either black or white. More bits will allow us a greater number of color variations, and the use of multiple bits for each component of an image is what allows us to store captured imagery with realistic color information.

The number of bits per component is known as the component's (and the channel's) **bit depth**.[2] The bit depth is actually a way of measuring the **color resolution** of a given image.[3] Just as a larger number of pixels in an image allows for finer image detail, so a larger number of bits allows for finer variations in color. As you will see, many of the issues we mentioned when discussing spatial resolution have counterpart issues when discussing color resolution. Another term for color resolution is **dynamic resolution**, referring to the greater dynamic range available when using a greater number of bits per component, and you will occasionally hear the term **chromatic resolution** as well.

Probably the most common bit depth for image storage is 8 bits per channel, which is also referred to as a "24-bit image" (8 bits each for the red, green and

---

[2] Although you will often see bit depth defined in terms of the number of bits per channel, this definition is technically inaccurate, since the channel of an image refers to the full array of pixels that makes up the image. Theoretically, the number of bits per channel for a given image would be the number of bits per component multiplied by the spatial resolution of the image. However, since "bits per channel" is the more common term, we will consider it to be synonymous with "bits per component" and will use the two interchangeably.

[3] For the purposes of our discussion, we'll consider "color" to include shades of gray as well. Thus, the number of bits dedicated to reproducing the gray tones in a monochrome image can still be considered a measure of its color resolution.

blue channels). Eight bits per channel means that each component of a pixel can have 256 (2^8) different possible intensities and the three components together can represent about 16 million (16,777,216 for the geeks) colors. Although this sounds like a lot of colors (most images will not even have that many pixels), it is often still not enough to reproduce all of the subtle tonal variations that are captured with some analog imaging formats. Feature film work, for instance, often represents digital images with as many as 16 bits per channel, which gives us a palette of 281 trillion different potential colors. On the other hand, lower-end formats in which color gradations are less important may be able to work with a much smaller color resolution. Many video games, for instance, work with only 4 bits per channel, or less!

Incidentally, there is unfortunate confusion about some of this terminology in the personal computer marketplace. The video devices on early PCs were limited in their ability to display a great number of different colors. Many of them could only devote 8 bits *total* to the color specifier. To work around this limitation, they would use these 256 values to look up colors in an index of many more colors. Two different images might not need the same group of 256 colors, and consequently the palette was often dynamically allocated as necessary.[4] Unfortunately, the correct terminology of "8-bit indexed color" was abbreviated in popular use to simply "8-bit color." When systems became available that could display a full 8 bits per *channel*, this then became referred to as "24-bit color." Throughout this book, we will always refer to an image's color resolution in terms of the number of bits per channel.

Plate 5 shows our original sample image (which was initially captured with eight bits per channel) after being decimated to only four bits per channel. Notice the **quantizing** that arises—the noticeable delineations between various bands of colors, particularly in the blue background. This phenomenon, also referred to as "banding," "contouring," or "posterization," arises when we do not have the ability to specify enough unique color values for smooth transitions between different shadings.

Strictly speaking, this noticeable banding should really be called a **quantization artifact**. Quantizing itself is merely the process of assigning discrete values to samples taken from a continuous (i.e., analog) signal. This step is necessary in order to store an image digitally, and if it is done with enough precision, you shouldn't be able to distinguish the digital copy from the original. However, if you do not allocate enough data to store the sampled information, artifacts will

---

[4] The use of such **indexed color**, while no longer common in display hardware, is still implemented with certain image file formats, such as GIF, and is also commonly used in most dedicated videogame hardware.

result. There is a huge body of information about the proper way to choose the amount of data necessary to accurately represent an original image, but for the purposes of the artist trying to produce a quality image, the main issue is to use enough data so that visual artifacts aren't created. As we'll see in later chapters, one often finds that not having enough color resolution in an original image may only cause problems much later in the process, after many operations have been performed on the image.

Normalized Values

Since different images may be stored at different bit depths, and consequently would be represented by different numerical ranges, it is convenient to refer to the numerical value of a pixel as if the values had all been normalized to floating-point (noninteger) numbers in the range of 0 to 1. Since a pixel with 8 bits per channel can have values in the range of 0 to 255 for each channel, we would divide each value by 255 to come up with these normalized numbers. For instance, a reddish yellow pixel in an 8-bit image might have RGB values of (255, 100, 0). This pixel's normalized values would be specified as (1.0, 0.39, 0). By the same method, a 10-bit image (which can have a range of 2^{10}, or 1024, values per channel) would have every value divided by 1023 to determine its normalized representation.

There are a number of reasons why this is a useful convention. First of all, it frees the user from having to worry about the bit depth of the source images that are being worked with. A good compositing system should be able to deal with images of a variety of differing bit depths and combine them easily and transparently. Additionally, math operations between images are made much easier. For instance, it is a normal mathematical assumption that multiplying any number by 1 will not change the value of the number. If we multiply an image by another image, it is convenient that any pixel that is white (1, 1, 1) does not change the value of whatever it is multiplied by, and multiplying every pixel in an image by a pure white image (i.e., a constant value of 1) will leave the image unaffected. Throughout this book we will assume that an RGB triplet of (1, 1, 1) refers to a 100% white pixel, a triplet of (0, 0, 0) is a 100% black pixel, and (0.5, 0.5, 0.5) is 50% gray.

Additional Channels

In addition to the three color channels, there is often a fourth channel, the **alpha channel**, that can be stored with an image. It is used to determine the transparency of various pixels in the image. This channel is also known as the **matte channel**, and we will use the two terms interchangeably throughout this book. As you'll come to see, nearly all compositing is based on the concept of the matte. Chapter

4 will cover the basic ideas behind mattes and the matte channel, and Chapter 5 will go into greater detail about some specialized processes used to create and manipulate these matte images.

The HSV Color Representation

Up until now, we have specified the color of an image as being based on red, green, and blue components. This model, or **color space**, is certainly the most common way to represent color when using a computer, but it is hardly the only way. A particularly useful alternate method for representing (and manipulating) the colors of an image is known as the **HSV color space**. "HSV" refers to the hue, saturation, and value of a pixel.[5] In many ways, HSV space is a much more intuitive method of dealing with color, since it uses terms that match more closely with the way a layperson talks about color. When speaking of color conversationally, instead of characterizing a color as having 85% red, 0% green, and 90% blue, we would tend to say that the color is a "saturated magenta." The HSV model follows this thinking process, while still giving the user precise definition and control.

The **hue** of a pixel refers to its basic color—red or yellow or violet or magenta, for instance. It is usually represented in the range of 0 to 360, referring to the color's location (in degrees) around a circular color palette. Plate 6a shows an example of such a circular palette. In this example, the color located at 90° corresponds to a yellow green, and pure blue is located at exactly 240°.

Saturation is the brilliance or purity of the specific hue that is present in the pixel. If we look again at our color wheel in Plate 6a, colors on the perimeter are fully saturated, and the saturation decreases as you move to the center of the wheel.

Value, for the most part, can just be thought of as the *brightness* of the color, although strictly speaking it is defined to be the maximum of red, green, or blue values. Trying to represent this third component means that we need to move beyond a two-dimensional graph, and so you should now look at Plate 6b. The value is graphed along the third axis, with the lowest value, black, being located at the bottom of the cylinder. White, the highest brightness value, is consequently located at the opposite end.

Even though we've talked about the HSV color space as an alternate method of representing data, it is generally *not* used to store images. Rather, it is much

---

[5] Variations on the HSV model include HSL and HSB, in which the third component is either lightness or brightness, respectively. HSV seems to be slightly more common with digital compositors, but just about everything we talk about applies equally well to these other models.

more commonly employed as a useful paradigm for manipulating colors. Chapter 3 covers this topic in greater detail.

IMAGE INPUT DEVICES

As we discussed earlier, images that are intended to be used in a digital composite can come from a variety of sources. Those images that were originally created by nondigital methods will need to be scanned into the computer, or **digitized**, before we can use them. "Still" images, images that are not part of a moving sequence, may be simply brought into the system using a wide variety of single-image scanning devices. Flatbed scanners for print material are common, and slide scanners can be used to digitize images that were originally captured on negative or transparency film. Most of the imagery that we will work with when creating digital composites will be sequences of images, not just a single still frame. Sequences of scanned images will probably come from one of two places: either video or film.

Video images, captured with a video camera, can simply be passed through an encoder to create digital data. High-end video storage formats, such as D-1, are already considered to be digitally encoded, and you merely need to have the equipment to transfer the files to your compositing system. Of course, there are a huge number of different video formats, each with its own set of protocols and specifications. This topic will be discussed further in Chapter 10.

Digitizing images that originated on film necessitates a somewhat different approach, and the use of a film scanner is required. Until very recently, film scanners were typically custom-made, proprietary systems that were built by companies for their own internal use. Within the last few years, several companies (such as Kodak and Imagica) have begun to provide off-the-shelf scanners to whomever wishes to buy them. The process of scanning a piece of film is conceptually straightforward. A light source illuminates the film from one side, and an array of sensors mounted on the other side captures the transmitted color. Depending on the device, the array is usually only a single pixel tall but wide enough to capture a full scan line, and the film moves slowly across this array each time a new scan line is captured. The rate at which a film frame can be scanned at high resolution will vary depending on the resolution you are trying to capture as well as the scanner itself—typical speeds can range from only a second or two per frame up to several minutes per frame.

If the intention is to transfer film directly to video, the scanning can be accomplished with a higher speed piece of equipment known as a **telecine** device. Telecine hardware is usually capable of digitizing images in real time, running the film at a rate of 24 frames per second, but the quality is not as high.

Typically, the original negative of the film is scanned, and then digital values are inverted to produce an image that looks correct. By scanning the negative, one is ensured of obtaining the highest possible image quality without suffering any generational loss from creating an intermediate print. The only disadvantage of this technique is that the original negative is essentially irreplaceable, and if it is somehow damaged during the scanning process, the consequences can be dire.

The science of how analog information (such as a piece of film or a video signal) can best be converted to a digital representation is a potentially immense topic. But, as mentioned, the important thing to remember is that the digitization of any image produces something that has a finite, limited amount of information associated with it. The only way to increase the amount of useful information in an image is to re-sample it at a higher resolution, and any additional processing that is applied to an image that has already been sampled can only decrease the accuracy of the data representation. This concept will be repeated and continually referenced throughout this book, as it is critical to always keep in mind the limitations of the images which with one is working.

DIGITAL IMAGE FILE FORMATS

Now that we have a digital representation of an image, presumably residing in the memory of the system used for the digitization, we need to store it in a file on the system's disk. There are a number of different **file formats** that one may choose to store an image. Each format has its own advantages and drawbacks, and as such there is no universally accepted standard format that everyone agrees is the best. File formats vary in their ability to handle a variety of important features, many of which are listed here.

File Format Features
Variable Bit Depths

Certain file formats may be limited to storing images with only a limited or fixed number of bits of data per channel. Other formats are flexible enough that they can store image data of arbitrary bit depth. A good compositing system should be able to read files with different bit depths and allow the user to combine these images without worrying about the original bit depths.

Different Spatial Resolutions

Although most popular formats can be used to store images of any spatial resolution, certain formats (particularly those that are designed to represent only video images) may be limited to specific, fixed resolutions.

Compression

In order to limit the amount of disk space that is used by an image file, certain file formats will automatically compress the image using a predetermined compression scheme. Other file formats may allow you to explicitly specify the type of compression that you wish to use, and of course there are some formats that use no compression whatsoever. The next section gives some information about the different types of compression that are commonly used with image data and also discusses which types of images work well with which compression schemes.

Comment Information in a Header

Some image formats may allow for just about any sort of commentary to be stored with an image, whereas other formats may have a set of predefined niches for comments. Typical information would be the date/time an image was created, the name of the user or piece of software that created the image, or information about any sort of color-correction or encoding schemes that may have been applied to the image before its storage.

Additional Image Channels

Beyond the traditional three color channels, images will often have additional channels that can be carried along with them, such as a matte channel for transparency information or a Z-depth channel for determining the relative distance that any given pixel is from a certain fixed location. Some formats will allow the user to store any number of arbitrary additional channels with an image. This can be useful as a method of preserving the identity of the multiple layers that are mixed together to produce a final image.

Vendor Implementations of File Formats

It should be noted that it is up to the vendor of a particular piece of software to follow the proper specifications for any file formats that they claim to support. There are dozens of examples where two different packages may both claim to support the TIFF file format, for example, yet neither package can read the TIFF files created by the other. Beware of these potential conflicts: It is always a good idea to double-check the entire pipeline that an image might travel before you embark on the creation of large amounts of data in a particular format.

We've included a list of the more popular file formats, along with some of their different characteristics, in Appendix C.

Compression

Because high-resolution images can take up a huge amount of disk space, it is often desirable to compress them. There are a number of techniques for this, some of which will decrease the quality of the image, others which will not. If the compression scheme used to store an image can be completely reversed, so that the decompressed image is digitally identical to the original, then the compression scheme is said to be **lossless**. If, however, it is impossible to completely recreate the original from the compressed version, then we refer to this as a **lossy** compression scheme.

As you will discover, there are almost always opportunities to trade quality for space efficiency. In the case of image storage, we may wish to sacrifice some visual quality to decrease the amount of disk space it takes to store a sequence of images. Fortunately, there are a number of excellent lossless methods as well. To get an idea about one of the methods used to compress images without loss of information, we will look at a technique known as **run-length encoding**. This is just one of many techniques, but it is a fairly common one and examining it will raise most of the typical issues one confronts when discussing image compression.

Run-Length Encoding

Run-length encoding (or RLE) is a fairly simple technique, yet in the best-case scenario, the resulting compression can be significant. Consider the image in Figure 2.2, a white cross on a black background. This figure is an extremely low-

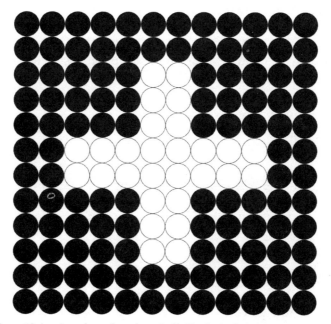

Figure 2.2   *12 × 12 image enlarged to show individual pixels.*

resolution image (12 × 12), enlarged to show the individual pixels. Also, to keep things simple, consider it to be a black-and-white image, so that we only need a single bit of information to determine a pixel's color. In this case, 0 will be a black pixel, 1 will be white. Thus, a numerical representation of this image would be as follows:

```
0 0 0 0 0 0 0 0 0 0 0 0
0 0 0 0 0 0 0 0 0 0 0 0
0 0 0 0 0 1 1 0 0 0 0 0
0 0 0 0 0 1 1 0 0 0 0 0
0 0 0 0 0 1 1 0 0 0 0 0
0 0 1 1 1 1 1 1 1 1 0 0
0 0 1 1 1 1 1 1 1 1 0 0
0 0 0 0 0 1 1 0 0 0 0 0
0 0 0 0 0 1 1 0 0 0 0 0
0 0 0 0 0 1 1 0 0 0 0 0
0 0 0 0 0 0 0 0 0 0 0 0
0 0 0 0 0 0 0 0 0 0 0 0
```

As you can see, we are using 144 characters in a simple matrix to accurately define this image.

Run-length encoding works on the principle of analyzing the image and replacing redundant information with a more efficient representation. For instance, the first line of our image above is a string of twelve 0s. This could be replaced with a simple notation such as 12:0. We've gone from using 12 characters to describe the first line of the image to a 4-character description. Using this convention, we can encode the entire image as follows:

```
12:0
12:0
5:0, 2:1, 5:0
5:0, 2:1, 5:0
5:0, 2:1, 5:0
2:0, 8:1, 2:0
2:0, 8:1, 2:0
5:0, 2:1, 5:0
5:0, 2:1, 5:0
5:0, 2:1, 5:0
12:0
12:0
```

The total number of characters we have used to represent the image using this new notation is 104. We have reduced the amount of information used to store the image by nearly 30%, yet the original image can be reconstructed with absolutely no loss of detail.

It should be immediately obvious, however, that this method may not always produce the same amount of compression if a different image is used. If we had an image that was solid white, the compression ratio could be enormous, but if we had an image that looks like Figure 2.3, then our same compression scheme would give the following results:

> 1:0, 1:1, 1:0, 1:1, 1:0, 1:1, 1:0, 1:1, 1:0, 1:1, 1:0, 1:1
> 1:1, 1:0, 1:1, 1:0, 1:1, 1:0, 1:1, 1:0, 1:1, 1:0, 1:1, 1:0
> 1:0, 1:1, 1:0, 1:1, 1:0, 1:1, 1:0, 1:1, 1:0, 1:1, 1:0, 1:1
> 1:1, 1:0, 1:1, 1:0, 1:1, 1:0, 1:1, 1:0, 1:1, 1:0, 1:1, 1:0
> 1:0, 1:1, 1:0, 1:1, 1:0, 1:1, 1:0, 1:1, 1:0, 1:1, 1:0, 1:1
> 1:1, 1:0, 1:1, 1:0, 1:1, 1:0, 1:1, 1:0, 1:1, 1:0, 1:1, 1:0
> 1:0, 1:1, 1:0, 1:1, 1:0, 1:1, 1:0, 1:1, 1:0, 1:1, 1:0, 1:1
> 1:1, 1:0, 1:1, 1:0, 1:1, 1:0, 1:1, 1:0, 1:1, 1:0, 1:1, 1:0
> 1:0, 1:1, 1:0, 1:1, 1:0, 1:1, 1:0, 1:1, 1:0, 1:1, 1:0, 1:1
> 1:1, 1:0, 1:1, 1:0, 1:1, 1:0, 1:1, 1:0, 1:1, 1:0, 1:1, 1:0
> 1:0, 1:1, 1:0, 1:1, 1:0, 1:1, 1:0, 1:1, 1:0, 1:1, 1:0, 1:1
> 1:1, 1:0, 1:1, 1:0, 1:1, 1:0, 1:1, 1:0, 1:1, 1:0, 1:1, 1:0

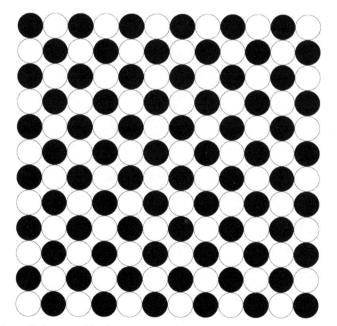

Figure 2.3 *12 × 12 image with alternating and white pixels.*

This change would be a bad thing, since we're now using 562 symbols to represent the original 144.[6]

The point of this example is not to prove anything specific about the run-length encoding method, but rather to underscore the fact that not all encoding methods work well for all types of images. There are certainly more efficient methods for encoding images, and in fact there are far more efficient variations of the run-length encoding scheme than the one shown here. As it turns out, run-length encoding tends to be a fairly good encoding method for computer-generated imagery that is produced by a 3D rendering package because this sort of image tends to have larger expanses of identically colored pixels. On the other hand, run-length encoding is generally a less effective method for storing images that have been digitized from an analog source, such as film or video, since grain, noise, and other irregularities inherent in a natural scene will cause nearly every pixel to be different from its adjacent neighbors.

Lossy Compression

As mentioned previously, a process like run-length encoding is lossless—no information is discarded when an image is stored in a format that uses this scheme. However, there are a number of formats that can compress the storage space necessary for an image by dramatic amounts as long as the user is willing to accept some loss of quality. Probably the most popular of these lossy formats is the one that uses a compression scheme defined by the Joint Photographic Experts Group. Generally, these images are said to be in **JPEG** (pronounced "jay-peg") format. The JPEG format has a number of advantages. First of all, it works particularly well on images that come from film or video, in part because the artifacts it introduces are designed to be less noticeable in areas with some noise. In particular, JPEG compression attempts to maintain brightness and contrast information (which the human eye is very sensitive to) at the expense of some color definition. The format also has the advantage that the user can specify the amount of compression that is used when storing the file. Consequently, intelligent decisions can be made about the trade-off between storage space and quality.

Consider Figure 2.4, in which the original image is shown in part (a) and the two compressed images in parts (b) and (c). Figure 2.4a is the original image, Figure 2.4b has been compressed with a quality level that is considered to be 90% as good as the original, and Figure 2.4c compressed with a quality level of only

---

[6] All but the most basic run-length encoding schemes are intelligent enough to deal with situations in which the encoding would increase the file's size. A final "sanity check" is performed after the image is encoded; if the encoded version is larger than the unencoded original, then the file will be written without any additional attempts at compression.

(a)

(b)

(c)

Figure 2.4 *Compression versus image quality. (a) Uncompressed original image. (b) Image compressed with 90% JPEG quality. (c) Image compressed with 10% JPEG quality.*

10%. When we examine the file sizes of the images that result from these compressions, we find that Figure 2.4b takes up less than ¹⁄₁₆th the space of the original, yet has suffered only minor visual degradation. Figure 2.4c is noticeably degraded, yet can be stored using less than ¹⁄₂₀₀th of the disk space needed to store the original!

JPEG compression is by no means an ideal scheme for compressing every type of image. As mentioned earlier, synthetic or computer-generated scenes will tend to compress quite well using lossless schemes, and in fact the artifacts introduced by JPEG compression are *most* noticeable on synthetic images. Look at Figure 2.5a as compared with 2.5b. Figure 2.5b is a close-up of a section of an image that was compressed for storage using JPEG compression. When decompressed, we can

(a)

(b)

(c)

Figure 2.5 *Compression and types of images. (a) Original sample image. (b) Image after JPEG compression, showing artifacts. (c) Image after GIF compression, with little or no noticeable artifacts.*

see that noticeable artifacts around the edges of the text have obviously been introduced. The compression reduced the file size by about two-thirds, but the quality loss may be unacceptable. This is particularly true when you consider Figure 2.5c. This image was saved in the GIF file format, which uses a limited color palette coupled with a compression scheme that is well suited to this type of image. Figure 2.5c actually takes up slightly *less* disk space than it took to store 2.5b, yet appears to be far more accurate.[7]

The only foolproof method for determining the best possible compression scheme for a particular image is to do an exhaustive test. This goal is encouraged, certainly, but it should also be stressed that the blind pursuit of compression is *not* the best way to approach the issue of deciding on a file format. Ultimately, the amount of compression that can be obtained should only be one of many factors that one should take into account. The next section will encourage you to consider a multitude of issues before you make your decision.

Choosing a File Format

By now you've probably realized that there are no definitive guidelines that can help us determine exactly which file formats should be used for a given type of image. Certainly the content of the image is one of the things that we may consider when choosing a format, but the primary determining factor will be the actual scenario for which the images are being used. The only definable guideline is to choose the best compression possible that still produces the desired image quality. Although the amount of compression is an easily measurable quantity, the "desired image quality" is a bit more subjective.

If you are working in a situation in which quality is the top priority, then generally you will not want to use lossy compression schemes at all. You will want every image that you create to be as high quality as possible. But even if you know that your final output images are going to be something like JPEG, it is probably a good idea to use a lossless format for all of the intermediate compositing work that you do. That way you will not be subject to quality loss each time you write out one of these images, accumulating artifacts with each step. Once you have produced your final imagery, *then* convert them to your space-saving file format, choosing the quality level that you find acceptable.

Always be aware of whether the file format you are using is going to lose data, and don't be led into a false sense of security just because you think you are

---

[7] If you look around the Internet, you can find countless examples of people using GIF files to store digitized images and JPEG files to store images of clean text and illustrations. Not only does this practice waste huge amounts of disk space on the server where the files are located, it also causes Web page updates to be dramatically slower than necessary.

using a lossless format. Even if the format doesn't do any explicit compression, there may be some other factor that reduces the image quality. It may not support the bit depth that you need, for instance, which can translate into a huge quality degradation if you are not careful. This information is not always obvious, but a little research into the file format in question (and your software's support of this format) can prevent some catastrophic consequences.

A number of other issues relating to this topic are dealt with in Chapter 11, "Quality and Efficiency."

Nonlinear Color Spaces

In addition to the standard data-compression algorithms mentioned earlier, there is a class of techniques that use specialized color encoding before an image is stored in order to make better use of the bit depth available. Images that are encoded in this fashion are said to be stored in a **nonlinear color space**. Although the topic is fairly complex, the basic process of converting an image into a nonlinear color space is essentially quite simple. First, a specialized color or brightness correction is applied to the image. Then, the image is saved into a lower bit depth than the one in which it was originally stored. The lower bit depth obviously reduces the amount of disk space that is needed to store the image, while the specialized color correction helps to bias the data loss so that more important information is retained.

There are a number of different scenarios that make use of nonlinear color space encoding. In the video world, it is usually referred to as the "gamma" with which an image is stored, while those compositors who work with film imagery will more commonly encounter files stored in the "logarithmic color space" that is used with certain film-specific file formats. To be sure, there are many scenarios in which you may never need to deal with nonlinear color spaces, but both film and video make use of these techniques. Understanding them can therefore be extremely useful in certain situations.

A more precise description of the reasoning behind the use of nonlinear color spaces, as well as the proper way to work with (and even view) such images, is not a trivial subject. This fact, coupled with the consideration that many compositors will not need to deal with nonlinear data at all, has prompted us to reserve any further discussion of the topic for Chapter 15.

CHAPTER THREE

Basic Image Manipulation

Now that we have a basis of understanding for the digital representation of images, we can start to look at methods for modifying these images. Most of the tools we will be discussing initially fall into the category of traditional **image processing** operations.

Throughout this chapter, and really throughout the rest of the book, we will be discussing tools and procedures that modify images. It is extremely important to understand that these modifications do not come without a price. Of course it will take a certain amount of time to perform any given operation, which must be planned for. But more important is the fact that just about *any* image manipulation will ultimately degrade the image. In some cases this degradation will be slight, even imperceptible, but in others the problem can be extreme. A digital image starts with a finite amount of data, and each step in the compositing process can cause some of that data to be lost. The issue of how to recognize and minimize any image degradation is covered in much greater detail in Chapter 11, but you will also find related discussions throughout the book. Because the problem can occur at every single step of the process, it is not possible to present an overall solution. Rather, a good compositing artist needs to learn which operations (or combination of operations) are more likely to introduce artifacts or cause data loss.

We will certainly not be able to provide a detailed description of every possible image processing operator, but will instead discuss several of the most common as well as those that best illustrate a specific concept. Most other tools are merely variations or combinations of the ones that we will be discussing. Appendix A gives a short description of several more of these tools, and the bibliography lists some relevant books that are more dedicated to the topic.

We will first discuss *single-source* operators, that is, operators that take a single image or sequence as their input and produce a new, modified output. This process is in contrast to what will be discussed in the next chapter, where we see how two (or more) different sources can be combined using multisource operators to produce a result.

TERMINOLOGY

Throughout our discussion of various tools (in particular those which modify the color of an image), we will occasionally show graphs of how the pixels in the image are affected. Graphing the behavior of a function is a useful way of getting a more intuitive feel for how the image will be modified. Our graphs will all follow the format shown in Figure 3.1. Here, the X-axis represents the value of pixels in the original, source image. The Y-axis is the value to which the pixel has been converted after our color-correction operator has been applied. Thus, an uncorrected image would look like the graph in Figure 3.1, in which a pixel that starts with a value of 0.5 would still have a value of 0.5 after the operation.

Let's assume that we take an image and multiply every pixel by a certain constant value. This is known as a "brightness operation." We'll start with the image shown in Plate 4. The application of a brightness of 2.0 produces Plate 7;

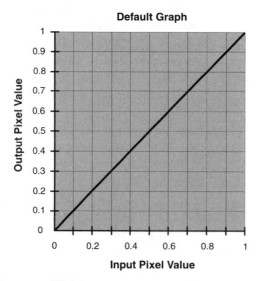

Figure 3.1   *Graph of an unmodified image.*

the graph of the "brightness 2.0" operation is shown in Figure 3.2. Examining the graph, we can see that a pixel value of 0.5 (midtone gray) maps to a pixel value of 1.0 (white) in the new image. In other words, every pixel is now twice as bright as it was before the operation. As usual, normal pixel values are assumed to range from 0 to 1, and any values that are pushed outside this range may or may not be **clipped**, depending on the compositing tool you are using. In our current example, any pixels whose values were pushed out of range were clipped, which is why any input pixels that were originally above 0.5 are now all equal to 1.0. Chapter 11 discusses the issue of data clipping in greater detail.

For some of the more simple tools, we also provide a brief equation to describe the operator. For these equations, we usually treat the entire image as if it were a single variable. In these cases, we use the following conventions:

I = Input image

O = Output image

Thus, $O = I \times 2.0$ would refer to our brightness example, in which every pixel in the input image was multiplied by 2.0 to produce the output image.

Now that we have our terminology in place, we're ready to start discussing some of the basic image processing tools we can use when compositing a scene. We will go over a number of different tools, but we will not yet discuss how these tools can interact with one another or how they can be combined to produce a

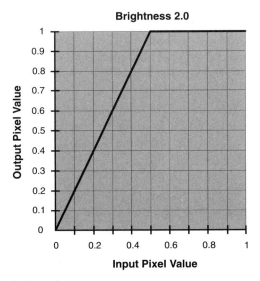

Figure 3.2 *Brightness 2.0 graph.*

multiple-step compositing script. Chapter 11 provides more information on this topic.

Single-source image processing operations can be broken down into three basic categories: color manipulations, spatial filtering, and geometric transformations. Our example, the brightness operation, would be considered a color manipulation, and we will discuss this category first.

COLOR MANIPULATIONS

As mentioned, we consider the brightness operation that we've just covered to be a color manipulation. While the layperson might not consider an apparent brightness change to be a shift in color, we'll see that it is really just a simplified case of an operation that *will* produce a visible color change. Thus, in the image processing and digital compositing world, operations that affect brightness and contrast are all classified as color-correction tools. Brightness is a specialized version of a more general tool, called simply the "Multiply" operator.

RGB Multiply

The brightness example had us multiply every pixel by a constant value to produce a new result. But if you recall from the last chapter, we often find it useful to work with digital images as a group of channels instead of whole pixels. If this is the case, we can actually apply a multiplication to each component of the pixel separately, and not necessarily equally. Thus, instead of multiplying each channel by 2.0 to create an overall brightness shift, we could apply a multiplier of 0.1 to the red channel, a multiplier of 1.25 to the green channel, and leave the blue channel unmodified (i.e., multiply it by 1.0). The result of such a procedure is shown in Plate 8. As you can tell, we've dropped the amount of red in the image significantly and boosted the green a bit, producing an image that is much more greenish blue than the original. The graph of the equivalent function is shown in Figure 3.3.

Most of the color-correction operators that we discuss can be applied either to all the channels of an image equally or to individual channels in varying amounts. When applied equally, the result will tend to be an overall brightness or contrast modification. When different amounts are applied to different channels, a visual color shift will usually take place as well. For the most part, our examples show the operators as they apply to the image as a whole, but you should assume that they can also be limited to individual channels as well.

Add

Instead of affecting the apparent brightness of an image by multiplying, we can instead add (or subtract) a constant value from each pixel. Consider the situation

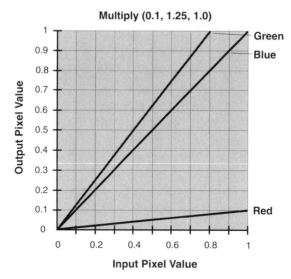

Figure 3.3 *Graph of RGB multiplication.*

in which we wish to add a value of 0.2 to every pixel in the image (O = I + 0.2). The resulting image is shown in Plate 9, with the graph shown in Figure 3.4.

Notice that, unlike the multiplication operation (which keeps the deepest blacks at the same level), the blacks in this example have gone to gray, or "washed out."

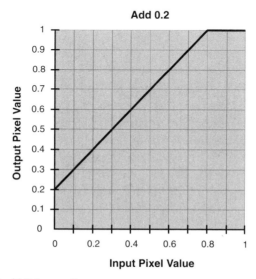

Figure 3.4 *Graph of add 0.2 operation.*

The reason should be obvious: With the Multiply operator, a value of 0 will remain 0 when multiplied by any other number, and small numbers tend to stay small. In the case in which we *add* a value to every pixel, then even the pixels that start as 0 will end up being changed to whatever value we added to the image, in this case 0.2.

We've just discussed two different tools that can change an image to be brighter than it was to begin with. Phrases such as "make it brighter" are ambiguous at best, and it generally ends up being the job of the compositing artist to decide which tool would be best for producing the desired result. Using a multiplication is probably more common, simply because the loss of rich blacks when using the Add operator is usually an undesirable artifact. However, you will notice that both of these tools will push pixels to pure white (a value of 1.0), causing bright areas of an image to look "blown out" or "burnt." Fortunately, there is another tool that is commonly used for making an image appear brighter, yet which doesn't exhibit the same sort of problems, either on the high *or* the low end. This tool is known as the Gamma operator.

Gamma Correction

The Gamma Correction operator uses the following exponential function:

$$O = I^{1/Gamma}$$

In other words, we raise the value of each pixel to the power of 1 divided by the gamma value supplied. If you have a calculator handy, you can see how different values of gamma will change the brightness of a given pixel. For instance, a pixel whose initial value is 0.5 will end up with a new value of 0.665, if a gamma of 1.7 is used.

The real reason why the Gamma operator is so popular becomes apparent when you examine what happens when you raise 0 to any power: It stays at 0.[1] A similar thing happens when 1.0 is raised to any power: It stays at 1.0. In other words, no matter what gamma correction you apply to an image, pixels with a value of 0 or 1.0 will remain unchanged. The only effect that the gamma operator has will be on nonblack and nonwhite pixels.

Don't worry too much about the math behind the Gamma Correction tool. Rather, examine the graph of its behavior. A gamma correction of 1.7 is depicted

---

[1] The exception, of course, occurs when you raise anything to the zeroth power, which is defined as producing a result of 1. However, since applying a gamma value of 0 to the above equation would produce a divide-by-zero problem, the generally accepted convention is that applying a gamma of 0 to an image will produce a black frame.

in Figure 3.5 in our graph format, and the effect on our example image is shown in Plate 10. As you can see in the graph, the endpoints of our brightness range remain fixed, midrange values are affected the most, and the effect gradually tapers off as you reach the extremes. Examining the resultant image will show that it is primarily pixels that were of medium brightness that have been boosted. The image does indeed appear brighter, but there are none of the problems we've seen with earlier tools, where the blacks become washed out or bright areas are clipped to pure white. Not only does the image tend to look more natural, but there is also much less chance for the types of data loss that can plague other operators.

Incidentally, please be aware that "gamma" is one of the most overused letters in the Greek alphabet. Ambiguity and confusion can arise because the term is commonly used to refer to a variety of totally unrelated nonlinear functions. Many other disciplines outside the image processing field use the term, and even *within* the field of digital compositing, "gamma" may be used to refer not only to the specific image processing operation we've just discussed but also to a nonlinear data encoding method (as discussed in Chapter 2), or even to the characteristic response of a piece of film to light exposure.

Invert

An extremely simple operator, yet one that will be used a great deal, is the Invert operator. The basic math behind the tool is merely

$$O = (1 - I)$$

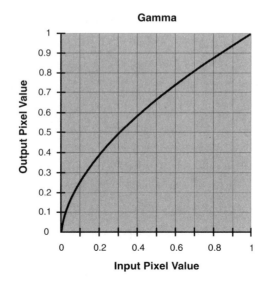

Figure 3.5 *Graph of gamma correction of 1.7.*

In other words, every pixel is replaced by the value of that pixel subtracted from 1.0. When working with color images, the result is an image that appears to be similar to the photographic negative of the original. Colors are converted to their complementary colors, bright areas become dark areas, and vice versa. The Invert operator is also referred to as the Negate operator on many systems.

Although the need to produce the negative of an image may seem limited, a much more common use of the Invert operator is to modify images that are being used as masks or mattes. Such images are discussed further in Chapter 4.

Contrast

The Contrast operator is a tool for changing the brightness relationship between the upper and lower color ranges of an image. Increasing the contrast causes dark areas to get darker and bright areas to get brighter. Decreasing the contrast will bring the apparent intensity of lights and darks closer together. There is no universal standard for exactly how the contrast operator should be implemented, so we'll look at the graphs of a few different possibilities. A very rudimentary contrast could be implemented using a combination of the tools that we've already discussed. For instance, if we wanted to increase the contrast of an image, we could first subtract a constant value and then multiply the result by another constant. The graph of this (from the equation $O = (I - 0.33) \times 3$) is shown in Figure 3.6.

Contrast as applied in this manner is a less than ideal operator, since both the low end and the high end treat the image's data rather harshly. A better system

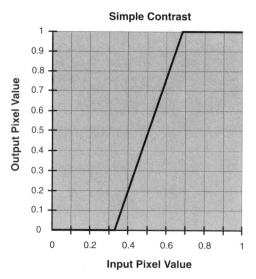

Figure 3.6 *Simple contrast operation.*

is to apply gammalike curves to the upper and lower ranges, as in Figure 3.7. This method tends to give a much cleaner image, particularly at the low and high ends of the brightness spectrum. Plate 11a shows an image that has been affected by the original contrast we showed in Figure 3.6, whereas Plate 11b was modified by our smoother contrast.

Ideally, our operator will also allow us to explicitly choose the boundary between what are considered the highs and the lows in the image, giving us a "biased contrast." In the graph in Figure 3.7 you'll notice that the point at which the curve goes from being concave to convex happens at exactly 0.5. Everything above 50% brightness is made brighter; everything below is made darker. This is fine if our image is relatively normal in its distribution of light and dark areas, but if the image tends to be very dark or bright overall, we may wish to adjust the midpoint where the transition occurs. Given a dark image, in which nothing in the frame is brighter than 0.5, we might want to set our bias point to be at 0.25 instead. If we *didn't* do this, then everything in the scene would become even darker, since all values fall below the threshold for what is considered the "dark" areas of the frame. Figure 3.8 shows a graph of a biased contrast in which the bias is set at 0.25.

Channel Swapping

There may be situations in which one actually wishes to reorder the channels that make up an image—placing the blue channel into the green channel, for instance. Simple reordering within the R, G, and B channels is not used a great deal, since it is a fairly brute-force and nonintuitive method of modifying an image's color.

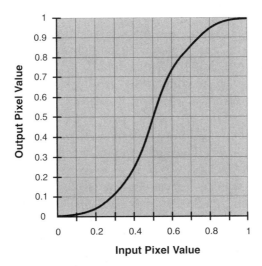

Figure 3.7 *Smoother contrast graph.*

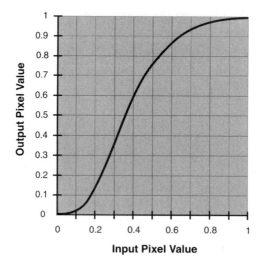

Figure 3.8   *Graph of biased contrast (bias = 0.25).*

More common is the need to move data to and from the matte channel. Channel substitution techniques are also commonly used as the basis for certain color-difference methods, as discussed in Chapter 5. It is usually more common to use channel swapping in conjunction with some sort of expression language, which we will discuss later in this chapter.

HSV Manipulations

As mentioned in Chapter 2, there is an alternate way to represent the colors in an image, known as the HSV model. This model is particularly useful as a tool for color correction, since it can be used to deal with concepts that would normally be very inconvenient were we limited to viewing color as simply a mix of red, green, and blue. For instance, affecting the saturation of an image merely by adjusting RGB values can be rather cumbersome, but using the HSV model allows us to directly access the saturation component, making manipulation trivial. An example is shown in Plate 12, in which the image's saturation has been reduced by about 50%.

Because HSV represents hue in a circular fashion (as shown earlier in Plate 6b), we can now "rotate" all the colors in an image by a certain amount. Plate 13 shows our test image after it was rotated by 180° through the color spectrum. You'll notice that every color in the image has been shifted to its complementary color, while still preserving the brightness and saturation relationships.

Look-up Table Manipulations

We've shown a variety of graphs for various operators in the last several pages, where we plot the output color as it compares with the input color. But instead of merely viewing the results of an operation with such a graph, we ideally should be able to create a graph manually and then allow the software to apply this function to the image directly. In essence, the software will evaluate the value of the graph for every input value and determine what the corresponding output value should be. This input-to-output mapping is known as a **look-up table** (or a **LUT**), and consequently such a feature is usually called a LUT-manipulation tool. Such a tool can give an extremely fine amount of control, even allowing specific color corrections across a narrow range of values. It will also often prove useful as a tool for creating and manipulating mattes. The sample image shown in Plate 14 has had all three channels modified by the set of curves shown in Figure 3.9.

This method of using user-defined curves to manipulate the colors of an image is not limited to merely modifying the brightness of certain regions in a given channel. Given a flexible enough software package, one can choose to arbitrarily modify one channel based on another channel. This operation can be particularly useful if you are able to include HSV color space in the mix. For instance, we may wish to modify saturation based on a particular hue. The diagram in Figure 3.10 shows a tool for performing this operation. The X-axis maps out the full range of hues available in an image, while the Y-axis controls the relative saturation. In

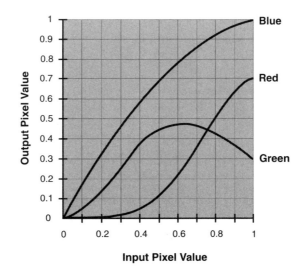

Figure 3.9 *Graph of arbitrary look-up table curves.*

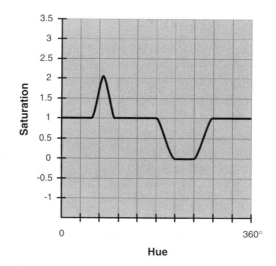

Figure 3.10   *Graph of hue versus saturation operation.*

the example shown, the center of the *Y*-axis is defined to be the point where saturation is unchanged. Pulling the curve upward will increase saturation, while moving it downward will decrease it. As you can see, we have chosen to desaturate anything that is blue, while at the same time we supersaturate a narrow range of green values. The resulting image is shown in Plate 15.

Expression Language

Finally, if all the other built-in techniques are not able to achieve the result you desire, a good compositing system should allow the user the ability to define arbitrary mathematical expressions to modify the color of an image. This type of tool is essentially a simplified computer language with support for a wide variety of expressions and mathematical constructs. It should be robust enough that the user can create very complex expressions. Since this type of tool can vary widely between different packages, we will define a few basic conventions and then give some examples that follow those rules. This pseudocode should be easily translatable to a number of different systems. In general, the syntax for most of these manipulations is assumed to be C-like, and certain built-in keywords and functions are assumed to be predefined.

As was the case with the LUT manipulations, we will use this tool to modify the value of the channels in our image. But instead of creating a user-defined curve, the color change will instead be based on some sort of algorithm or equation. Let's start off with a very simple example, in which we modify the entire image by multiplying each of the R, G, and B channels by a constant value. In this case we'll modify each channel by 0.75. The expression for such an operation might look like this:

$$R = R \times 0.75$$
$$G = G \times 0.75$$
$$B = B \times 0.75$$

The resulting image would be darkened by 25%. This isn't necessarily the best use of an expression language, since the identical result could have been obtained much more simply by merely applying a brightness of 0.75 to the entire image.

Let's look at another example, one that produces a monochromatic image from the color source by averaging the three channels together:

$$R = (R + G + B)/3$$
$$G = (R + G + B)/3$$
$$B = (R + G + B)/3$$

A more proper expression, which takes into account the fact that the human eye perceives the brightness of red, green, and blue differently, would be obtained by the following:

$$R = (R \times 0.309) + (G \times 0.609) + (B \times 0.082)$$
$$G = (R \times 0.309) + (G \times 0.609) + (B \times 0.082)$$
$$B = (R \times 0.309) + (G \times 0.609) + (B \times 0.082)$$

Again, however, similar results could have been obtained by using other operators, in this case some sort of desaturation or monochrome effect.

Instead, consider a situation in which we wish to have a conditional requirement carried out by the expression. In particular, examine the next scenario, in which only the green channel is being modified. The red and blue channels remain unchanged:

$$R = R$$
$$G = R > G \ ? \ (R + G)/2 : G$$
$$B = B$$

For those of you unfamiliar with the shorthand syntax used in this expression, the English translation is as follows:

> If a pixel's red value is greater than its green value, then set the pixel's green value to be equal to half of the red value plus the green value. If the pixel's red value is not greater than the green value, then leave the pixel's green value unchanged.

The result of the application of this expression is shown in Plate 16. As you can see, well-thought-out equations can quickly produce results that would otherwise have required the combination of several different methods.

SPATIAL FILTERS

So far, all of the image manipulations that we have talked about involved a direct mapping between a given input color and a given output color. This color mapping could be described by a simple function, and the only thing necessary to compute a pixel's output color was the equation and the original color of the pixel. Now we will look at a new class of tool that takes into account not just a single input pixel, but also a small neighborhood of pixels surrounding the input pixel. This type of tool is known as a **spatial filter**.[2]

Convolves

The most common spatial filter is known as a **spatial convolution**, or simply a **convolve**. It iteratively considers a specific pixel, as well as a specific number of adjacent pixels, and then uses a weighted average to determine the value of the output pixel. This group of pixels that will be considered is known as the **kernel**, and is usually a square group of pixels that has an odd number of rows and columns. By far the most common kernels are 3 × 3 and 5 × 5, but there are occasions where larger kernels may be used. As we said, the convolve operator uses a weighted average of the existing pixels to determine a new pixel value. To control this weighting, we define a specific **convolution filter** that is used for the computation. This filter is the same size as the kernel we plan to use and contains a series of different numbers in the shape of a square matrix. The numbers in this matrix will dramatically affect the resulting image.

Although usually the compositing artist won't need to do much more than choose a specific filter from a list of options and then allow the computer to apply the convolve process, we'll take a moment to look at an example of how the math is actually applied for a simple 3 × 3 kernel. We start with the following matrix:

$$\begin{matrix} -1 & -1 & -1 \\ -1 & 8 & -1 \\ -1 & -1 & -1 \end{matrix}$$

---

[2] The term "spatial filter" is actually rarely used in the digital compositing world. Very often you will see packages try to group the operators that we discuss in this section under either color-correction tools or geometric transformation tools. Since they do not really fit into either category, we have decided to refer to them in a manner that is consistent with most image processing books.

Think of this as a mask that will be laid over our source pixel, where the source pixel is aligned with the center of the matrix and each of the eight neighboring pixels is aligned with its positional counterpart. We then multiply each pixel by the coefficient with which it is aligned. In this example, the value of every neighboring pixel is multiplied by -1, and the source pixel itself is multiplied by 8. Now we add together all of these values to get a new number. This number becomes the value of our new pixel in the destination image. (Numbers above 1.0 or below 0 are clipped.) This process is repeated for every pixel in the source image until we have created a new image, point by point.

If we consider a section of an image whose pixels have the values shown on the left in Figure 3.11, applying the convolution filter we've just discussed will produce the results shown on the right. The particular filter we applied in this example is one that is designed to detect edges in an image. As you can see, it produced a bright pixel wherever there was a transition area in the original image, and produced dark pixels wherever the source image had a constant tone. To see this more clearly, examine the result of applying this same convolution filter to a larger image. Figure 3.12a is our original image, with some very high-contrast transition areas. Figure 3.12b is the resulting image after applying our edge-detection convolve.

There are a large number of different convolution filters that are commonly used for processing images. A few more of these will be mentioned in a moment, but you will probably need to consult a book on image processing if you are looking for a specific effect. Most compositing software will also come with a large number of prepackaged filters already implemented.

Blurring

There are many different algorithms for blurring an image, all of which produce slightly different results, but the basic concepts remain the same. The colors from neighboring pixels are partially averaged with the current pixel to produce a new image. Visually, the end result is an apparent reduction in sharpness.

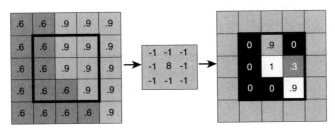

Figure 3.11 *A convolve operation.*

(a)

(b)

Figure 3.12 *(a) Original image. (b) Image after applying an edge-detecting convolve.*

Probably the most common blurring algorithm uses a simple convolve. For instance, a 3 × 3 convolve using the filter

    1 1 1
    1 1 1
    1 1 1

will result in a slight blur, as shown in Figure 3.13. Using a larger kernel, and thus averaging a larger area together, can cause a much greater amount of blurring, albeit at the expense of speed. Convolve-based blur algorithms can be extremely slow, particularly for large amounts of blur.

Also be aware that certain blur algorithms can animate *very* poorly. Visual steps between blur levels can be noticeable, causing blurs that change over time to be unacceptable. As usual, you may want to test the particular system that you are working with to see if it suffers from these problems.

Finally, although simple blur algorithms are often used to simulate the effects of an out-of-focus lens, a visual comparison between a "real" defocus and a simple blur will show decidedly different results. Chapter 12 discusses this topic in greater detail.

Figure 3.13 *Slightly blurred figure (3 × 3 convolve).*

Sharpen

Given the fact that we can blur an image, it seems that one should be able to sharpen an image as well. To a certain extent this *is* possible, although it's really somewhat of a trick. The Sharpen operator actually works by increasing the contrast between areas of transition in an image. This, in turn, is *perceived* by the eye as an increased sharpness. Keep in mind that sharpening tools can never actually create or restore lost information. There is really no detail being added to the scene, only the perception of it. The trick only works up to a certain point, and results can often include undesirable artifacts.

Sharpening can either be done by using a convolve with a filter such as

$$\begin{matrix} -1 & -1 & -1 \\ -1 & 9 & -1 \\ -1 & -1 & -1 \end{matrix}$$

or via other techniques, such as **unsharp masking**. It doesn't really matter which specific mathematical technique you use—the principle is the same, as illustrated by the simplest-case scenario discussed next.

Figure 3.14a shows an enlarged look at an edge in an image—in this case a straight-line transition from dark gray to light gray. Figure 3.14b shows the same area after some sharpening has been applied. If we create a graph based on the values of a horizontal slice of the original image, it would look like Figure 3.15a, whereas Figure 3.14b corresponds to Figure 3.15b. Notice the boosted contrast at the transition juncture: The bright area gets slightly brighter, the dark area slightly darker. A good sharpening tool should let you choose the amount of the sharpening, as well as the extent of the sharpening. If we happen to be using a convolve

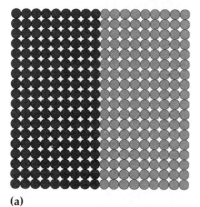
(a)

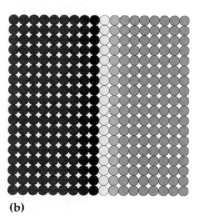
(b)

Figure 3.14 *Close-up of a sharpen operation. (a) Original edge. (b) Same area after sharpening has been applied.*

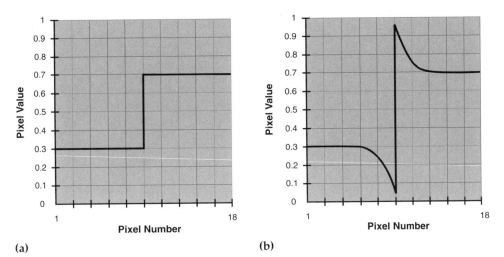

(a)   **(b)**

Figure 3.15 *(a) Graph of Figure 3.14a. (b) Graph of Figure 3.14b.*

to do our sharpening, increased sharpening amounts would be produced by increasing the weights of the coefficients in our matrix, and an increased extent would be produced by using a larger matrix.

Plate 17a is an original image, with no sharpening applied. Plate 17b has had a slight sharpening applied, with subtle but noticeable results. Plate 17c has had a far greater amount of sharpening applied, to demonstrate the type of problems that can show up. Now that you are familiar with what sharpening is really doing, it should make sense that oversharpening will cause you to see noticeable **ringing** along strong transition areas, such as the edges of the stones against the sky in the example. You should also be able to see that the sharpening has increased the amount of apparent grain in the image—an artifact that would be even more noticeable if it occurred on a sequence of images.

Median Filter

Certain spatial filters do not use a specific weighted matrix to determine the way pixels are averaged together. Instead, they use other rules to determine their result. One such filter is the **median filter**. Quite simply, it ranks all of the pixels in the kernel in terms of brightness and then changes the value of the pixel in question to be the same as the median, or center value, of this ranking. The net result is that the median filter does an excellent job of removing single-pixel noise artifacts, while causing only a slight reduction in the sharpness of the image.

Figure 3.16a is an image with some noticeable noise spikes—small bright and dark spots. Figure 3.16b is the same image after the application of a median filter.

(a)   **(b)**

Figure 3.16   *(a) Image with noticeable noise spikes. (b) Same image after application of a median filter.*

As you can see, the bulk of the noise has been eliminated. Applying the filter again in a second pass would probably eliminate the rest of the noise. This process does not come without a price, however, since each time a median filter is applied the image will be slightly softened. For this reason, median filtering is usually applied only within a certain threshold. The only pixels that will be replaced with the median of their neighbors are those pixels that vary by more than a certain amount from the original image. Areas that do not have any noise are not changed, and the overall image suffers far less softening than a normal median would produce.

GEOMETRIC TRANSFORMATIONS

The next class of operations we will be discussing all fall under the category of geometric transformations, or simply "transforms." A transform operation causes some or all of the pixels in a given image to change their existing location. Such effects include **panning**, **rotating**, **scaling**, **warping**, and various specialized distortion effects. We'll first consider the three simplest transformation effects: pan, rotate, and scale.

Whenever we talk about moving images around, we must realize that they have to be moved relative to something. It's easiest to just consider that the image is being moved relative to some predefined frame. In most day-to-day compositing work, the first thing we tend to do is define our working resolution, and everything is moved around inside of this frame. What we call a **working resolution** is typically the resolution of the image that will be produced once we are finished with our compositing operations.

For the purposes of the next few examples, let's assume our working resolution is 1200 pixels wide by 900 pixels tall. Let's also assume that the input or source image that we'll be dealing with in these examples is a slightly smaller resolution, say 900 × 600. There is at least one more item we need to know about the system we are working in, namely, what is considered the *origin* of our system. In other words, what part of the frame is considered to have the (*X,Y*) location of (0,0). This point may vary between different software packages, but the most common assumption is that the origin is located in the bottom left corner of the frame. Thus, our example image when placed (without any additional transformations) into our working resolution frame is shown in Figure 3.17.

Panning

Let's say we wish to apply a simple translation to the image, offsetting it in both *X* and *Y*. Such a translation is usually referred to as a **pan**.[3] In this case, we will

Figure 3.17 *Image in a working resolution frame.*

---

pan the image by 150 pixels along both axes. The new image produced is shown in Figure 3.18, with the original image more or less centered within the frame of our new output image.

What happens if we move the input image 700 pixels in X instead, causing part of the input image to be moved beyond the borders of our working resolution? The result will usually be something like what is shown in Figure 3.19a. However, the issue of what is done with the rest of the image that has moved out of frame is dependent on the compositing system that is being used. On most systems, the rest of the image will be cropped, or discarded. Any additional transformations to this image will be performed with the truncated image, and any portion of the image that was moved out of the working area will be unrecoverable. A few systems are able to deal with this problem in a more robust fashion, allowing the off-screen information to be preserved so that it can later be brought back into frame if needed. There is also a common option in most systems that lets the user

Figure 3.18   *Image from Figure 3.17 panned by 150 pixels along both axes.*

effect is applied over time, we have decided to refer to either a static or a dynamic reposition as a "pan."

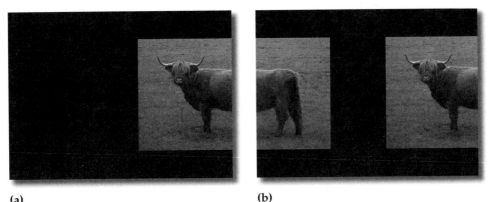

(a)   **(b)**

Figure 3.19 *Panning. (a) Image panned off-screen. (b) Image panned with wrapping.*

specify that the image "wraps" around to the other side of the frame, as shown of this is shown in Figure 3.19b.

Rotation

Let's **rotate** an image now. The two parameters needed to control a simple rotation are the *amount* of the rotation (usually specified in degrees) and the *center* of the rotation. Changing the center of rotation can dramatically affect the result. Compare Figure 3.20a and Figure 3.20b. Both images have been rotated 30° clockwise, but in the first the center of rotation was the origin, (0,0), whereas in the second the image was rotated about a point that is approximately its center.

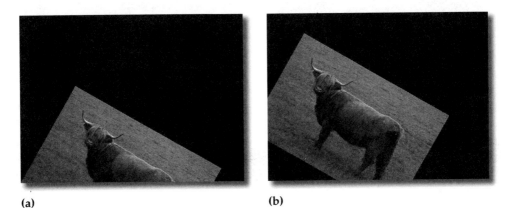

(a)   **(b)**

Figure 3.20 *Rotation. (a) Image rotated 30° clockwise about the origin. (b) Image rotated 30° clockwise about its approximate center.*

Scale

Now we will look at the case of **scaling** an image. Again, if your compositing system supports it, the ability to scale around a user-defined point is useful. Figures 3.21a and 3.21b show an image scaled down by 50% (or scaled by 0.5) around the same two origins that we used for our rotation examples. If for some reason your compositing system does *not* support scaling around a user-defined origin, don't be too concerned, since it is really just a shortcut that can easily be duplicated by panning the resulting image into the position we desire.

Although this example shows an image scaled by the same amount (0.5) in both X and Y, we can certainly scale nonuniformly instead, say by 0.3 in X and by 1.2 in Y. Note that we can also "flip" or "flop" an image by scaling it by -1 in the X or Y direction, respectively. Remember that flipping an image is *not* the same as merely turning it upside-down (i.e., rotating it by 180°). Instead, flipping produces a *mirror* image along the X axis. This can be very useful when faking shadows or reflections in a composite. Figure 3.22 illustrates the difference between an image that is flipped (3.22a) and one that is merely rotated (3.22b).

3D Transforms

So far we've confined our discussion of various transformations to what are considered to be 2D transforms. We can also choose to rotate an image as if it were being moved about within a 3D environment. Various perspective[4] effects

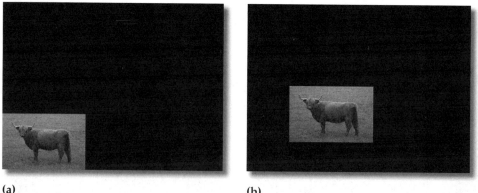

(a)   **(b)**

Figure 3.21   *Scaling. (a) Image scaled by 50% around the origin. (b) Image scaled by 50% around its approximate center.*

---

[4] Perspective is discussed in greater detail in Chapter 12.

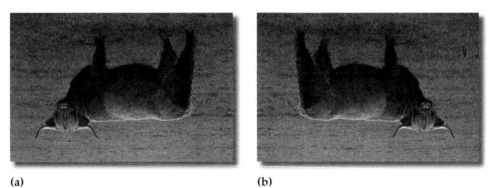

(a) **(b)**

Figure 3.22 *(a) Flipped image. (b) Rotated image.*

will consequently be introduced. Without going into great detail to define the information needed to extend our discussion into this third dimension, let's just look at a simple example of transforming an image in 3D space. Figure 3.23 shows an image that has been partially rotated around the X-axis. You can see the obvious

Figure 3.23 *Three-dimensional rotation around the X-Axis.*

perspective effects, whereby foreshortening causes the bottom of the image to be compressed and the top of the image to be enlarged.

Even if your compositing system doesn't support the concept of perspective transformations, it may support something known as "corner-pinning," in which the user can manually reposition the four corners of an image to create any arbitrary tetrahedron. The end visual result should be similar.[5] In general, most 3D transformations can be emulated using 2D transforms.

Warping

An even more sophisticated method of distorting an image is known as **warping**. Conceptually, it is easiest to think of warping as if your image were printed on a thin sheet of flexible rubber. This rubber sheet can be pushed and pulled by various amounts in various areas until the desired result is obtained. Image warping is usually controlled by either a grid mesh or a series of splines. (Spline-based systems ultimately create a grid as well—they just do a better job of hiding it from the user.)

Although warping is a powerful tool for manipulating images to obtain effects that would otherwise be impossible, for illustrative purposes we will use it for a slightly less serious result. Consider Figure 3.24a, which shows our sample image with a grid laid over the top. In order to control the warping of this image, we will manipulate this grid; the corresponding warp will be applied to the image. Thus, if we stretch our grid as shown in the right half of Figure 3.24b, the resulting warped image would be similar to that shown in Figure 3.24c. Later, in Chapter 15, we will also touch on the technique of **morphing**, a sophisticated combination of warping and dissolving between two images over a period of time.

Expression Language

Just as we saw with the color-correction tools, the ideal compositing system will allow you to resort to mathematical expressions to define warping parameters. The syntax will follow the same format as we defined for our color-correction example, only now we will be dealing with X and Y transformations. The degenerate case, in which we are merely mimicking something simple like an X translation, could be represented as

$$X = X + 30$$

---

[5] The primary difference is that the perspective may not be exactly the same. A good 3D transform will let you choose a true 3D position, which will in turn affect the resulting perspective of the image.

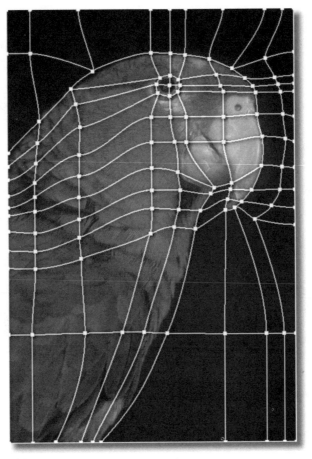

(a)

Figure 3.24 *Warping. (a) Sample image with grid laid over it.*

This transformation would shift every pixel to the right by 30 pixels.

More complex equations can easily be extrapolated. For instance, using a periodic function like sine, we can create a wavy offset:

$$Y = Y + 50 \times \sin(X \times 0.02)$$

In this example, the sine function returns a value between -1 and 1 depending on the value of X. The multiplication by 50 magnifies the effect so that pixels are offset in the range of -50 to 50. (Multiplying X by 0.02 before passing it to the sine function will control the frequency of the wave.) The result of this warp operation is shown in Figure 3.25.

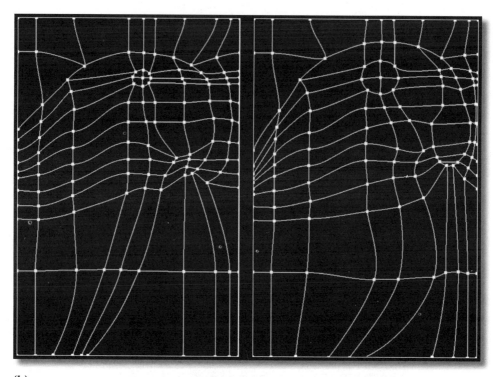

(b)

Figure 3.24   *(b) Grid before and after distortion.*

Filtering Algorithms

Every time a geometric transformation is applied to an image, there is a step in which the computer samples the original image and creates a new one. Within this step, there is a choice of what type of **filter** will be used to produce the new image.[6] Consider the situation in which we want to scale an image down to one-tenth its original resolution. There are a number of ways that we could go about this. We could simply use every tenth pixel, for instance. This technique is a very simple filter, generally known as an **impulse filter**. It is a very fast method of reducing an image, but unfortunately not a very good one, since it completely ignores 90% of the data that makes up the original image. Consider the worst-case example of how this can be undesirable. If pixel number 1 and pixel number

---

[6] From a mathematical point of view, these filters are essentially the same as the spatial filters that we have already described. However, their implementation here is different, and the compositing artist will use them differently.

(c)

Figure 3.24   *(c) Resulting distorted image.*

10 in the image are black, but pixels 2 to 9 are white, our scaled-down image would use a black pixel to represent the new pixel number 1, even though the average value should be closer to white. Better filtering algorithms look at all of the pixels in the original image and selectively average these pixels together to obtain a new pixel that more accurately reflects the data in the original image.

Choosing a specific filter is not just something that we do when scaling an image down (or up). Every geometric transformation (from a rotation to a warp) will use some kind of filter to compute the resulting image. Presumably, your compositing system will allow you to choose a specific filter for most geometric transformations. (If it doesn't, it is probably time to get a new compositing system.) Advanced systems may give you a variety of different filters to choose from by

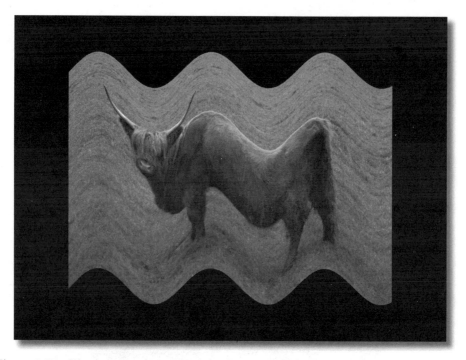

Figure 3.25 *Warping operation performed using a sine function.*

name, whereas less sophisticated systems may just limit your choices to simple options such as "low-quality" or "high-quality."

Different types of filtering can produce vast changes in the quality of the resulting image, particularly when dealing with a moving sequence of images. For instance, when animating a pan be sure to choose a filter that is able to deal with increments of less than a pixel. Such a filter, known as one with **subpixel** accuracy, is designed to prevent your image from popping to whole-pixel boundaries as it moves—a visual artifact that is surprisingly noticeable, even when working at high resolutions. On the other hand, if you are using a geometric transformation to merely reposition an image (i.e., without any scaling, rotation, or animation), then you would be better off choosing a filter that does *not* resample, but instead preserves the original data exactly.

Although the perfect filter does not exist, there are a variety of different filters that are typically used with image processing algorithms. The following list mentions a few of the filters that would normally be available for image resizing, with a look at the pros and cons of each. A resizing filter can act in the same fashion as a sharpening operator, where subtle application will appear to increase sharpness but at the risk of introducing ringing artifacts. Other resampling filters may introduce noticeable softness into an image or may result in **aliasing**. Higher-quality filters are more expensive in terms of memory and CPU usage, not surprisingly; therefore you should be aware of what type of filter you are using for a given operation. The use of a lower-quality filter for intermediate test work may be justified, as long as you intend to switch to a higher-quality one for the generation of your final imagery.

- The **impulse filter** is the fastest method for resampling an image, since it will sample only a single pixel in the original image to determine the value for a given pixel in the new image. It is also known as a **Dirac filter** or a **nearest-neighbor filter**. Although fast, it generally produces a significant amount of aliasing in just about any situation. In general, it should only be used when the need for speed is paramount.
- The **box filter** is of slightly better quality, but still tends to produce a lot of artifacts. When scaling an image up in size, it will result in a boxy look.
- The **triangle filter** considers slightly more area when resampling, and is used a fair amount as a quick method for resizing an image for viewing purposes.
- The **Mitchell filter** is a good balance between sharpness and ringing, and is often the best choice when scaling an image to a larger resolution.
- The **Gaussian filter** is a common filter that is virtually free of aliasing or ringing artifacts, but tends to introduce noticeable softening in the image.
- The **sinc filter** does a very good job of keeping small details without introducing much aliasing. It is probably the best filter to use when scaling an image from a larger resolution to a smaller.

CHAPTER FOUR

Basic Image Compositing

Now that we've taken a look at a number of different methods to modify a particular sequence of images, we can start to discuss the manipulated combination of *multiple* sequences. This process, combining two or more image sequences, is the true heart of digital compositing. It requires the use of special operators that are capable of dealing with more than a single input sequence, and so we will refer to these operators as "multisource operators." As was the case with our discussion of basic image manipulation tools, we will only take an in-depth look at a few of the most important image-combination tools. There are numerous others, for many of which we provide a bit more information in Appendix A.

We'll start this discussion with one of the most common multisource operators. It is also one of the simplest, and we'll refer to it as simply an Add. If you recall, in the last chapter we discussed a single-input Add operator that added a constant value to each pixel in an image. Although we'll be using the same name for the multisource operation we're about to discuss, the difference should be obvious. By using the same names, we're following typical nomenclature used in the industry; because of the obvious difference in the situations in which the two operators will be used, there should be little room for confusion. A number of the basic mathematical single-source operators, such as Subtract or Multiply, have dual-input equivalents.

Adding two images together involves, not surprisingly, the addition of each pixel in the first image to its corresponding pixel in the second image. Plates 18a and 18b show the two source images we will be using to illustrate some of our multi-input operators. Combining these two images using an Add produces the image shown in Plate 19. As you can see, the result is similar to a photographic double exposure.

While this effect is certainly useful in a variety of situations, it does not give us the impression that any sort of layering has occurred. There is no sense that certain portions of one image are actually occluding the second image. To accomplish this, we need to introduce the concept of a **matte**.

THE MATTE IMAGE

Combining different image sequences needs to be a process with as much control as possible. We need to be able to limit which portions of the various images will be used, and which will not. We need to be able to control the transparency of the various layers so that they don't completely obscure everything that they are covering. And we need to have a method for defining and controlling these attributes that is intuitive and consistent with the rest of the image processing we will be performing. This is what the matte image gives us.

First of all, understand that a matte image is no different from any other image, in terms of the data used to represent it. It can generally be treated and manipulated in exactly the same fashion as other images, but it is considered to have a different *purpose* than those images. Instead of providing a visual representation of a scene, it is more like a utility image, used to control individual compositing operations.

Mattes are used during compositing when we only wish a portion of a certain image to be included in the result. You may also hear the term "mask" used when referring to mattes, and it is not uncommon to find the two terms used interchangeably. For sanity's sake, we will try to limit the use of the word "mask" to refer to a general image that is used to control or limit certain parameters in an operation, such as a color correction.

To complicate things even further, both "mask" and "matte" may also be used as either nouns or verbs. The terms can refer to the image used in the process of protecting or excluding a section of an image, or they may refer to the process itself. Consequently, we may "matte out" a section of the foreground so that the background is revealed, or we may "mask off" the bottom third of an image when we color correct it so that the correction doesn't affect that area.

Mattes are generally considered to be single-channel, grayscale images. There is no need for three separate channels, as there is when specifying color, since the transparency for any given pixel can be described by a single numerical value in the range of 0 to 1. Many systems and file formats support single-channel images, whereas others will simply place a copy of the same information into all three channels of an RGB image. While this method is redundant (and wastes disk space), it does sometimes provide a simpler model for both the user and the programmer.[1] Ideally, the compositing system will store a single-channel matte

---

[1] Matte images tend to contain large areas of identical pixels, usually black or white, and as such will compress dramatically using one of the better lossless compression schemes. Consequently, there

image as efficiently as possible, yet still allow the compositor to treat it as if it were a normal RGB image when necessary.

Depending on the software package you are using and the file format you have chosen, a matte can also be bundled along with a three-channel color image as a discrete fourth channel. When the matte image is part of a four-channel image, it is known as the **matte channel** or the **alpha channel**.[2] In the next section we will discuss four-channel images in greater detail, but for the time being we will consider the case in which our matte is a separately stored image.

Let's look at a very simple example of how a matte image is used, given our original two images (Plates 18a and 18b) and a third matte image shown in Plate 20. We will use this matte channel to isolate or extract a foreground piece of Plate 18a and will then place it over the background of Plate 18b. The resulting image is shown in Plate 21.

This example is simply to give you an intuitive idea of how a matte channel might typically be used. As you can see, areas that are white (have a pixel value of 1.0) in the matte channel are used to specify that the corresponding area of the foreground image is kept at full opacity. This is said to be the "solid" area of the matte. Conversely, the black areas of the matte are used to specify that the corresponding pixels in the foreground image will be transparent, or effectively removed, when it is placed over the background. Intermediate gray levels of the matte channel provide a continuum of transparency, with brighter (higher-valued) pixels specifying more opaque areas and darker pixels specifying more transparent areas. The same behavior can be seen if we look back at the image from *James and the Giant Peach* that we discussed in Chapter 1. Plate 2e shows the matte that was used to extract the peach from Plate 2a in order to place it into the scene shown in Plate 1.

In the preceding examples, we have only shown matte images as being distinct entities, completely separate from normal color (RGB) images. Any operation that is used to combine two images would need to reference the matte image as a third image in order to control varying levels of transparency. This need not always be the case if we are working with a system that supports four-channel images.

THE INTEGRATED MATTE CHANNEL

As stated earlier, very often an image will be stored with not only the three basic color channels, but also a fourth channel, the matte channel. But there is more to

---

is often less concern about the amount of disk space that is taken up by a matte image.

[2] The concept of a matte image that could be integrated as a fourth channel to a normal color image was developed and formalized by Ed Catmull and Alvy Ray Smith at New York Institute of Technology in the late 1970s.

the process than simply attaching that matte channel to an image. Usually, when a fourth channel is added to an image, the color channels are modified as well, to include some of the information that comes from the matte channel. In fact, the standard definition of a four-channel image assumes that the red, green, and blue channels have already been multiplied by the integrated matte channel. Such an image is referred to as a **premultiplied image**,[3] and it is most commonly produced as the output of a 3D rendering and animation package. (Occasionally there are situations in which you may have a three-channel image that has already been multiplied by an external matte. This too could be referred to as a premultiplied image, but this scenario is much less common.)

Plate 22 shows an image whose color channels are the result of multiplying Plate 18a by Plate 20 to produce a premultiplied image. As you can see, everywhere that the matte was black (having a digital value of 0), the color channels have become black, or 0. Wherever the matte was a solid white, the color channels are unmodified. Less obviously, in areas where the matte had some intermediate gray value, the corresponding pixels in the RGB image have been darkened by a proportional amount.

Premultiplied images can be a great source of confusion, primarily because in certain situations this multiplication step is done automatically but in other situations (or using different software packages), the process must be dealt with explicitly by the user.

Whether or not an image is premultiplied can significantly affect the compositing process and the resulting imagery. Using premultiplied images with tools that aren't expecting them can be disastrous, as can the reverse. This is particularly true when dealing with certain layering operators such as the Over tool, which we will discuss in a moment. Toward the end of this chapter we will spend even more time discussing these concepts.

Before we take a look at some additional multisource operators, it will be useful to stop and describe a few notations that we will be using in conjunction with our definitions.

MULTISOURCE OPERATORS

Many of the multisource operators that we will be discussing will support images that carry an auxiliary alpha channel. Unless otherwise specified, assume that the operation discussed is independent of whether the images contain integrated

---

[3] The premultiplied image (as well as a number of the multisource operators that can take advantage of a premultiplied image) was first described in a classic paper that Tom Porter and Tom Duff presented at the 1984 **SIGGRAPH** conference.

matte channels. For those operators where it is applicable, we will first discuss the process as it relates to images without any integrated matte channel and then will look at the same operator's behavior with four-channel images. When we do need to make a distinction about separate image channels, we will use the following notation. For any image A,

A_{rgb} = The RGB channels only.

A_a = The alpha, or matte channel, only.

A = All the channels (be there three or more) of the image.

Finally, just so that we can put some of these descriptions into equation form, we'll define "O" to represent our output image, just as we did in Chapter 3. We will also occasionally use "M" whenever we need to denote an image that is used exclusively as a matte channel. Such an image should generally be thought of as a single-channel (grayscale) image.

Using these notations, the Add multisource operator that we originally discussed could be simply represented as

$$O = A + B$$

A and B are our two source images and O is the resulting image. Since the Add operator behaves the same with either three- or four-channel images, there is no need to mention any specific channels in this particular equation, and it should be obvious that in actuality,

$$O_{rgb} = A_{rgb} + B_{rgb} \quad \text{and} \quad O_a = A_a + B_a$$

Now that we have a common language that we can use to discuss some of these concepts, we can finally begin to talk about some of the more powerful compositing operators. Most of these are not just two-source operators such as the Add we just saw, but instead can accept several inputs, including matte inputs that may be used to control which portion of one image is combined with another image. By far the most common operator for selectively combining two images is the Over tool.

Over

Since the Over operator is such a crucial, often-used tool, we will examine it in great (some may say excruciating) detail. Even if you feel you are very familiar with using Over for compositing, it is worth understanding the exact algorithm that is used, since a number of problems can be diagnosed when you are armed with this knowledge.

The Over operator takes two images and, using a third image as a controlling matte, lays a portion of the first image on top of the second. It was the operator we used to illustrate the matte channel early in this chapter, producing the image in Plate 21. Intuitively, people understand compositing with the Over tool as if the matte were a cookie cutter that removes all excess information from the foreground image. Once this cutout is created, the result is then pasted on top of the background.

Here's what really happens, mathematically, when we place image A (the foreground) over image B (the background), using image M as the matte for image A.

$$O = (A \times M) + [(1 - M) \times B]$$

Let's break this down into the specific steps as they occur. First, the foreground image is multiplied by the matte image (A × M). In our example, this was already shown to produce the intermediate image shown in Plate 22. Again, everything outside of the matte has become black, and the portion of the image that is located within the solid, or white, area of the matte remains unchanged.

The second step is to take the inverted matte image (Plate 23a) and multiply that with the background image. This multiplication produces a new intermediate image with a black hole where the foreground will go (see Plate 23b). To complete the process, these two intermediate images are then added together, creating the final output, which we already saw in Plate 21.

This example underscores an important point about most image-combination tools. They are often just a group of even more simple operations applied sequentially. If you find yourself trapped on a desert island with a compositing system that has only a limited number of tools, you will usually be able to recreate a large number of more complex tools as necessary.

For those of you who are accustomed to working with images that already have an integrated matte channel (such as those rendered by a 3D animation package), the equation describing the Over operation may seem to contain an additional step. In fact, the first stage of our Over equation (described by (A × M)) is designed to produce a normal premultiplied image that would behave identically to an image produced by 3D rendering software.

If we look again at the Over operation, this time simplifying for the case of an image with an integrated matte channel, the equation becomes

$$O_{rgb} = A_{rgb} + [(1 - A_a) \times B_{rgb}]$$

Note that the color channels of the output image are independent of the background image's matte. However, the output image's matte channel is composed as follows:

$$O_a = A_a + (1 - A_a) \times B_a$$

We could also write the simplified equation for all four channels as

$$O_{rgba} = A_{rgba} + [(1 - A_a) \times B_{rgba}]$$

As mentioned earlier, be sure you understand exactly what type of scenario your compositing operator is expecting in terms of premultiplied images, so that you can avoid the problems we'll be discussing at the end of this chapter. Let's look now at a few more common image-combination tools that you will probably find useful.

Mix

A mix is the weighted, normalized addition of two images. In other words, the two images are averaged together, often with one of the images contributing a larger percentage to the output. Plate 24 shows the result of mixing 75% of image A with 25% of image B.

The equation for such a mix, where "MV" refers to the mix value (the percentage of the first image that we will be using), is as follows:

$$O = (MV \times A) + [(1 - MV) \times B]$$

This operation is usually known as an "additive mix," since the weighted averages are added together.

To "dissolve" from one image to another over a given period of time, one merely animates the mix value so that it initially displays 100% of image A and then eventually displays 100% of image B.

Subtract

The Subtract operator causes every pixel in image A to be subtracted from its corresponding pixel in image B. Quite simply,

$$O = A - B$$

Note that Subtract is not a symmetrical operator. The order in which the two images are specified is important to the result. Be aware of which multisource operators are symmetrical and which are not, since it will determine whether or not you need to be concerned about the order in which you combine images. Thus, $(B + A)$ equals $(A + B)$, but $(A - B)$ does *not* equal $(B - A)$.

Most implementations of the Subtract operator will allow you to choose whether to clip all values that go below zero, or to take the absolute value of the result, in which negative numbers are converted to positive. The absolute value method is particularly useful for difference matting, which we'll discuss in Chapter 5. A subtraction that returns the absolute value of the result becomes a symmetrical operation, so you no longer need to worry about the order of the two image sequences that you specify.

In

There are certain multisource operations that require only a matte image for the second input. (The matte image can either be a single-channel image or the alpha channel of a four-channel image.) The In operation is one of these. As you can see from the equation, it pays no attention to the color channels in the second image, even if it is a four-channel image:

$$O = A \times B_a$$

When we describe the use of the In operator, we usually say we are placing image A *in* image B; the result is an image that consists of only the areas in image A that overlapped with the matte of image B. An example of this is shown in Figure 4.1. On the left, we see image A (the dark gray circle) placed in a certain position relative to image B (the light gray square). Both images are assumed to have an integrated solid matte channel that corrresponds to the shape you see. "A in B" is shown on the right.

Out

The Out operation is the inverse of the In operation—it results in a new image that consists only of pixels from image A that did not overlap the matte of image B. We say that A was "held out" by B.

$$O = A \times (1 - B_a)$$

This result is illustrated in Figure 4.2.

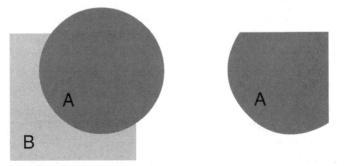

Figure 4.1   *A in B.*

Figure 4.2 *A held out by B.*

Atop

As mentioned, many image-combination tools can be used in tandem to produce new tools. Most of these combinations are given different names by different software vendors, so we will not attempt to list them. But to give an example, we show a fairly common one, usually referred to as an Atop operator. It places image A over image B, but only in the area where image B has a matte. We say we are placing A "atop" B.

$$O = (A \text{ in } B) \text{ over } B$$

An example of this operation is shown in Figure 4.3.

Although most of these image-combination operators are really just very simple mathematical calculations that work with images and mattes, more complex operators certainly exist. **Morphing**, for instance, combines the animated warping of two images over time with a controlled dissolve between the two sequences.

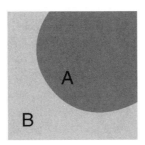

Figure 4.3 *A atop B.*

MASKS

There are times when we wish to limit the extent of a certain operator's effect. A particularly useful method for doing this involves the use of a separate matte as a control image. Whenever a matte is used in this fashion, it is usually referred to as a **mask**. In essence, the use of masking with a single-event operator implies a multisource scenario, with the original sequence as the first source and the mask as the second. Just about any operator should be something that can be controlled by an external mask, and so we'll look at a fairly simple example.

Consider the matte image shown in Plate 25a. Let's say we wish to decrease the brightness of our parrot image, but we want to limit that attenuation as a function of this mask. The result of this is shown in Plate 25b, where we used a brightness value of 0. If we hadn't used a matte to limit this operator, the entire image would have gone to black, but instead the darkening was only applied where the mask allowed it to be. In the areas where the mask was completely solid, the resulting pixels remained unchanged. Where the mask was transparent, or black, the full attenuation could be applied. In any areas where the mask had intermediate gray values, the brightness was applied by a proportionally smaller amount.

If your system does not support masking to control operations, you can still accomplish the same effect manually, using some of the image-combination tools that we have already discussed. You would first apply the effect to the entire frame and then use the mask to isolate the proper area and combine it with the original, unaffected image.

COMPOSITING WITH PREMULTIPLIED IMAGES

It is extremely important to understand exactly what type of image (premultiplied or not) your system's compositing operators expect. Some systems assume that they will always be dealing with premultiplied images; others may require the image and matte to be brought in separately so that they can be recombined during the operation in question. If you do not use the proper type of image, you run the risk of introducing a wide variety of unacceptable artifacts. Let's look at some different scenarios. We'll use an example based on the Over operator, but the same problems can show up with other tools as well. The matte in our example is intentionally very soft-edged, since this is the most problematic situation.

Consider Plate 26a, the image that we will use for our foreground. It features a dog standing in front of a gray wall. Plate 26b is a soft-edged matte to extract the dog from the scene. Plate 27 shows the background image that we will be using. It features the same wall (shot from an identical camera position), only with a cat standing in front of the wall.

If we premultiply our foreground image (Plate 26a) by its matte (26b), the result is shown in Plate 26c. Now, if this result is placed over the background in a system that assumes that the images you are providing are all premultiplied, the proper result is obtained, as shown in Plate 28. The soft edges blend well with the background and there are no noticeable artifacts.

However, if we combine Plate 26a with Plate 27 *without* premultiplying the color channels, we have an image that will not be handled properly if our Over operator is expecting a premultiplied image. The result of placing such an image over the background is shown in Plate 29. Note that the foreground element, in areas where its matte is supposed to be 0, is still contributing to the result. If you were to check out the math of what is happening, you'd see that in those areas of the result image, it is exactly as if we had simply added the two images together.

Equally damaging problems can occur in the other direction, that is, if we feed premultiplied images to a system that is expecting to combine the image with the matte itself. Such a system will automatically multiply the image by its matte channel, even though this has already been done in a normal premultiplied image. In this situation, we have effectively multiplied the image by its matte channel *twice*, thereby darkening all areas of soft-edged matte. The result of such a mistake is seen as a dark halo around the foreground, as shown in Plate 30.

Although the preceding examples resulted in some very obvious problems, an improper image/matte relationship can be the cause of some very subtle artifacts as well. Such artifacts can show up even if we have properly synchronized our image types with what the operators are expecting. One of the more common places these will occur is when we are trying to color correct images that have already been premultiplied.

Color-Correcting and Combining Premultiplied Images

Whenever we premultiply an image by a matte, there is a very specific brightness relationship between the pixels in the color channels and the pixels in the matte. Systems that assume you are working with premultiplied images will rely on this image/matte relationship; consequently, the brightness of any color channel can no longer be modified without taking the alpha channel into account (and vice versa). Thus, any time you apply a color correction to a premultiplied image, you run the risk of producing a new image whose matte/image relationship is no longer "legal." If you look at the math that is used when we premultiply an image by a matte, it should be obvious that the brightness of any given red, green, or blue channel in such an image can never exceed the value of the alpha channel. This can sometimes be used as an indicator that there has been some kind of operation performed on the image after the premultiply occurred. The result of compositing with this image will vary, depending on the extent of the change made to the different channels, but generally it will manifest itself as a slight brightening or darkening of the composite in areas where the foreground matte was semitransparent. More extreme changes to the color or matte channels will obviously result in more extreme artifacts.

A particularly common problem will occur when some color correction has been applied to a foreground premultiplied image that causes the blacks in the scene to be elevated above a value of 0. Now, even though the matte channel may still specify that the surrounding field is black, the RGB channels may have some small, often visually undetectable, value. The problem will show up when one attempts to layer this element over a background. The resultant image will show a noticeable brightening of the background in the area outside the foreground's matte. As one becomes a more experienced compositing artist, artifacts like this become the clues that let one track down exactly which layer in a composite is causing a problem. In this case, the clue is the fact that the background gets brighter. As you can imagine, it may be very difficult to determine if this problem exists, since at first glance an improperly modified image may appear perfectly correct.

Because inevitably you will find yourself with a need to color correct a premultiplied image, there is usually a tool on most systems to temporarily undo the premultiplication, at least in the critical areas of the image. We will refer to this tool by the rather unwieldy name of "Unpremultiply." Essentially, the tool redivides the image by its own matte channel, which has the effect (except in areas where the matte is solid black, or 0) of boosting the areas that were attenuated by a partially transparent matte back to approximately their original values. An example of this is shown in Plate 31, which is the premultiplied image from Plate 26c after redividing by its matte. (Areas where the matte was equal to 0 have been set to be pure white.) Although this is obviously not a completely perfect recreation of the original image, it restores enough information in the edges so that appropriate color corrections can be applied.

If your system does not have an explicit tool to perform this operation, you can try using some other tool to simulate it. For example, if there is a simple expression language available, you can modify the image so that

Red = Red/Matte

Green = Green/Matte

Blue = Blue/Matte

Once the image has been unpremultiplied, any necessary color corrections can be applied without fear of corrupting any semitransparent areas. The result should then be remultiplied by the original matte channel, which will restore the element to one whose image-to-matte relationship is correct.

For slight color corrections, or when using images that have very hard-edged mattes, you may get perfectly acceptable results without going through this process. As usual, use your best judgement, and if it *looks* correct, then by definition it *is* correct. But if there is any doubt in your mind, or if you are having problematic edges, you may want to take a moment and compare the results of performing your color correction before and after the image is multiplied by the matte.

By default, all the major 3D packages will render elements that have been premultiplied by their matte channel. As we've seen, this is not always the ideal scenario and in many situations may actually be counterproductive. Assuming that the 3D element is perfectly ready for integration into the scene, having it delivered already premultiplied by its matte channel will be fine. But as often as not, this conceit is not really the case. You may want to determine if there is some way of overriding this premultiplication behavior in the 3D package, so that you can have unpremultiplied images available for your compositing work. This ability will be particularly important if you are in a situation in which you will be performing a good deal of color correction on the 3D element.

Luminosity

When working with four-channel premultiplied images and using the Over operator, there is an additional effect that can sometimes be useful. It involves selectively manipulating the alpha channel of the image to intentionally modify the image-to-matte relationship. This operator is often referred to as a "Luminosity" tool.[4] By decreasing the value of the alpha channel before placing an object over a background, the object will appear to become brighter in the result. In addition, the background will become more visible through the foreground element.

An example of this effect is shown in Plate 32. In this case, the matte channel for the foreground image was multiplied by 0.6 before being placed over the background. In fact, as the matte channel is decreased toward 0, the result becomes more and more like an Add operation instead of an Over. This can be proven by examining the equation for Over again. If the matte of the foreground object in a premultiplied image is set to 0, the Over operator will produce the same results as an Add.

---

[4] The other common name for this on many systems is the "Opacity" operator, even though this name is less descriptive of the visual result this tool produces.

CHAPTER FIVE

Matte Creation and Manipulation

❦

In the last chapter, we introduced the concept of a matte image and gave some examples to show what an important role these images play in the digital compositing process. But unlike most other images that you will be dealing with when compositing elements together, matte images are not scanned into the computer from some outside source. Rather, they are almost always generated within the computer, as a part of the compositing process. There are many different methods used to generate mattes for compositing, just as there are many ways that a matte image can be used. The process of generating a matte, particularly when automated, is referred to by a variety of terms, including "matte extraction," **pulling a matte**, and **keying**. Keying is actually a broader term, in that it is often used not only to describe the process of creating a matte but also to include the process of combining one element with another. Thus, you might "key" a blue-screen element over a background. This chapter will look at methods for manipulating as well as creating mattes.

An example of a situation that would require a very simple matte would be a split-screen composite. This is a situation in which (for example) the left half of the image comes from one source and the right half of the image from another. The matte would be a fairly simple shape that defines the boundaries of the split—often just a straight line that separates one plate from another. Such a matte is easily created using simple paint or shape-generation software. More often, however, we need to place an object whose outline is much more complicated into a scene. We need a matte that accurately represents the boundaries or outline of the object and that fully encloses all solid areas of the object's interior.

In the case in which this object does not move, it is still conceivable that such a **static matte** can be hand-painted. But even with an unmoving subject it can be difficult to accurately paint something that properly captures the desired edge qualities (such as transparency and softness) of a given object. Instead, one will tend to use certain software algorithms, discussed later in this chapter, to help isolate an image from its background.

When compositing sequences of images, situations involving static mattes are fairly rare. Far more often we find the need to create a matte for an object that is moving within or through the frame. We require the use of a moving matte, or **traveling matte**. There are two approaches we can take to generate these mattes. The first would continue the methods we've talked about already, that is, hand-drawing a matte for the object in question over every frame of our sequence. This process, known as **rotoscoping,**[1] is still done, but only after all other options have been exhausted, since hand-drawing a matte for every frame of a sequence is time-consuming and error prone. Common problems produced by a series of hand-drawn mattes include edges that slide, jitter, or crawl.

One slightly less brute-force method of manually generating a traveling matte involves the use of splines to rotoscope a basic outlined shape for an object. The rotoscope artist specifies certain key shapes, and the software smoothly interpolates any in-between frames. Unfortunately, objects that move or change shape a great deal may end up needing a key shape defined for every frame anyway! In any event, this technique still does not do a very good job of isolating extremely fine detail (such as hair or fur) and has less control over areas of partial transparency than is usually desirable.

Ultimately, we will need to rely on more *procedural* techniques—semiautomated processes in which some initial parameters are determined that are capable of extracting a matte, and then the software is allowed to apply these same parameters over a sequence of images.

PROCEDURAL MATTE EXTRACTION

We will briefly touch on a number of different methods that may be employed to procedurally extract a traveling matte from a sequence of images. The efficacy of these methods is highly dependent on the image in question, and often you will find it necessary to try a number of different tools before obtaining a result that you are happy with.

The best methods of extracting a matte for an object rely on the fact that we (usually) know in advance that we are planning to place the object in question into a different scene. Consequently, we can choose to photograph this subject in

---

[1] The **rotoscope** was a device patented in 1917 by Max Fleischer to aid in cel animation. The term is now used generically to refer to the process of creating imagery or mattes by hand on a frame by frame basis.

a manner that greatly simplifies its matte extraction. Typically, this involves the use of a special background that is placed behind the subject we wish to isolate. This background (or **backing**) should be a uniform color, ideally a color that is not significantly present in the subject itself. The exact choice of what color to use will be determined by the extraction technique that will be employed, but by far the most common color that is employed is blue. Thus, the process of shooting in front of any colored background is sometimes generically known as **bluescreen photography**. Not all of the extraction tools we will discuss rely on a uniform backing, however, and many of them can be used to help extract mattes for objects that were not shot with any special attention or intentions. We will look at these tools first.

Keying Based on Luminance

One of the most common methods used to extract a matte for a given item is based on manipulating the luminance values in a scene. This is usually known as **luma-keying** and involves the application of some basic image processing operators to choose the luminance values that one wants to include or exclude from the matte.

The technique is generally most useful when the feature you wish to extract from the scene is significantly brighter or darker than the background from which you wish to separate it. The ideal case would be a bright object shot over a black background, but you'll find that there are often situations in which the brightness difference between foreground and background is enough to extract a decent matte.

Consider Figure 5.1a. A bit of manipulation can quickly produce the image shown in Figure 5.1b. As you can see, we now have something that could easily be used as a crude matte, and additional digital manipulations could continue to refine the result. This situation would also benefit greatly from the use of an interior **garbage matte**, which we will discuss in a moment.

Keying Based on Chrominance

Chroma-keying is a bit more sophisticated, but it still makes use of some of the basic tools that we discussed in Chapter 3. In the case of a simple chroma-keyer, the process is to pick a certain range of colors or hues and to define only the pixels that fall within this range as being part of the background. Generally, a good chroma-keyer will have additional tools that let you specify not only a specific hue range, but also a particular saturation and luminance range to further control the matte.

A good chroma-key tool can be used to pull a matte from a bluescreen or a greenscreen, but it should not be confused with some of the more sophisticated color difference methods that we'll discuss in a moment.

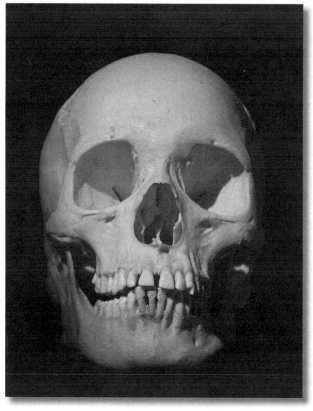

(a)

Figure 5.1   *Luma-keying. (a) Skull image on a dark background.*

Incidentally, the terms "chroma-key" and "luma-key" originally came from a process that used specialized hardware for real-time keying on a video signal. A standard video signal natively represents image information in terms of both luminance and chrominance values, and this keying hardware would use modified luma or chroma components to key elements together.

Difference Matting

In theory, if you have an image that contains the subject you wish to isolate, and another identically framed image that does *not* contain the subject, subtracting one from the other will produce an image that consists of information only where the subject was present. This process is known as **difference matting**.

In practice, slight lighting discrepancies, shadows, and grain make the difference between the two images unpredictable and the results less than perfect. Difference matting is thus usually not considered a complete solution, but rather

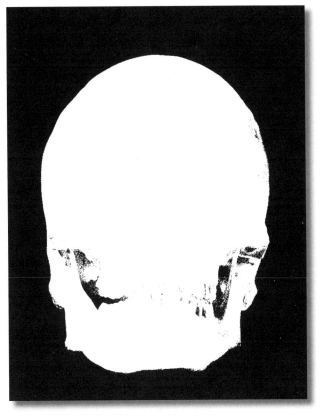

(b)

Figure 5.1 *(b) Matte extracted by luminance-based keying.*

as a very useful first-pass method that can then be cleaned up using other methods. Since a difference matte requires two separate images with the same lighting and camera setups, it is a limited tool, and using it to produce a traveling matte from a sequence of images would require either an unmoving camera or some method of perfectly synchronizing the camera movements between the two plates.

In spite of these limitations, difference matting is an extremely useful tool in certain situations because it can be used to extract a matte from just about any background. Consider the example image shown in Plate 26a as compared to Plate 33a. As you can see, the dog is present in the first image but not the second, yet everything else is identical. If we subtract Plate 33a (which is known as a "clean plate") from 26a, the result is shown in Plate 33b. While this is by no means a perfect matte, it is not a bad starting point and can probably be digitally manipulated to produce something that is more acceptable.

The Color Difference Method

By far the most popular (and effective) method for procedurally generating traveling mattes is known as the **color difference method**. This method was actually developed and patented in the 1950s by Petro Vlahos as an optical matte extraction process, and was first used in a major theatrical production for *Ben Hur* in 1959. The steps used, which involved selectively combining the different color records (or channels, to use digital terminology) of a piece of film to produce the resulting image, can be easily converted into equivalent digital formulas. We will describe the basic steps here so that you can get a better idea of exactly how the technique is applied, but understand that this will be a very simplified version of a more complex process.

The first thing that we should mention is that the color difference method is not just a matte-extraction tool. It is actually a combination of steps that includes matte extraction, color correction, and image combination. Although the matte-extraction step *will* produce a matte that could be used in other situations, the basic definition of the color difference method must include all of the steps to be complete, and so we will describe the entire process in this section.

Assume we are working with an image shot on a blue background. The first step in the color difference method involves the creation of a new image in which this blue backing is suppressed to black. This is done by selectively substituting the green channel for the blue channel in every pixel in which the existing blue component has a greater intensity than the green component. In other words, for each pixel,

If Blue > Green

then New Blue = Green

else New Blue = Blue.

An example of this process is shown in the color section: Plate 34 is our original bluescreen element, and Plate 35 is the result after applying the operation. Since the green channel should have a value of 0 in areas of pure blue backing, the primary result of this substitution is an image in which the blue background has gone to black. Additionally, anything in the foreground that has a heavy blue component (i.e., blue or magenta areas) will be modified. Although this effect is a problem if there is any blue coloration in the foreground that we wish to keep, it is also a benefit in that it will neutralize any blue **spill**—blue lighting from the backing that has inadvertently fallen onto the foreground. This step, known as "spill suppression," is usually applied with a few more parameters than we have just described. Additional thresholds are added so that there is control over exactly how much blue is removed and to compensate for any change in brightness that the channel substitutions might cause. The use of spill suppression to better integrate an object into a scene will be discussed again in Chapter 14.

The second step in the color difference method involves the creation of the matte itself. This is simply a matter of subtracting the maximum of the red or the green component from the blue component. It is this difference between the blue channel and the other channels that gives the technique its name. To restate the step mathematically:

$$\text{Matte} = \text{Blue} - \text{Maximum(Green, Red)}$$

This operation will actually produce what we would normally think of as an inverted matte—the foreground area is black and the background area is white. This result is shown in Plate 36.

We now simply multiply this inverted matte with our intended background—a step that results in a background with a black hole in the shape of our foreground element. The final step would be to add our modified foreground to this intermediate background, producing an integrated result. As you can see, the final steps of this process are identical to the way that the Over operator works.

Of course, the steps described are merely a basic template for the process. If you were to apply these *exact* steps to any given bluescreen image, the chances are high that you would not be terribly happy with the result. In our example images, you'll note that the background of Plate 35 did not become perfectly black, but rather a dark gray. The matte created in Plate 36 is also less than perfect—the areas that should theoretically be pure white are only about 85% white. In practice you would want to have additional control over the various steps as they are being applied in order to deal with such issues. You would adjust the relationships between the channels, thresholding certain values and multiplying others, until a visually acceptable result is obtained for the final composite. This type of control is exactly what the Ultimatte system, described in the next section, allows.

The color difference method always involves shooting the foreground object we wish to isolate in front of a uniform-colored backdrop. What's more, this method works best when the backing is a pure primary (red, green, or blue) color. Its effectiveness is greatly reduced if the backing is less pure. Chroma-keying tools have an advantage in this respect, in that they are not biased toward any particular hue. If you are confronted with an image that has an off-color background, these tools may be a better choice. Chapter 13 goes into much more detail about choosing a backing color for optimal matte extraction.

Specialized Keying Software

Above and beyond the standard compositing tools that are used to extract a matte from a scene are custom software packages that are designed explicitly for this purpose. These custom packages can almost always produce far better results, due to the specialized algorithms they employ.

The value of these custom packages lies not only in their excellent matte-extraction tools, but also in the methods they use to integrate an element into a scene. Color correction, spill suppression, and edge treatments can all be dealt with when using these packages. Of the packages in question, by far the most common are the tools provided by the Ultimatte Corporation. Ultimatte was actually founded by Petro Vlahos, the creator of the color difference method, and the Ultimatte software and hardware that it provides are extremely evolved versions of that process.

Yet another common tool for matte extraction and bluescreen compositing is the software known as Primatte. This software is essentially a very powerful chroma-keyer, allowing the user to choose a large number of different chroma values at the same time from which to key, and also allowing the user to deal with spill areas explicitly. Both of these tools are available as adjuncts to most of the common compositing packages or can be purchased as stand-alone software.

Many complete compositing packages will also provide their own custom matte-extraction tools, most of them based on some of the techniques that we have already discussed. Depending on the software, these tools can range in quality from barely acceptable to extremely powerful.

Ultimately, no single tool or technique is necessarily "better" than another. Each can be useful in a particular situation, and the choice of which tool to use will often be determined by a number of tests. Some packages or techniques work better for some images and worse for others, and it can be very difficult to predict this in advance.

MATTING TECHNIQUES

We first need to correct the common misconception among novice compositors that the process of pulling a matte off a bluescreen should be a simple, one-step process. In the real world, especially for high-end work, this is true so rarely that it is definitely the exception rather than the rule. Even the best tools can have problems with certain images, and typical production situations often deliver plates to the compositor that are less than perfect in terms of evenness, graininess, and freedom from objects that are not intended to be seen in the final composite.

A typical matte extraction usually involves *several* steps, a great deal of interactive testing, and often requires that specific tools be used for specific problem areas. You may also find that whatever tools you use to extract a matte will need to be modified at different points in time. Unavoidable changes to the backing's illumination (such as an inconsistent light source) may require that the settings be animated throughout the duration of the sequence on which you are working.

Garbage Mattes

Very often one will use **garbage mattes** to help simplify the process of creating a clean matte. A garbage matte is a loose-fitting shape designed to address specific problem areas, and will almost always be used in conjunction with a more exact matte. Garbage mattes should be quick and easy to create; usually they will have very little to do with the edges of the object in question. By definition, their purpose is to remove any obvious "garbage," or extraneous information. This garbage will usually be something exterior to the chosen foreground subject, such as a piece of rigging that is hanging into frame or a defect in the bluescreen itself. The matte shown in Plate 2e was actually created with the aid of a garbage matte similar to the one shown in Figure 5.2. This matte, in conjunction with some more standard matte-pulling software, was used to quickly remove the support pole that is visible in the original bluescreen plate (Plate 2a).

Garbage mattes can also be used to explicitly *include* a portion of an image, such as areas that would otherwise be problematic due to their color similarity with the backing. Thus, it is not uncommon to create both an inner and an outer garbage matte for any given image. This underscores a particularly salient point: The most important thing that any automated matte-extraction technique will give you is a high-quality edge. Everything that is *not* an edge may very well be something that can be addressed with far less effort using other techniques.

Figure 5.2 *Garbage matte.*

Edge Mattes

Since it is usually the edges that we spend the most time with when working on a matte, it is extremely useful to have a way of limiting certain operations so that they affect only these edges. One of the best ways to limit these operations is by using yet another matte, usually referred to as an **edge matte**. An example of an edge matte for the peach from Plate 2a is shown in Figure 5.3. As you can see, this is a matte that is solid only along the edges of an element and is transparent elsewhere. It can be created either directly from an image or, probably more commonly, from another matte. For instance, if we pull a very high-contrast matte for our foreground element, we can then use an edge-detection algorithm to define only the edge. In this situation, the original matte we pull should be as hard-edged as possible, since edge-detection algorithms will work more effectively with this scenario. Then, depending on the edge-detection tools you have available, you may need to do some additional processing to create a thicker edge.

Edge mattes are worthwhile for a number of reasons. First of all, when coupled with a few simple operations they can be used to create a very accurate inner and outer garbage matte. They can also be very useful as a mask for controlling additional effects that are used to help with the integration. For instance, one could use an edge matte to more easily control the softness or transparency of the foreground's edges. Or a soft edge matte might be used to help with spill suppression around the edges of the foreground element. There may even be occasion to use an edge matte to apply effects after the layering is finished. It

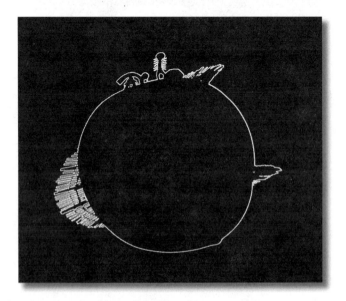

Figure 5.3   *An edge matte for the peach in Plate 2a.*

may be worthwhile, for instance, to apply a slight blur along the edge where the foreground and background meet *after* they have already been composited together. When done sensibly, over a very small area, this can look far superior to simply blurring the edges of the foreground element before creating the composite.

Combining Mattes

Instead of using a single technique to create a single matte, it is often the case that a number of different mattes are generated, each targeted to a certain portion of the image. For instance, certain settings may pull an excellent matte around a character's hands, yet these same settings may produce absolutely unusable results on hair blowing in the wind. A second pull may be tuned to deal with the hair, and the matte image that this produces can then be manually combined with the matte that works well on the character's hands.

Combining these mattes will require finesse in and of itself. Since the different settings will produce different edge qualities, a hard-edged split will tend to show this transition area. Instead, you will probably need to use an additional matte with a soft transition edge to split the different procedural mattes together.

Manipulating Mattes

Since a matte image is really just like any other image, it means that we can use our standard image processing operators to modify these mattes as needed. We already discussed this a bit when we looked at the luma-key, where we used a combination of operations to tune a matte. No matter what method we use to extract a matte, procedural or manual, there may be times that we wish to tweak that matte by a slight amount—to expand it or shrink it or soften the edges a bit. This practice is perfectly acceptable, but is abused so consistently in the industry that we want to be very careful about recommending it. Postprocessing a matte to soften edges is not a substitute for pulling a proper key in the first place. Even though some of these techniques can modify mattes so that they look acceptable at first glance, significant loss of detail may have occurred. This detail may have been something that could have been preserved had a bit more time been spent tuning the original matte-pulling parameters instead of quickly resorting to postprocessing the result.

Having said this, we'll now assume that you have spent the time necessary to convince yourself that the matte you have pulled is the best possible using the tools you have available. If this is the case, yet your matte still does not feel acceptable, then it may be time to resort to other tools. We'll mention a few of the more typical problems that are seen with mattes that are procedurally generated and then suggest some possible remedies. These are only suggestions, and may be totally inapplicable to your particular situation. In fact, many of these suggestions could easily cause more problems than they solve, depending on the matte in question.

Remember that *any* changes you make to the matte channel must also be reflected in the RGB channels if you are already dealing with a four-channel, premultiplied image. Do *not* simply blur or dilate the matte channel of a four-channel image, or you will most likely end up with a noticeable matte line when you go to composite your element over a background. We will assume that you are working with matte images that are separated from the RGB images and consequently will not remind you of the matte/image relationship for every situation in which it may be applicable.

Holes in the Matte

It is not uncommon to find that a particular matte pull has some undesirable "holes" in it. These holes are usually caused by grain or noise in the bluescreen element—grain that contains enough variance so that certain particles have coloring identical to the backing. The ideal way to eliminate this sort of thing is with the use of garbage mattes, but if this is not practical, you may be able to apply something like a median filter, which will remove single-pixel anomalies.

Another technique for dealing with excessively grainy bluescreen elements is to apply a very slight blur to the original bluescreen element, extract a matte from this blurred element, and then use this extracted matte in conjunction with the *original* bluescreen plate. By slightly blurring the bluescreen plate, the most egregious grain or noise will be toned down, and a cleaner matte can then be pulled. However, we don't actually want to have a softened foreground element in our scene, so we revert to the original, unblurred element for our image. This can be combined with our clean matte to produce what one hopes is a better composite.

Incidentally, there may be situations in which a few small holes in the foreground matte are not going to be noticeable. If the background is not significantly brighter or darker than the foreground, the holes will reveal something that is fairly neutral and innocuous. They will, at worst, appear to be a bit of grain on the element.

Hard Edges

Attempts to create a solid matte for the subject while completely removing the backing area will often involve a distinct threshold between the two areas. This can, as a side effect, produce a fairly hard edge to the matte. This is usually undesirable, since in the real world, even very sharp objects will have a slightly soft edge when viewed from a distance. The simple solution is to apply a slight blur to the matte channel, although by doing so you run the risk of introducing a matte line, since a blur will typically spread both outward and inward. You may end up doing some additional processing on the matte after the blur, to alleviate such problems. If your matte was too hard only in certain areas, you should use some sort of mask to control the blur, or limit its extent to only areas that are problematic.

Ill-Fitting Mattes

Very often we will find the need to slightly increase or decrease the coverage of a given matte or a portion of a matte. Many compositing packages will provide tools for doing this directly, using algorithms typically known as Dilate and/or Erode. These increase or decrease the relative amount of dark and light pixels in an image. Figure 5.4a shows a close-up of a small portion of a matte; the result after applying a simple Dilate tool is shown in Figure 5.4b.

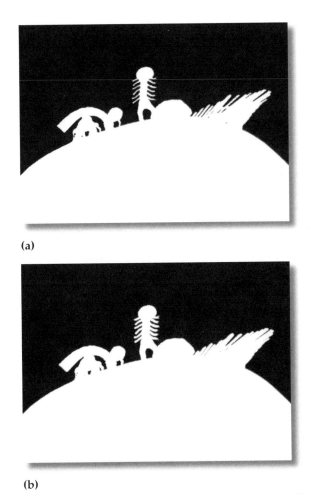

(a)

(b)

Figure 5.4 *Fixing ill-fitting mattes. (a) Close-up of a portion of a matte. (b) The matte after applying a dilate tool.*

If your software does not have an explicit Dilate/Erode tool, you can usually come up with fairly similar results by using a combination of other operators. For instance, to dilate a matte, you can apply a very slight blur to it and then use an additional brightness or gamma to manipulate the medium-gray pixels that are created. There are any number of additional scenarios that might require explicit modifications to a matte. Some later chapters of this book will look some more at specific considerations that should be taken into account when creating a matte for an object.

CHAPTER SIX

Time and Temporal Manipulations

Although everything that we have discussed up to this point is related to the topic of digital compositing, most of it would also fit just as well into a book about using computer-based paint programs. We have talked about a variety of tools for combining and manipulating images, but primarily have looked at these tools only as they are applied to a single, static image. The focus of this chapter is to move beyond the single-frame mentality into a discussion about how the concepts that we've been discussing apply to a sequence of images.

Certainly a good deal of what we have already discussed is easily understood in terms of a moving sequence. Just about any compositing package (and even some paint packages) will allow you to apply the tools we have discussed to a sequence of images. But the reason digital compositing *must* be treated as a separate issue from simple digital painting is that techniques that would be perfectly acceptable when dealing with a single image become not only cost ineffective but sometimes completely unusable when the need arises to produce a sequence of images.

Before we go into more detail about methods for dealing with image sequences, let's take a moment to discuss the difference between viewing a single still image and a sequence of them.

APPARENT MOTION

The eye has a natural ability to perceive movement when shown a sequence of still images, assuming that the rate of viewing is high enough and the distance any given object moves within the scene is small enough. This illusion is known by a variety of names, including "stroboscopic motion," the "phi phenomenon," or simply "apparent motion."

There is a common misperception that the reason we can see motion when viewing a succession of unmoving frames is that the human eye has a tendency to continue to transmit a signal to the brain for a few moments after the image is removed from view. This phenomenon is known as **persistence of vision**. Persistence of vision *does* explain why we do not see flicker when viewing a sequence of images at a high enough rate, particularly with a medium such as film or video, in which is a brief moment between each frame when the screen is actually blank. Persistence of vision will eliminate flicker only if the rate at which images are displayed is high enough. Film running at 24 frames per second (fps) is actually too slow to completely eliminate flicker; consequently, theatrical motion picture projectors are designed so that they show each frame *twice*, running at a rate of 48 frames per second. Even a rate of 30 fps is not really enough to completely eliminate flicker, which is why video was designed to show two interlaced field images at a rate of 60 fps instead. (This topic will be discussed in greater detail in Chapter 10.)

However, it is really a combination of both apparent motion *and* persistence of vision that allows us to be fooled into believing that we are seeing a moving scene when shown a sequence of still pictures. Apparent motion can actually happen at extremely slow frame rates, although generally a rate of about 16 frames per second is considered a reasonable minimum. This was the rate used for most of the original silent films.[1] Both the rate at which one views a sequence of images and the rate at which that sequence of images was acquired are important factors in digital compositing. We need to be aware of both, not only so that we can judge movement, but also because of the greater storage and processing requirements that arise when the number of frames increases.

TEMPORAL RESOLUTION

Just as is the case when dealing with a single image, in which we have a certain number of pixels to work with, when dealing with a sequence of images we will have a certain fixed number of these images, or **frames**, to work with. The more frames that are sampled over a given period of time, the greater the amount of information we have about the scene and the motion within it. In essence, this is yet another way of increasing the resolution of our imagery. We will refer to this as the **temporal resolution** of a sequence.

---

[1] Interestingly, the reason that the standard speed for film projection was increased to 24 fps was primarily to improve the *sound* quality for the new "talkies."

For the time being, let's assume that the images we are dealing with were captured at the same rate as that at which they will eventually be displayed. This rate is equivalent to the temporal resolution of a sequence and is usually measured in frames per second, or simply **fps**.

Most current feature films are captured and displayed at a rate of 24 fps. This is actually a fairly slow rate, bordering on the limits of the eye's ability to perceive flicker. Many artifacts, such as the distracting "strobing" one gets when the camera pans quickly, are often more pronounced in film than when dealing with higher-speed media.

Video in the United States is considered to run at a rate of 30 fps, although this is somewhat of a simplification, as we'll describe in Chapter 10. Various other countries may have different video standards: PAL, for instance, which is the video standard used in much of Europe, specifies a rate of 25 fps.

Other specialized film formats, such as the one known as Showscan, are designed to be played at even greater speeds. (In the case of Showscan, the rate is 60 fps.) The advantage of a format that is designed to display frames at a higher rate relates to the perceived increase in the "realism" of the experience for the viewer. The artifacts caused by a low temporal resolution (such as flicker, strobing movement, and noticeable grain) are all minimized. High-speed formats are usually coupled with increased spatial resolution as well, to give a much more satisfying image. The disadvantage of high-speed systems from a digital perspective is that they require significantly more data for any given amount of time. Even if you choose to scan and store your images at a similar spatial resolution as you would for regular film, the fact that the projection speed is 60 fps instead of 24 means that you need more than twice the amount of storage space for the same length shot.

Frames, once digitized, are usually numbered sequentially for the sequence, although often they will not necessarily be used exactly the way they were created. Two sequences of images need not be of the same length to be combined, and they need not be combined with their frame numbering, or even their acquisition rate, synchronized.

TEMPORAL ARTIFACTS

As mentioned, there are certainly a number of issues that start to become problems once we are dealing with sequences of images instead of just a single frame. Some of these problems, such as the large amount of data that must be managed, are reasonably well defined. If we want to work with 100 frames instead of just one frame, the amount of disk space will probably be about 100 times greater. But there are other problems that arise as a result of our moving image. Many of these problems will fall into the category we refer to as **temporal** artifacts. The definition of this term should be fairly obvious—it refers to some visually notice-able problem that is a result of viewing moving images over time.

Very often you will find yourself putting together a composite and testing a number of different frames in the sequence. Each individual frame may look perfect, with nothing to belie the fact that it is actually a composite. With full confidence you process the entire sequence and send it to a viewing device. However, once you look at the result at the proper speed, everything falls apart. Matte edges crawl, objects moving around the scene are jerky and irregular, elements flicker, and you realize that a composite is more than just a collection of stand-alone images.

The eye is very sensitive to small movements. This is almost certainly a survival trait, a way of sensing danger in one's surrounding environment. Any sudden anomaly in the field of view, any unusual motion, will trigger a warning some-where in the back of the brain. Unfortunately, this means that many small artifacts that are unnoticeable with a single image can become dramatically more visible when viewed as a sequence. Just about any movement can be a problem if it is not smooth and regular. An object's edge that does not have good frame-to-frame continuity due to an irregular matte will become immediately obvious when played at speed. Small changes in the rate of movement—accelerations and decel-erations—will be noticeable and distracting. There is no single magic solution to these problems. The compositor should constantly test short sequences, not just single frames. Every effort should be made to ensure that techniques are smooth and continuous over time, and always make sure that you look at the complete moving sequence before you show it to your client or supervisor.

Now that we're aware of some of the problems that can arise when working with image sequences, let's go ahead and look at some of the ways we can work with and modify the timing aspect of image sequences. The next section will cover some general-purpose methods for modifying the speed of an image sequence. The reader should also be aware that a very specific timing conversion—the conversion between 24-fps film and 30-fps video—will be covered in Chapter 10.

CHANGING THE LENGTH OR TIMING OF A SEQUENCE

Whenever a sequence of images is captured, there is a certain rate associated with it, and this rate determines the number of frames that are captured for a given shot. The person capturing the images may have some control over the rate at which they are shot, but once a particular event is captured it will have been recorded using a specific number of frames. If, for some reason, the number of frames proves to be inappropriate for the desired shot, it will be up to the composi-tor to modify the sequence so that it is useful.

A number of tools and methods exist that can be applied to a sequence of images to modify its length or **timing**.[2] The most simple method entails the removal of certain frames from the sequence in order to produce a new sequence. For instance, we may wish to use only the first 120 frames of a 240-frame sequence. Or we may use some range of frames from the middle of the sequence, say frames 100 to 200. Note that choosing a continuous range of frames out of a larger sequence will certainly give you a shorter shot, but it does not actually change the *speed* of the action in the shot. Say we have a 100-frame sequence of images that shows a ball rolling from the left side of the frame to the right. At frame 1 the ball is just entering the frame; at frame 100 it is just exiting. If we need a shot that is only half this length (50 frames long), then using only frames 1 to 50 from this sequence would seem to fit the criterion. But the new shot will be that of a ball that starts at the left frame line and rolls only to the middle of the screen. The action of the shot is quite a bit different, and the ball itself still appears to be rolling at the same rate.

Instead of this shot, let's say that we need a 50-frame shot in which the ball's action is the same: It should still be seen to enter and exit frame over the course of the shot. The simplest method would be to reshoot the scene and just roll the ball twice as fast (or run the camera at half its normal rate). This is often the best solution, but may be impractical for a number of reasons. As we'll see in many other places in this book, the "simple method" for solving problems (reshooting the scene) is often *not* an option, which is why digital compositing becomes necessary in the first place. So, let's assume that we are not able to reshoot our scene and therefore need to come up with a solution that makes use of the existing frames.

The most basic method for increasing the apparent speed of the action in a sequence of frames is to remove, or "drop" selected frames. For instance, if we wish to make the sequence appear to be twice as fast, we could just remove every other frame. In our rolling ball example, we will be left with 50 frames, but they will contain the full action desired (the ball rolling from left of frame to right), and consequently the ball will appear to be rolling at double the original speed. By the same token, if we wish to change a sequence so that things appear to be moving twice as slow, we can double every frame. Unfortunately, these methods often result in a new sequence in which the action doesn't appear quite as smooth

---

[2] "Timing" is yet another potentially ambiguous term, particularly if you work in the film world. Film, when being developed and printed, goes through a color-correction step that is known as "color timing." In conversation especially, you may find people abbreviating this term and referring to the "timing" of a shot when they are discussing its color balance. *Usually* the context of the discussion will make it obvious whether they are talking about color or temporal issues, but not always.

as it should. The eye can perceive the artificiality of the process. In the case in which we double the speed of the sequence by dropping frames, for instance, we may see a noticeable strobing or jerkiness in the motion. This effect is mostly due to the fact that, had the moving object actually been traveling at twice the speed, the camera would register a larger amount of **motion blur**. Motion blur is literally a blurring or smearing in an image that is caused by the distance an object moves while it is being captured. An example of motion blur is shown in Plate 45, and the phenomenon is described further in Chapter 12.

In many situations, the lack of motion blur can be compensated for by adding a subtle blur to the shot, although you may find that it is necessary to restrict the blur to the proper areas of the frame, depending on the type of action. For instance, if the camera is unmoving and all the action is coming from an object moving across the frame, then any additional blur should be applied *only* to the moving object.

Slowing down the action in a scene by doubling frames is also subject to visual artifacts. In this situation, since the motion is effectively being reduced from (in the case of film) 24 frames per second to 12 frames per second, we are approaching the threshold at which apparent motion no longer works. The brain may start to realize that it is seeing individual images instead of a scene in motion.

Depending on the software you have available, there are a number of methods to help alleviate some of the artifacts inherent in simply doubling or dropping frames. One of the most common methods involves selectively mixing, or averaging, frames together. Let us look again at the case in which we wish to have a sequence move at twice its original speed. Figure 6.1a shows our original frames, numbered sequentially. Instead of dropping every other frame, we do a 50/50 mix between every pair of frames to produce a new frame. Our new sequence would be as follows:

1&2, 3&4, 5&6, 7&8, 9&10, 11&12, . . .

Thus, our new first frame is composed of both frames 1 and 2 of the original sequence, averaged together. Frame 2 is a mix of frames 3 and 4, and so on, as shown in Figure 6.1b. This method produces a sequence that is half the length and visually twice the speed of the original. It has the additional benefit of

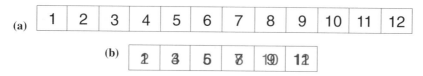

Figure 6.1   *Averaging frames to change length and timing. (a) The original sequence of frames. (b) Double-speed image sequence.*

producing images that will appear less artificial. The process of mixing two frames together essentially gives a crude approximation of a motion blur effect for objects that are moving.

The ability to produce a new sequence by mixing together additional frames becomes even more important when you need to create sequences that are not whole-number multiples of the original sequence. Consider a situation in which we want to increase the speed of the animation by only 50% instead of 100%. Using an intelligent averaging tool, we can produce a sequence whose frames consist of the following:

$$1\&2, 3, 4\&5, 6, 7\&8, 9, 10\&11, 12, 13\&14, 15, \ldots$$

Most of today's compositing systems will allow the user to either enter a compression ratio (e.g., "reduce speed by 33%") or specify a frame-range mapping (e.g., "change the timing so that frames 1–8 of the new sequence are composed of frames 1–12 of the original sequence"). The system may even allow you to create a curve that controls the weighting of the various frames that make up your new frame. If your system does not support any of these tools, then you may find it necessary to create the intermediate averaged frames manually—potentially an extremely tedious task!

Finally, there is an even more sophisticated tool for modifying the timing of a sequence of images. It is currently available almost exclusively on high-end systems and is usually an extremely compute-intensive process. Using sophisticated algorithms, it can analyze the motion of individual areas (or even pixels) within a frame and actually produce new intermediate frames that are created via some specialized interpolation and warping parameters. It is fully expected that this technology will become increasingly available and will soon be a standard option on all compositing packages.

KEYFRAMING

Now that we have discussed some of the ways that we deal with sequences of images in our compositing system, let's go to the next step and discuss how the various tools that we defined in earlier chapters are extended to work on these sequences. Digital compositing is based on the notion that just about any sort of manipulation you may use to produce or enhance a single image can then be similarly applied to a sequence of images. This is not to say that such an application is necessarily trivial, and certain techniques, such as those involved when using a digital paint system, do not easily translate from a single image to a sequence.

Even with tools that can just as easily be applied to a sequence of images as to a single frame, we will soon realize that instead of applying the same settings to our entire image sequence, we will want to modify certain parameters so that they change, or animate, over time. This raises the question of what the best way to animate these parameters would be. Obviously it could be quite painful to manually specify a different value for a particular effect on every frame of our sequence. Fortunately, there is a better way—a way that makes the job of animating values over time a relatively painless task. This technique is known as **keyframing**. Keyframing is a process in which, instead of explicitly defining a value for every frame of the sequence, the artist chooses certain "key" frames, assigns values to those frames, and then allows the computer to interpolate the values for the remaining frames. **Interpolation** is the process of using certain rules or formulas to derive new data based on a set of existing data. With keyframe animation, we are deriving values that fall between the existing keys that we have chosen and that will appear to make smooth transitions as we move through time.

Most books on computer animation techniques will give a great amount of detail about the process of using keyframe animation, but for the purposes of our discussion we will work with a simple example that explains the basic concepts. We'll look at how we might use keyframe animation to vary the brightness of an element in order to properly integrate it into a scene. Consider the case of an actor shot on bluescreen who is walking toward the camera. Let's assume that we've already done a wonderful job of pulling a matte for the actor, using some of the techniques discussed in Chapter 5. Now all we need to do is color balance him to the background plate in which he's supposed to appear. The only slight difficulty is that the plate dictates that he is walking from the far end of a shadowy corridor into a well-lit room. The bluescreen element was shot with constant lighting, so obviously we'll need to deal with animating the brightness of the character as he walks toward the camera. (Note: Animating the brightness of an element to simulate a change in lighting is common, but not ideal. A better composite would result had the element actually been shot correctly, with lighting that mimicked the background plate.)

Using basic keyframing techniques, we'll start with determining a proper brightness for the character at the first and last frames. At frame 1, we determine that applying a brightness of 0.4 to the foreground produces a pleasing, visually integrated result. At frame 300 (after he has completely entered the well-lit room), we decide that a brightness of 1.1 is most appropriate. By default, our software will probably linearly interpolate these two values to determine values for the intermediate frames. (There are a number of different ways to interpolate data between control points. We'll look at another in just a moment.) Figure 6.2 shows a graph of the linear interpolation between our keyframes. As you can see from the graph, at frame 150 (halfway through the sequence), the software has chosen a value of 0.75 (halfway between 0.4 and 1.1). Unfortunately, when we go look at frame 150, we notice that the actor has still not entered the room and consequently appears to be too bright for the scene. On closer examination, we realize that the

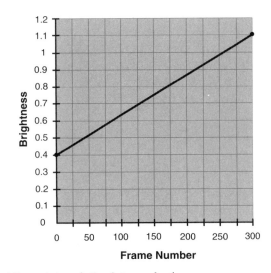

Figure 6.2 *Graph of linear interpolation between keyframes.*

actor doesn't enter the room until about frame 200, and should therefore remain fairly dark up until that point.

We then go back and look at a few more frames and determine proper brightness values for those frames. Figure 6.3 represents a graph of those new values, where we have added keyframes at frames 200 and 250. Note that we have changed our

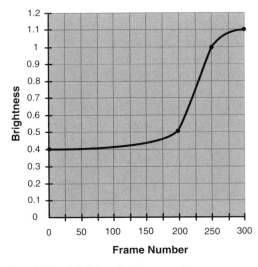

Figure 6.3 *Graph of values interpolated from keyframes using a more complex (nonlinear) method.*

interpolation method, so that instead of drawing straight lines between our key points, we are now using a smooth spline to create our curve. As you can see, the foreground element's brightness slowly increases as the actor approaches the room. Then, as he steps through the doorway, which occurs at about frame 220, there is a more rapid increase in brightness, lasting a few frames. Finally when he is fully in the room, where the lighting is constant, the value essentially levels off for the rest of the sequence.

This situation is, of course, a very simple example of how a single parameter might be animated over a range of frames. More complex scripts may involve animated parameters for many different layers.

There are a number of different ways to animate a parameter over time. Instead of using keyframes, we might simply use an equation, or we may import data from an outside source. If we are animating the movement of an object, it might be simpler to draw the motion path of the object and then control the speed at which the object moves along that path. Not all software will support all methods, but usually the same results can be achieved using a variety of methods.

CHAPTER SEVEN

Image Tracking and Stabilization

If you examine the history of visual effects in feature films, you'll notice that the vast majority of composites, be they optical or digital, occur in scenes in which the camera isn't moving or zooming. This setup is known as a **locked-off camera**, and until fairly recently it was almost a mandatory requirement for visual effects shots because it was extremely difficult to synchronize multiple elements in the same scene if their camera moves weren't exactly the same. However, it is often not possible, or even desirable, to use a locked-off camera. Multiple shots without camera moves can become boring and lifeless, and with today's sophisticated audiences may even cause the viewer to *expect* a visual effects shot.

Some of this problem has disappeared since the invention of the **motion-control camera,** which gives the camera operator the ability to repeat any given camera move multiple times. A background plate can be shot with a motion-control (or "moco") camera move, and then at a later time the foreground element can be shot with the same move. Motion control has a number of disadvantages, however, including the fact that it requires setting up a good deal of extra equipment (such as camera dollies rolling on a prelaid track). It also tends to be limited in terms of what type and speed of moves it is capable of performing. In many cases motion-control equipment can also be fairly noisy while in use, thus limiting its acceptability when shooting scenes with dialogue in them.

In situations in which the need arises to composite together elements that were shot *without* identical camera moves, one can now turn to a technique known as **tracking**. Tracking is the process of selecting a particular region of an image and determining that region's movement over time (i.e., on a sequence of images). Once the information about the movement of a region (or group of regions) is obtained, a variety of operations (which we'll discuss in a moment) can be applied much more effectively.

As we've seen with many other digital compositing tools, even a process such as tracking is something that was possible to do within a traditional optical compositing system, although the time it took to manually track an object was considerable. Additionally, it took a very skilled, patient operator to accurately hand-track an object into a scene. Today's digital tools, however, make it much easier to approach a shot in which the camera was not locked down. A great deal of work has been done to automate the tracking process,[1] and almost all compositing packages now include the ability to exactly determine the movement of a particular feature over a sequence of images.

TRACKING AN ELEMENT INTO A PLATE

There are a variety of situations in which tracking can be used, but probably the most common is when you need to synchronize the movement of an object you are adding to the scene with something already in the scene. The object in the scene may be moving, or the camera may just be moving relative to the object.

Consider the sequence of images in Figure 7.1. We'll use this image sequence as our example footage to help us explain the specific steps that are involved when tracking an element into a scene.

These steps will vary somewhat depending on what software you are using, but the concepts are fairly universal and the tools for automatically tracking a certain region of an image are all based on the same basic principles. Let's say we intend to add an object into the scene that appears to be attached to the front

Figure 7.1   *Image sequence for tracking example.*

---

[1] Tracking as an automated process was actually developed by the U.S. Defense Department to aid in missile guidance.

of the ship as it moves through the frame. First, you choose the feature in the image that you wish to track. (The next section gives some suggestions on how to go about choosing a feature that will track effectively.) Specifying the feature is done by outlining a **region of interest** (usually abbreviated as **ROI**) with a bounding box. An example of this is shown in Figure 7.2, where we have placed our ROI so that it outlines a small outcropping on the bow of the ship.

This region will now be used as a pattern that the software attempts to locate in all the other frames in the image sequence. Let's assume that you specify this region while looking at the first frame of the sequence, as shown in our example. The tracking software takes this reference ROI from this frame and begins by comparing it with the same location in the second frame. But not only does it compare the sample with the *same* location in the next frame, it also compares it with regions that are slightly *offset* from the original location. For instance, it pans

Figure 7.2   *Choosing an area to track using a bounding box.*

the source ROI by one pixel to the left and does a similar comparison. Then it pans two pixels to the left and does the comparison. Every time it tests a new offset, it keeps a record of how much that tested area deviates from the original sample. Eventually, after doing an exhaustive search, there will almost always be a region that matches far better than any of the other tests with the original pattern. This region is then accepted as the new location of the feature in frame 2. For instance, our tracking software may have gone through its exhaustive search and concluded that the best match with the original ROI from frame 1 occurs when it moves the sample two pixels to the right and three pixels down.[2] In order to properly match this movement, the element you are adding into the scene will need to be moved by an equivalent amount—two pixels to the right and three pixels down. Usually this movement is done automatically by the tracking software, once it determines the proper new location. The value of this new location is also entered into a table that keeps track of the movement of our pattern for every frame that we are tracking.

The software can now move on to frame 3, repeating the same process of searching for a pattern match with our original ROI. Eventually these steps are performed on every frame of the sequence, generating a move for our new element that corresponds exactly to the movement of the region that we have selected to track.

As you can imagine, this can be a fairly time-consuming process, particularly if the computer needs to search for pattern matches over a series of very high-resolution images! To make the process more efficient, there is at least one more region that the user is asked to define before the software begins tracking. This region is known as the "search area" and is also specified with a region-of-interest box, larger than the first and surrounding it. This box limits the area that the tracking software needs to consider on the subsequent frames in order to obtain a pattern match. Limiting the search area in this fashion speeds up the tracking process significantly, since areas of the image that are outside the search area are never examined. Just as the choice of what feature one wishes to track is not an exact science, so too is the choice of how large a bounding box should be drawn to define the search area. Some of these considerations will be looked at more thoroughly in a moment.

Although the example we have given discusses the process as if it were only testing areas that are whole-pixel offsets from the original, in actuality a good tracking system will exhaustively check subpixel offsets as well. Very few things will conveniently move a whole-pixel offset between every frame, and the ability to track accurately at the subpixel level is one of the things that distinguishes a

---

[2] Incidentally, the algorithms used to determine what exactly constitutes a "match" can vary quite a bit between different pieces of software; consequently, the accuracy can vary quite a bit as well.

mediocre tracking system (of which there are many) from an excellent one (of which there are very few).

Choosing the Feature to Track

Probably the most important thing that experienced trackers have developed an instinct for is how to choose the right area to track. The first step of this decision-making process is to visually examine the entire sequence with which you are working. There are a number of reasons for this step. Obviously, one of the primary reasons has to do with the fact that you are looking for a feature that remains visible throughout the necessary duration of the shot. If the feature you are tracking becomes obscured or leaves frame, you will need to expend some additional effort dealing with this problem, as described in the section entitled "Human Intervention."

Secondly, you are looking for a feature that remains fairly constant in terms of its shape and color. The tracking algorithm will usually be trying to find something that matches the original sample, and if the pattern changes over time it will no longer be such a match. Fortunately, there are methods for tracking objects that vary over time. Generally they involve choosing to periodically update the sample region you have chosen, replacing the original pattern with the most recent successful match. This change needs to be fairly gradual for the algorithm to deal with it, and a sudden, drastic change in the region that occurs over only a few frames will probably still cause the tracker to lose the region in question. Depending on the situation, this process of redefining the sample pattern may occur any number of times throughout the duration of the shot. As usual, the degree to which this process is automated will depend on the software that you are using.

Not only do we need to worry about the visibility and constancy of our ROI over the length of the sequence, but we also need to make sure that the ROI moves in a way that is appropriate for the element we are adding. In our example we chose to track the tip of the ship because we were planning to attach an object to this point. But we don't always need to track the exact attachment spot, as long as it does not move *relative* to that desired location. In other words, tracking some other feature on the front of the boat would probably also give us data that was reasonably accurate. But the farther away from the actual attachment point we move, the less accurate the data becomes, since these areas are moving differently. If you look at the example images in Figure 7.1 again, you can see that the rear of the boat is actually rising as the bow is descending. Obviously, if we wish to attach something to the front of the boat, it would be useless to track the back of the boat.

Finally, there are some specific visual characteristics that we look for in the region that we are choosing to track. Generally, you will want to pick a high-contrast area, with noticeable variations in color and brightness. Certain software or scenarios may work better if you preprocess your element to increase the necessary qualities. Usually this entails some kind of overall contrast manipulation in an attempt to emphasize specific features that you would like to use as a tracking target. Be careful not to emphasize undesirable artifacts (such as noise) at the same time, or you may actually decrease the accuracy of the resulting track.

The feature chosen should have variations along as many axes as possible to minimize the chance of the software coming up with a false match. For example, choosing an ROI like that marked as A in Figure 7.3 could prove to be a problem, because all the test regions that lie along this section of the mast look extremely similar to the original sample and will probably cause the software to be unable to accurately lock to a particular point. The ROI marked B has the same problem in a different direction; if you attach an object to this point, you will probably notice that your object slides up and down along this diagonal. A much better

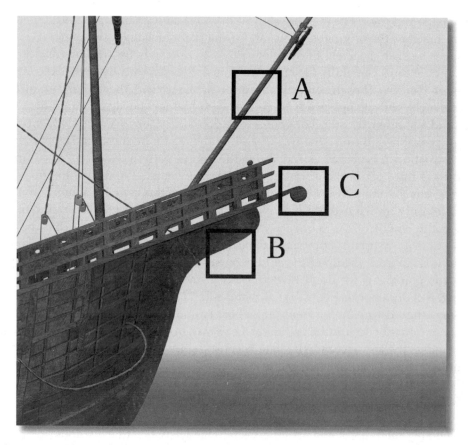

Figure 7.3   *Three possible tracking locations.*

area to choose would be something like that shown in choice C, where movement along any axis would be unique.

If you know ahead of time that you intend to track something in a scene, you may even be able to add something to the scene that will be easier for your tracking software to identify. By placing specific **witness points** into a scene, you will be assured that there are high-contrast, uniquely shaped references that the software can track to. Ideally, you will be able to place them in locations that will not be obscured or suffer problems with lighting variations. Depending on the scene, these witness points may or may not need to be removed from the final shot. They may be covered by the new element that you are tracking into the scene, or they may be innocuous enough (such as strategically placed props in a scene) that they can remain. If you do need to remove them, the tracking data they provide may simplify the process of tracking a neutral piece of imagery to cover them.

Limiting the Search Area

Another important reason to examine the entire sequence ahead of time is so that we can get a rough idea about the maximum amount our feature will move between any two frames. This information is important because it will help us to choose a search area that is no larger than necessary. This choice is generally a trade-off, since searching a too-large area will result in the search taking far longer than necessary, but choosing too small a box runs the risk of not including the proper area in certain frames. For features whose motion relative to the camera is fairly small, your search area box can also be fairly small, but if you are tracking an object that is moving significantly between every frame, then you'll need a wider search area (and consequently the tracking process will take longer).

Ultimately, you don't want to spend a great deal of time worrying about the size of this search area. It's better to err on the side of caution and choose a search area that is larger than you think necessary. These days, tracking algorithms are fast enough that the extra time it will take to search an overly large area will probably be negligible.

HUMAN INTERVENTION

Although most people would like to think that tracking an area in a scene is a completely automatic process, this is rarely the case. There are any number of reasons why the software may not be able to track certain things properly. Consider the case in which something else in the scene moves to obscure the object you were trying to track. Suddenly there is nothing in the search area that even remotely matches your sample. It need not be something as drastic as having an object move in front of our area of interest. Something as simple as a quick shift in lighting in the scene, caused by a light turning on or a surface catching a reflection, can confuse a tracking algorithm. Film grain may even cause enough variation between frames to introduce inaccuracies.

It is not uncommon for problems like this to show up several times during the process of tracking an area through a sequence of images. Generally, one has two choices. If the problem only happens for a few frames, you may be able to just manually enter in your best guess for where you think the feature would be on those frames. It will be much easier to make this guess if the object's movement is smooth and predictable. Erratic movement that varies significantly on every frame or a feature that is obscured for a larger period of time will require a second method. In this case you should try to choose a *different* point in the scene from which to continue your tracking, making sure that the new region is moving equivalently with the original ROI. Sophisticated software will usually be able to make a transition to this new point with little or no difficulty, but on some systems you may need to manually deal with the offset in the tracking data that happens when you switch points. Usually this intervention merely involves subtracting a constant X and Y offset from each frame's data after the changeover occurs.

Using Tracking Curves Manually

Although most software will allow you to simply specify the element you wish to attach to the feature in question and will automatically deal with tracking *and* moving it, there may be times when you need to interact with the tracking data directly.

Once a feature has been tracked, your software should have in storage a sequence of either pixel locations or pixel offsets for every frame of the shot. Some software returns the data based on the absolute pixel position of the image you tracked; others return the data as relative offsets from your original position (now defined to be [0,0]). Ideally, you have some way of examining a curve that is a plot of this data. This visual test can immediately show any gross problems or mistrackings that have occurred. For instance, Figure 7.4 shows a graph of the X movement that the tracking software has calculated for an object. The chances are high that the tracker encountered some problems around frame 40, indicating that you may wish to either retry the tracking or manually intervene.

Instead of having the software automatically apply any tracked movement to an element, you may wish to do it yourself. In this case you will need to attach the movement curves to a general Pan operator explicitly. By doing so, you will have additional flexibility, and you can easily modify the data first or use it in conjunction with a secondary move.

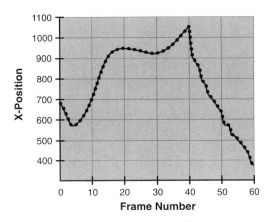

Figure 7.4   *Graph of tracking curve with a potential problem.*

STABILIZING A PLATE

Tracking techniques are also commonly applied when one needs to **stabilize** a sequence of images before they are used within a composite. This need tends to arise most often when the sequence was originally intended to be locked off but something happened during the shoot that compromised that intent. Any number of factors could conspire to produce such an "unstable plate." The camera might have been bumped or jarred while the film was rolling, a strong wind may have caused a slight wobble, or there may have been mechanical problems with the camera itself that caused the normally stable registration of the film as it moves through the gate to be less than acceptable. In this situation, the motion of the plate itself is tracked and analyzed, and then the unwanted movement is removed.

To do this, we still begin by tracking some feature in the frame to determine its motion over time. But instead of choosing a moving object in the scene, we will choose an object or feature that we believe is supposed to be stable and unmoving. By tracking this allegedly stable point, we can determine how far it deviates from a locked-down condition. Now we can take the resultant data and invert (negate) it so that we can move the plate in the *opposite* direction on each frame. We are effectively subtracting the plate's natural motion from itself to produce a new plate that no longer moves. (Again, applying our tracking curves in this fashion is assuming that our software isn't being used to automatically do this process for us.)

A modification of this technique can even be used to remove high-frequency jitter from an otherwise desirable camera move. Consider a tracking curve such as that shown in Figure 7.5. We can see that the motion has a lot of small, erratic

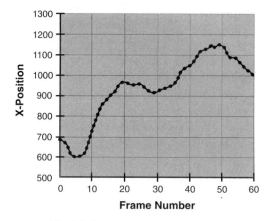

Figure 7.5   *Tracking curve with high-frequency noise.*

moves over time, yet there is also a large overall camera move. In this situation, where we are looking at the *X*-translation curve, we see that the high-frequency noise is moving by up to 20 or 30 pixels in *X*, whereas the overall curve covers a range of nearly 600 pixels over the 60 frames shown. If we want to remove only the high-frequency artifacts, we need to create a curve that does the same basic overall move but has none of the noise. Figure 7.6 shows such a curve.

Depending on your software, you can either create this second curve manually, matching the overall move as much as possible, or use your software's built-in tools for smoothing a curve to remove high-frequency noise. In either case, once this new, smooth curve is available, we subtract it from the original. (Essentially,

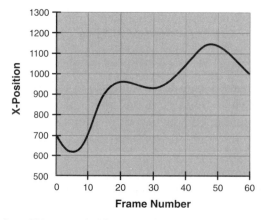

Figure 7.6   *Smoothed tracking curve (without noise).*

we subtract the value of the curve at each frame from the value of the original curve at that frame.) The resulting curve is shown in Figure 7.7; it is now a curve that contains *only* the unwanted high-frequency noise from the original.

If we invert this curve and use it to pan the original plate, we will end up with a plate that still has the required move yet doesn't exhibit any annoying extra jitter.

TRACKING MULTIPLE POINTS

So far, we have talked only about one-point, or single-point, tracking. It is capable of giving us the X and Y position for a single point on an image so we can attach an element to it or stabilize the image based on that point. Single-point tracking only gives us enough information to deal with simple, overall positional changes.

If, instead, we track *two* points in a scene, we now have enough information to accurately reproduce any rotational changes that occur between the two points. What's more, by measuring the change in distance between the two points, changes in scale for a given object can also be computed and mimicked. (Again, most systems would automate this process, but if not, you could also compute this information manually.)

Taking this concept even further, four-point tracking gives enough information to calculate simple warps that mimic perspective shifts. We can track the four corners of a moving object and lock an image or element inside those points, often creating a perfect match for any transformations caused by object or camera moves. The logical extension of four-point tracking is a system in which multiple points in a scene are tracked and then used to control some sort of warping

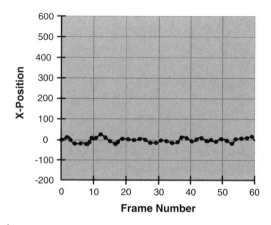

Figure 7.7 *Noise-only curve.*

tool. Every moving point modifies the warp on the image, so that very complex movement and distortions can be matched.

Finally, tools are now becoming available that can take tracking data from multiple points and, sometimes in conjunction with proper survey data for the scene in question, recreate the full 3D camera move for the shot. This data can then be fed back to a 3D animation system that will be able to render elements that exactly match the moves from the real scene.

CHAPTER EIGHT

Interface Interactions

Although all digital compositing systems share the same basic concepts and algorithms, the method by which a user interacts with the system can vary widely. This interaction is primarily determined by the **user interface** that is provided with the software in question. These days, this user interface is typically a graphical front end to the tools, and hence is usually referred to as simply the **GUI**, the **graphical user interface**. It would be pointless (and impossible!) to try to discuss the specific quirks of all the various interfaces out there, so instead we will attempt (somewhat arbitrarily) to define certain user-interface categories, discuss the different philosophies behind various working methods, and then spend some time looking at basic tools that have similar equivalents on all common platforms.

Because the process of digital compositing is an interactive one, requiring extensive feedback at every step of the way, it is very important that your compositing software does not hinder your efficiency. Certainly a great deal of this ease of interaction will have to do with how experienced and familiar you are with the particular paradigm that your software employs. Just about any system, including a completely text-based command-line compositing system, can be used to produce high-quality images. But the best systems recognize that the operator's time is a significant cost factor in producing imagery, and consequently will provide as many tools as possible for optimizing the process.

We will break user-interface-related issues into two primary categories. The first is the more complex of the two and deals with how a compositing artist combines and controls the various tools that were discussed in Chapters 3 through 7. The second category, discussed in Chapter 9, encompasses the use of specific tools for viewing and analyzing images and sequences of images.

Different software packages may have extremely different methods of interacting with certain tools. Even the hardware that is used may be different: Certain compositing software may support a keyboard-only interface, other software may expect that your primary interaction will be with a mouse, and some packages dictate that you work primarily with an electronic pen and tablet. But the concepts *behind* the hardware are well defined and vary little from platform to platform. These concepts are what we will focus on in this chapter (and the next). The most important issues are related not to the interfaces used for specific tools, but rather to the overall working methodology that the software allows you to develop—the workflow.

WORKFLOW

Up to this point, we've primarily treated the various image manipulation and combination tools as if they were isolated entities. In other words, we have mostly discussed how a single operator affects a single image. In the real world, the compositing process is one of applying *combinations* of these tools, each modifying some aspect of the image sequence until the final, intended imagery is produced. There may be situations in which dozens or even hundreds of these tools are used. To see an example of this, examine Plate 93, which is a graphical representation of all the operators that were used to produce a single specific shot for the movie *Titanic*. Each box represents a single operator, and the overall structure and grouping of the boxes is based on the order in which these operators were applied. Essentially, these numerous discrete operators were combined in an intricate fashion to produce the complex, custom-designed machine that was needed to produce the finished shot. For the bulk of our discussions in this chapter, we will try to use slightly less complex examples than the one shown in Plate 93.

Whether one is working with a large, complex composite or a small, simple one, the basic workflow is essentially the same. The flowchart in Figure 8.1 covers the basic steps. Note that this process is fairly recursive, since newly created image sequences will often be treated as source elements for the next step in a composite.

Let's look at the individual steps as they occur. In step 1, the images with which we will be working are imported into our system. Files of various types may be brought in, and, depending on the software that you are using, there may be a need to do some specialized processing to format the images in a particular way. (Chapter 10 discusses format issues in much greater detail.) Certain high-speed compositing systems may require you to preformat the images so that they can be rapidly stored and retrieved from a special area of the disk, for instance. Other systems will simply keep track of the image sequences' locations in a general file system and will read images into memory as needed. To speed up

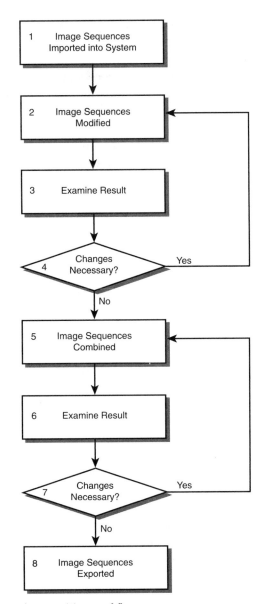

Figure 8.1 *Flowchart of compositing workflow.*

the interactivity of the process, the software may let you work with low-resolution **proxies** of the original frames. This option is discussed in a later section of this chapter.

In step 2, we start applying the image processing operators from Chapter 3 (and Appendix A). This process could include any number of color corrections, geometric transforms, or spatial filters—everything from brightness to blurs to rotations.

Now we take a look at the result of the operations we've applied to the sequence and decide whether we're satisfied with the result. This is step 3, the "visual feedback" step, which may cause us to return to step 2 for additional adjustments. We may bounce back and forth between steps 2 and 3 several times until we have a result with which we are happy. (Understand that you do not necessarily need to decide on all the image processing operations that you will use before you start to combine images. Most systems will allow you to add additional effects to the original layers as necessary, although your flexibility may be more limited with certain types of systems.) Also, although the steps are represented as single boxes in our flowchart, in a real composite we may go through these same steps with any number of original source sequences.

At some point we will need to combine some of these modified sequences, using tools such as those discussed in Chapter 4. This process is represented by step 5 in our diagram and is immediately followed by an analysis (usually visual) of the result. Once again we go into a feedback loop, with potentially a large number of iterations in which changes are made and the results are examined. In this case, we have the added complexity that the changes may need to be made to the operator that combines the images (step 5) or to one of the original image modification tools (step 2).

The flowchart obviously represents a very simplified view of the process. The actual method of interacting with your compositing package will depend heavily not only on the specifics of the user interface, but also on the basic paradigms your software uses. One of the most important distinguishing factors is whether your system is considered to be a **batch compositing** system or an **on-line** (or interactive) **compositing** system.

ONLINE VERSUS BATCH

Although it is convenient to try to divide compositing software into the categories of either "batch" or "on-line," the distinctions between the two are no longer all that clear. Historically, a batch compositing system was one with virtually no interactivity. It would generally rely on text-based scripts, include no graphical user interface, and would provide little or no immediate feedback for any image processing operations. On-line systems, on the other hand, usually consisted of some dedicated hardware that was capable of applying a limited set of operations to an image sequence, creating a new sequence with each step. If the compositor needed to apply several operations, each one would be done as a discrete step, producing a modified sequence that would then have the next operator applied to it. These days, pure on-line systems tend to exist only in the video world, where dedicated hardware is used to rapidly process the imagery in question. Such systems are fast, but lack a great deal of functionality and flexibility.

More general-purpose compositing systems are now available that combine functionality from both paradigms. This evolution is not surprising, since ultimately the actual operations that are applied are no different between the two systems. It is the way in which the compositing artist interacts with the software that is different. Even today, different systems will tend to enforce different workflows. The most important distinction is whether or not the system is designed primarily to create a compositing script or to iteratively produce new image sequences with every step. This distinction is an important one, and consequently it is still useful to categorize compositing systems as either on-line or batch. Let's look at the typical workflow for each category in a bit more detail.

On-line systems tend to work in the following fashion. First, a sequence of images—or several different sequences—is brought into the system. The sequences are imported, either from videotape or from the general file system of a computer, into a specialized disk that allows for much quicker access to the images. The system is capable of viewing these sequences (often called **clips**) interactively, displaying them at the proper frame rate as needed.

The user then decides on the first compositing effect that is necessary (a color correction, for instance) and applies it to the image sequence in question. The clip is then processed frame by frame (but usually fairly quickly) with this effect, producing a new image sequence. The compositor then uses this clip as the source for the next operation (combining it with a different clip, perhaps), and yet another clip is generated. The process continues, with a new sequence of images produced at each step, until the final composite is complete. The intermediate image sequences are not destroyed at every step, but rather remain available should the need arise to redo any of the earlier steps in the process. These clips can, at some point, start to take up a good deal of disk space and memory, and thus one will often need to dispose of sequences that are less likely to be needed again. This will be a judgement call, and disposing of a particular sequence may require the user to manually redo a number of steps if that sequence later proves to be necessary.

Batch systems take a different tack. Although one still works by manipulating and combining elements, there is no explicit processing of these operators to produce a new sequence at each step. Instead, one is working to produce a specialized script that, once perfected, can be run as a batch process. Each operator that is to be applied to an image sequence is tested on a few select frames. Once the desired parameters are determined, an instruction is recorded into the script that describes this operator and the parameters it is using. The script will continue to grow, and any number of effects or layers can be added, but the only processing that is taking place is being done on just a few selected frames, probably at a lower-than-normal resolution in order to speed up the testing process. The lower-resolution image that is being used for testing purposes is known as a **proxy** image, which will be discussed in a moment.

Eventually, the compositor has built a script that describes all the steps that will be needed to create the completed composite. Only then will the compositor choose to execute the script. The compositing software reads the script and applies all the operations that are necessary to produce the final composite. This step generally does not require any user supervision, since all the steps are already contained within the script. The process also does not necessarily need to run on the same machine as that on which the compositing artist created the script, and in fact it often does not, particularly if there are a number of machines in a network that can be used to share the workload. Ultimately, the script finishes executing and the new images that make up the final composite are stored on the computer's disk.

The process of building a script instead of actually processing and viewing each layer as it is created can be cumbersome, although this is as much a product of poor interface design as anything. The benefits of a script-based system are many, since complex, multistep processes can be modified and automatically rerun as necessary. Many on-line systems would require the operator to manually redo several of the same steps if there arose a need to change one of the original elements or effects that had been applied.

In general, on-line systems tend to be set up on machines that have a good deal of CPU and graphics-processing horsepower, which they will need in order to be interactive. Batch systems, on the other hand, tend not to need such extreme interactivity and consequently can run on much less expensive hardware platforms. The distinction between the two types of systems is starting to become less and less extreme, however. Most systems these days are, in fact, hybrid systems, with varying levels of interactivity and scriptability. Very few on-line systems do not offer at least some ability to group multiple operations together before computing a new result, and very few batch systems do not offer a number of tools that increase interactivity and provide reasonably rapid feedback. Ultimately there is no reason why software cannot be written that is both highly interactive as well as being fully scriptable.

For the duration of this chapter, as well as in certain other places in this book, we will discuss compositing systems primarily from a script-based point of view. This is done for a number of reasons. First, even if you are working on a system that has no ability to create a batch-processing script, you should still think of compositing in terms of the entire *process*, as opposed to individual steps. Second, script-based systems are much more common and tend to be less expensive, and as such are available to a much wider audience. Third, on-line systems that have poor or limited script-generating ability are really missing a significant piece of functionality, and we cannot ignore that functionality if we wish to give a complete overview of the compositing field. Finally, it is much easier to write about compositing in terms of a script-based system, since it allows us to represent the entire process of creating a composite in the same fashion as most script-based systems represent their data to the user—via a set of graphs or flowchartlike diagrams.

METHODS OF REPRESENTING THE COMPOSITING PROCESS

We need to define a few conventions here so that we can better discuss large compositing scripts. Let's walk through the creation of a very simple composite, defining a few terms and conventions as we go along. We begin with two source sequences, labeled "Foreground" and "Background." Our goal is to combine the two images so that the foreground is over the background and the two sequences are well integrated. Let's say that the foreground image is initially too dark, so a brightness layer is added to it. The background needs to be defocused a bit, and so a blur layer is added to that. We also decide that the background is a little too bright, and so a brightness modifier is added there as well. Finally, the modified foreground is layered over the modified background.

There are any number of ways to formally define this process. We could use an interface known as "English," since it is presumably something that most readers of this book are familiar with. To describe this process as succinctly as possible in English, we might say:

> Read in an image sequence labeled "Foreground," apply a brightness of 1.2 to that and then place the result of this operation over the image sequence that is created when you read in a sequence labeled "Background," apply a blur of 4.0 to it, and apply a brightness of 0.8 to that.

As you can see, the English language is not necessarily the best tool for describing compositing operations. The above description is fairly wordy and is probably not as precise as it should be, since the brightness of 0.8 could potentially be interpreted as needing to be applied *after* the Over operation occurs.

Now, if we were to represent this process using a simple text-based compositing system, the syntax might look something like this:

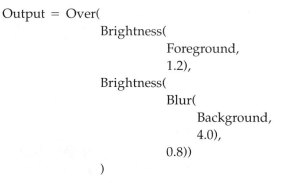

```
Output = Over(
            Brightness(
                    Foreground,
                    1.2),
            Brightness(
                    Blur(
                        Background,
                        4.0),
                    0.8))

        )
```

For those of you who are accustomed to working with a compositing system that has a nice GUI, this may look like a crude and cryptic way of representing a simple compositing script. But it certainly contains all the important information. We can see that a brightness of 1.2 has been applied to the sequence called "Foreground." We can see that a blur value of 4.0 has been applied to the "Background" layer, and then a brightness value of 0.8 is added above that. Finally, the Over operator takes the two sequences and combines them.

Consider now the chart shown in Figure 8.2, which is yet a third way of representing a compositing script—using a hierarchical "tree." For most people, Figure 8.2 is far more intuitive than either of the first two descriptions. It quickly shows the complex relationships between the images and operations in an easy-to-read format.

Each box in this tree is usually referred to as a "node" of the graph. The flow of this graph is from left to right. That is, when the operations are executed, the first nodes that are evaluated are those at the left of the graph, and then the operators to the right of that are evaluated, and so on, until the final node, at the far right of the graph, is executed. Any node that feeds directly into another node is considered to be the "parent" of that node; consequently, any node that is immediately *to the right of* the parent node is considered to be a "child" node. Thus, the Over operator is the child of both of the Brightness operators.

One thing that you will immediately notice about the diagram in Figure 8.2 is that you do *not* see the values of the variables assigned to each operator. This is

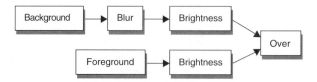

Figure 8.2   *Simple compositing script represented by a hierarchical tree.*

intentional, and common with most systems. Once we start to create larger scripts, we will find a need to limit the amount of information that our GUI is presenting us in order to better grasp the overall flow of the script. There is usually some method (such as double-clicking on one of the node boxes) that gives an expanded view of the specifics of that node, including the value of any associated variables. Your particular software may have many additional features; you should try to become as familiar as possible with them. Some software may allow you to explicitly name each node or to attach notes to them. This information can be helpful if your script grows to be large or if someone else will also be modifying parts of the same script.

Throughout the rest of this book we will use this simple tree format to depict groups of compositing operators. Again, we must stress that this is merely one of many possible ways to look at this kind of data: Your interface and mileage may vary. Most good compositing systems will give the user a multitude of different ways to view the data that is being manipulated, allowing the user to choose which method is most efficient for a given person or situation.

Take a moment now to look again at the script shown in Plate 93. This is a large script, but not unprecedentedly so. Composites produced for film, where attention to detail is critical and the increased resolution allows for a huge number of relatively small elements, can easily take months to set up and finesse.

Compressed Trees

As you can imagine, it can quickly grow difficult to keep track of where individual nodes are located in a large compositing script. This certainly underscores the importance of organizing your data efficiently and naming your nodes coherently and consistently. There are, fortunately, some other tools that can make the task a bit easier. One of the most important is the ability to select a portion of a graph and "compress" it, that is, to replace it (visually) with a simplified representation.

Consider a tree like the one shown in Figure 8.3. As you can see, our background image has several image processing operations layered on top of each other. Let's say that we've precisely tuned these layers to where we want them and that we no longer want to worry about them as individual objects. We can select the five

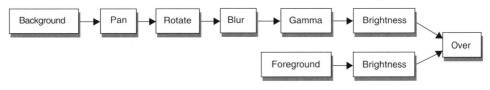

Figure 8.3 *More complex compositing script.*

layers and group them as a new compressed layer, which we'll call "BG_fixes." The simplified graph would look like Figure 8.4.

As usual, remember that not all software packages may support this sort of functionality, and even if they do, the paradigm may be different. If your software doesn't support this type of grouping directly, you can sometimes accomplish a similar effect by the use of precomposites, discussed more in Chapter 11.

Timelines

While the tree-based graph is very useful for viewing complex scripts, there is one piece of information that such a display does *not* address well, namely, the timing relationship between nodes, particularly for image sequences that are offset in time relative to one another. To better represent this information, we will use a **timeline graph** instead. The timeline lets us lay out the various events not only relative to each other, but also to an absolute time. Depending on what sort of work you are doing, you may find it useful to display the units of this graph either in common real-world units, such as seconds or minutes, or simply as individual frames. If you wish to display your timeline with real-world units, your system will need to know what the frame rate of your output medium will be—24 fps for standard film, 30 fps for NTSC video, and so forth. We will show all our time-related graphs with the units representing frames.

When dealing with layers from a timeline point of view, we are really only interested in two pieces of information: the length of the image sequence in question, and the starting point of this sequence. (A third useful piece of information, namely, when a sequence ends, is obviously an easily computed byproduct of the first two.)

Consider the case in which we want to have an object not appear in the scene until several seconds have elapsed. Perhaps the object is an explosion that is only 48 frames long, and it needs to begin after our background has been running for about 100 frames. Figure 8.5 shows a way in which we might represent this scenario. As you can see, we have a representation of our two layers, as well as a scale at the bottom of the diagram that shows us an absolute range of frames. The layers that we have available are positioned relative to this scale, so that their starting points and their lengths can be accurately measured. This sort of view gives us a great deal of information at a quick glance. We can see the relative

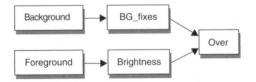

Figure 8.4 *Complex script represented by a hierarchical tree with a compressed branch.*

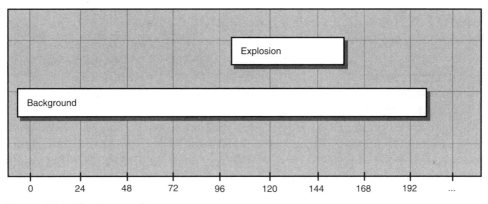

Figure 8.5   *Timeline graph.*

length of the two sequences—how the background is about 200 frames long and the explosion element is 48 frames long. We can also see that the explosion won't be used until about frame 100. This information would be far more cumbersome to determine using any of the other display tools that we've discussed so far.

The timeline view is useful in a variety of different situations and should be considered an essential adjunct to the standard node-based view of a script. Not only is it useful for viewing information, but it can also be used for manipulating the script as well. For instance, to change the point in time at which a certain layer appears, you could simply grab the layer in the timeline view and drag it to the desired starting frame. The timeline view makes it much easier to visualize and manipulate operations that involve a transition between two different layers. A dissolve between two different sequences can be indicated as in Figure 8.6, and adjusted by simply sliding the second layer so that the amount of overlap is of the desired duration.

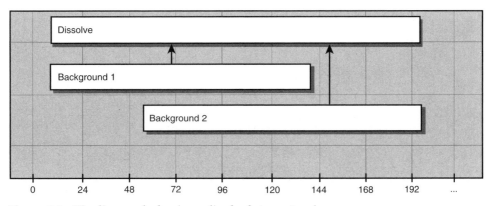

Figure 8.6   *Timeline graph showing a dissolve between two image sequences.*

CURVE EDITORS

As we've discussed in several earlier chapters, there are situations in which it will be convenient for the user to define a curve to control some aspect of a composite. This curve may represent a variable that changes over time, or it may represent a range of values in a look-up table. No matter what the eventual use of such a curve will be, there are some basic tools that are used for creating and manipulating curves. We usually call a group of such tools a **curve editor,** and we will present an example that uses many of these tools in a fairly standard layout. Some form of curve editing is available in most graphic packages. We will not go through the concepts in a great deal of detail, other than to define some basic terms and to highlight specific features that should be present in an above-average editor.

Take a look at Figure 8.7. We will use this diagram to point out some of these specific features. The diagrams show a number of curves that reflect variables that change over time. Thus, the X-axis represents time and is measured in frame numbers. The Y-axis represents the value of the variable in question. A curve that is not based on time, such as a LUT curve, would have differently labeled axes, but would otherwise be dealt with in exactly the same fashion as a time-variant curve.[1]

We are primarily concerned with a curve editor's ability to create, modify, and view a curve or group of curves. More specifically, a good curve editor should allow us to do the following:

- View multiple curves in the same window for direct comparisons. Multiple curves should be easily distinguishable, ideally through the use of color coding.
- Zoom in and out of a curve, scaling the X and Y axes nonproportionally as needed.
- View the specific numerical X and Y value at any location along the curve.
- Label individual curves with unique, user-defined names so that data can be better organized.
- View the **control points** on a curve and be able to directly access their specific numerical values.
- Create and manipulate individual control points.
- Insert and delete control points in an existing curve.
- Choose the type of interpolation used between control points. There are a wide variety of potential interpolation techniques, and different packages may vary slightly in what they offer. Figure 8.7a shows a curve with simple linear interpolation—the control points are connected with straight lines.

---

[1] Frame-based curves will usually limit you to nonfractional frame numbers, whereas other variables that can be controlled via a curve may not need such a limitation.

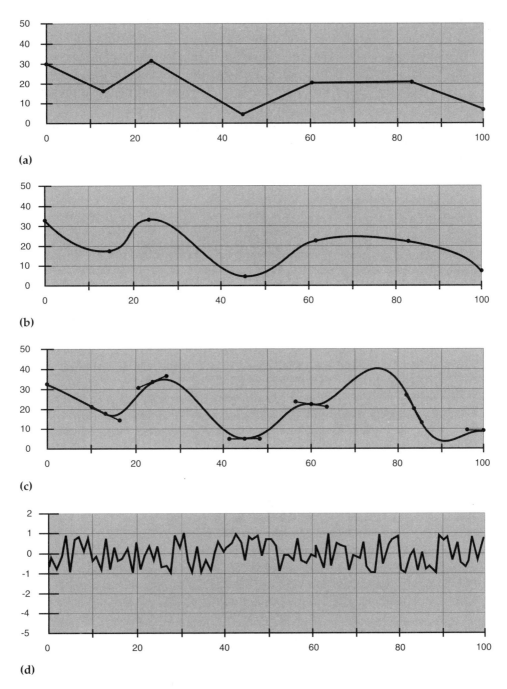

Figure 8.7   *Curves. (a) Linear interpolation. (b) Spline interpolation. (c) Hermite spline interpolation. (d) Function-based curve.*

Figure 8.7b uses the same control points, but interpolates with a smoother **spline curve** instead. Figure 8.7c uses a particularly powerful type of spline (usually known as a "Hermite spline") that allows one to control not only the position of the control points but also the tangents of the curve as it passes through these control points. These tangent controls are represented as additional "handles" that sprout from each control point.

- Create a curve based on a mathematical equation. The equation language should support standard functions as well as the ability to create a curve using random numbers within a given range. An example of this is shown in Figure 8.7d, a curve that is defined to be a random value between 1 and −1.

- Combine and manipulate curves based on mathematical expressions. This can work in a number of different ways—either a new curve is generated from the expression or the existing curve is maintained and the modifying expression is stored with it.

For example, we may want to take a curve which defines some fluctuating values and tie it to two different effects. The range of values for the curve is fine for the first effect, but the second effect may need a much larger range. In such a situation, we should be able to mathematically define a new curve that is simply a constant value multiplied by our first curve. This is shown in Figure 8.8, where the bottom curve is our first curve and the top curve is our second.

Notice that every value in the top curve is five times greater than the equivalent value in the lower curve for any given point in time. Ideally, the

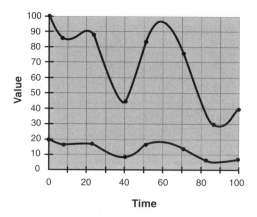

Figure 8.8   *Defining a new curve (top) mathematically based on a existing curve (bottom).*

second curve will still reference the first, and should we manually update the original, the second curve would automatically change as well.

- Apply arbitrary smoothing to an irregular curve. A number of different algorithms exist for smoothing a curve and removing unwanted noise or spikes. Figure 8.9a shows an unsmoothed curve, while Figure 8.9b shows the smoothed equivalent. Chapter 7 touched on some situations in which this capability is useful.
- Append two curves together to create a new curve. Ideally this operation includes the ability to apply some kind of smoothing to the connection point to prevent abrupt changes in value.
- Read and write a curve from or to a file on disk in a simple ASCII format. There is no industry standard for how a curve should be represented, but as long as the format that is used is text based and well documented, it is usually a trivial task to modify curves taken from one editor so that they can be read by another.
- Resample a curve to produce a new curve with a different number of control points. This capability is useful for a couple of reasons. First, you may wish to convert a simple curve that is defined by only a few control points into a curve that has a control point for every frame. This curve could then be written to a file and exchanged with any other package or device that works on a frame-by-frame basis—anything from a 3D animation system to a motion-control camera. It is also useful to do the reverse, that is, to import a

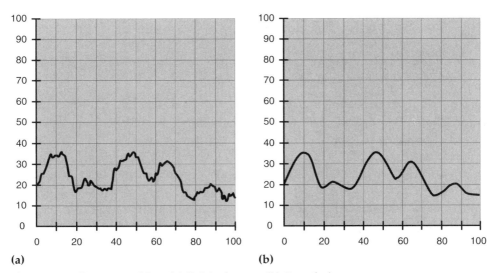

(a)   **(b)**

Figure 8.9   *Curve smoothing. (a) Original curve. (b) Smoothed curve.*

curve that is defined by an explicit value at every frame and convert it to a simpler representation that uses fewer control points. This curve will then be much easier to manipulate, as well as requiring less memory to represent it.

WORKING WITH PROXY IMAGES

If you are working on a computer that is not capable of displaying the images with which you are working in real time at full resolution, or if you do not wish to spend as much of your time waiting for the computer to process intermediate test images, you may wish to work with lower-resolution proxy images instead. A **proxy image** is a scaled-down version of the image that you are currently working on. The proxies are created either on the fly, as needed, or are precreated (manually by the user or automatically by the software). Working with proxy images usually requires (or at least implies) that you have some kind of batch-processing system available. The theory is that you can do the majority of your compositing work in low resolution; once you have taken it as far as possible, the steps you have defined will then automatically be converted and applied to the high-resolution equivalents. Some final tweaking will probably need to be done to deal with any unexpected problems that were not visible at low resolution, but the hope is that most of the work can be accomplished at low resolution in a much faster time. To best take advantage of the proxy image method, your compositing system should be **resolution independent**. This term means that the system can take a script created for low-resolution (proxy) images and apply it to the high-resolution equivalent images, while still producing the expected imagery.

Resolution independence is not as simple as it sounds, since a great number of image processing operations are normally specified in units that are pixel dependent. Something as simple as the parameters for a pan, for instance, are usually given in pixel units. If we specify a 200-pixel horizontal move for an image that is 400 pixels wide, we move that image by half its own width. If, however, we convert our script to high resolution, that same 200-pixel move applied to an image that is 2000 pixels wide will only move the image a fraction of its own width. A resolution-independent system either automatically converts the units to the new scale when we change our working resolution or simply represents all its operators in resolution-independent units in the first place. A pan, for instance, could be specified as a percentage of the image's width instead of as an absolute number of pixels. If you do not have a resolution-independent system, you can still work with proxies—you'll just need to do the conversion yourself. Knowing which operators need conversion can be tricky. Any operator that physically moves an element by a specific pixel value will usually need converting, but element scaling will not. Rotations will probably need the location of the center of rotation converted, but the angle of rotation would remain the same. Convolution-based effects such as simple blurs will need to be converted, but color corrections will not.

Most compositing systems will, at the very least, produce temporary low-resolution proxies to speed the interactivity of testing. This feature is different from a fully functional resolution-independent system, but it still can be very useful. It may be limited to single-image test frames, for instance, but will still allow you to preview certain operations at this lower resolution and interactively tune any necessary parameters before applying them to the full-resolution original.

CHAPTER NINE

Image Viewing and Analysis Tools

‿

In this chapter we will talk about a variety of ways to get information about the images with which one is working. This information is often visual in nature—certainly the most basic thing one can do with an image is to look at it—but there are also other tools that can be used to provide numerical or statistical data about an image. As was the case in the last chapter, different compositing systems may vary significantly in the way their tools deal with certain things, including the ability to view and analyze images. But the basic concepts are consistent throughout the industry, and consequently most of what we describe in this chapter will be available, in some form or another, on just about any basic compositing system. The processes and tools we describe will be useful *throughout* the compositing process. Before any operators are applied to an image sequence, you will need to know as much as possible about the images you will be using, and during the process you will constantly need information about the results of the various steps.

When it comes to viewing images, always keep in mind that the image you see represented on your computer screen is by no means guaranteed to accurately represent the way the image will appear in its final form. Ultimately, it is only by viewing your imagery in the format and medium for which it is eventually intended that you can be absolutely certain of what it will look like. Thus, if you are creating images for film, you must *see* them on film before you can be sure they are correct. While care should be taken to ensure that all viewing devices are calibrated to a consistent standard, don't assume that an image that looks acceptable on your computer monitor will look the same when it is displayed via a different method, even if that monitor is properly calibrated to some standard.

IMAGE VIEWERS

Certainly the most basic tool is one that can display a single image. It should allow the user to view individual channels of the image, including the alpha and Z-depth channels, and to zoom in and out of various areas of the image to see more detail. If the image you are viewing is of a greater resolution than your computer's monitor, your viewer should allow you to see a portion of the image at a true one-to-one pixel ratio and to resample the image so that you can see the entire image on your screen.

As you make iterative changes to your images, you will often need to do a detailed comparison between various trials. The best way is to be able to view the two images either by rapidly flipping between them or by interactively wiping or mixing back and forth between them.

If you are working with images that are stored in some sort of nonstandard color space, you may also find it useful to be able to apply a compensating LUT to the image when it is viewed. This LUT is strictly for display purposes: The data in the image is not changed; rather, the color conversion happens only in the viewing tool, for the benefit of the viewer. Chapter 15 discusses a couple of different situations in which this sort of functionality will be useful.

FLIPBOOKS

Not only will you want to view a single image, but most of the time you will also want to be able to look at a sequence of images, ideally at a fast enough rate so that they appear as a moving sequence. This type of viewer is often known as a "flipbook" tool, a term that goes back at least as far as the days of traditional animation, when one would quickly flip through a stack of sequential images to check the motion. The abilities of most flipbook tools are very tied to the hardware that you are using. Many flipbooks are reliant on the amount of main memory in the system for how many frames they can display as a moving sequence. Large images will mean that the system can display a shorter sequence, and smaller images will allow a longer sequence.

If you want to compute the amount of memory that will be needed for a computer to display a given image, don't assume that you can simply look at the file size of the image as it is stored on disk. Flipbooks generally need to uncompress an image before displaying it, and if your image file uses any compression then this size will not give you an accurate estimate. What you can do, usually, is to compute the amount of memory required by simply multiplying the width of the image (in pixels) by the height of the image (in pixels) by the number of bits per channel that your flipbook uses (which will generally never be more than eight, since this is the maximum most monitors will support) by the number of channels that the flipbook will display (usually three or four, depending on whether your flipbook loads the matte channel for animated playback) by the number of frames in the animation. This gives the total number of *bits* that it will take to load the given sequence, so divide by 8 to get the number of bytes.

Some systems may make use of specialized storage hardware to display image sequences directly from a hard disk, instead of consuming main memory. The speed of playback with either scenario is very system dependent. You will almost always want to view your sequence at the same speed as that at which it will eventually be used, but you may find that your system is unable to keep up with this rate if using full-resolution images. Usually this problem can be solved by displaying lower-resolution images instead. Consequently, you will need to determine on a case-by-case basis whether the particular test you are working on is something that you want to see at the proper speed or the proper resolution. A good flipbook tool will give feedback about whether it is able to maintain the speed you have chosen.

Most of the features discussed for a single-image display should also be accessible for the flipbook display. You should still be able to zoom in and out of the moving sequence, view specific channels of the moving sequence, interactively compare sequences, and view a sequence with a specialized LUT in place.

IMAGE STATISTICS

In addition to a variety of different viewing modes, you should be able to get some numerical or statistical information concerning the images with which you are working. You will certainly need to be able to determine the spatial resolution of an image, as well as its bit depth. Be aware that just because an image is contained in a file with a particular bit depth does not mean that that image actually has information commensurate with that bit depth. An 8-bit image can be saved in a 16-bit file format, but doing so does not actually create any new information.

Other information may or may not be available, such as the average color in an image, or the high and low extremes. This information will be useful in a number of situations, particularly those in which we are attempting to synchronize the colors and contrast between two images. Even more useful than an overall analysis of statistics is the ability to analyze specific *areas* of the image, a topic we will discuss next.

Pixel or Regional Information Tools

There are times when you would like to determine information and detail about a subregion or even a particular pixel of an image. Most software will allow you to turn on a mode in which you can point to an area of an image and get feedback about the exact X and Y coordinates that your cursor is indicating. You should also be able to determine the RGB value of an individual pixel or get some type of average value for a region. This information can be used to help with color-correction decisions or to check the solidity of a matte. Ideally, you will even be able to select the average color from an area and paste that value into a variety of different tools.

If you are viewing an image whose spatial or color resolution is greater than that of your display, be sure that any feedback tools you are using are providing information about the *original* image and not the proxy you are viewing. It is not uncommon, for instance, for nonprofessional viewing tools to simply return values from the image that is displayed on the screen, instead of looking back to the original image. If the original image was scaled to fit on your monitor, or if your tool is reading color values from an eight-bit video card, then the values returned from this image will be inaccurate relative to the original file.

Further statistics about an image can be determined using a specialized graph known as a **histogram**, which we will discuss next.

Histograms

A histogram is a way of displaying a plot of the number of pixels for each given brightness value in an image. Consider the four-bit, single-channel image shown in Figure 9.1b. With only four bits to represent the color in the image, each pixel can have one of 16 possible values. The graph shown in Figure 9.2 is a histogram of this image.

As you can see, there are a large number of pixels that have medium-gray values, but relatively few pixels that are pure white or pure black. In fact, we

(a)   **(b)**

Figure 9.1   *Sample image. (a) 8-bit image. (b) Image represented with only 16 colors.*

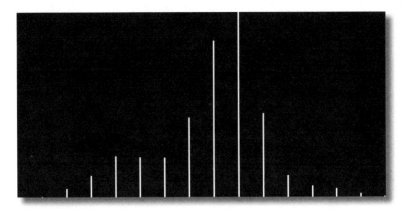

Figure 9.2 *Histogram of Figure 9.1b.*

could go so far as to tell that there are about 95,000 pixels with a value of 0.6 (60% gray), but only about 375 pixels with a value of 1.0 (pure white). The point of a histogram, however, is not to derive such *specific* statistics, but rather to examine overall data *trends* for the image.

Figure 9.3 shows the same type of histogram for the full eight-bit image, in which all 256 possible intensity values are graphed. This histogram presents a normal distribution of values, indicative of an image that was exposed and reproduced fairly normally. A histogram tool can also be useful for determining if an image has been artificially modified and if data has been lost. Unlike the uniform pixel distribution in Figure 9.3, Figure 9.4 gives a strong indication that the image has had some kind of image processing operation performed on it. The sharply

Figure 9.3 *Histogram of Figure 9.1a.*

Figure 9.4   *Histogram of an image with data loss.*

clipped region at the high end of the palette is almost certainly an artifact of some unnatural data truncation.

Determining whether an image has been digitally modified is one of the most useful pieces of information that a histogram can provide. Most color corrections, for instance, tend to create an image that has a less even distribution of colors, which will show up as noticeable gaps in an otherwise normal histogram. To understand why, think about the situation in which we apply a brightness of 2.0 to an image. This operation will multiply every pixel by 2, producing an image in which all the values of every pixel must be an even number. There can be no pixels with an odd value, and consequently the histogram will look something like that shown in Figure 9.5.

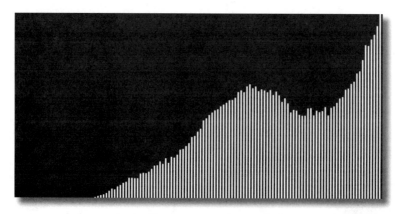

Figure 9.5   *Histogram of an image after a brightness of 2.0 has been applied. The histogram shows gaps due to an unequal distribution of colors in the image.*

Images that have been resampled from their original bit depth can also be detected via the use of a histogram. As mentioned earlier, if we create an 8-bit image from a 4-bit source image, we still really only have 4 bits of information present. Standard image-statistic tools will tell us that the image is an 8-bit image, but by examining a histogram of the image we would again see something like that shown in Figure 9.2. In this case, the regularly spaced gaps in the graph exist because the subtle color gradations that would be available in an 8-bit image were absent in the original 4-bit source. Although the difference between a 4-bit image and an 8-bit image is usually visible by viewing the color image directly, the difference between an 8-bit and a 16-bit image is much more subtle. Determining the true bit depth will require the use of a histogram or some other analysis tool.

CHAPTER TEN

Formats: Media, Resolution, and Aspect Ratios

Generally (we hope), when you set out to create a composite, you do so with the intention that it will be viewed via some specific medium. Whether you are providing images for broadcast video, CD-ROM, video games, feature film, or Web pages, you will need to have information about what the specific requirements are for that medium. In other words, you will need to know about the **format** that is being used.

Notice the usage of the term "format" here. It is another of those wonderfully ill-defined words that is extremely context dependent. In Chapter 2 (and Appendix C) we discussed digital image **file formats**—specific methods for storing digital images on a disk. This certainly may be part of the information required, assuming it is acceptable to deliver digital images directly. But more often the term "format" is used in the broader sense, referring to the specifics of the physical medium needed to capture or display the images being dealt with. Thus, film, video, 35mm, IMAX, VHS, Betacam, and so on would all be considered to be formats that we might use during the process of digital compositing. Some of the formats we just mentioned are subsets of others, which is part of the reason why it is so difficult to precisely determine what one is referring to when discussing the format. Care should be taken to ensure that all parties involved in the conversation are actually referring to the same topic.

In an attempt to organize the information presented in this chapter, we'll group the formats we discuss into three distinct categories: film, video, and other. Although this is an arbitrary classification system, there are certain basic traits for each category that make such a system worthwhile. This chapter will look at a variety of different formats within these categories, while keeping in mind that the point of this discussion is to present an overview that covers, in as simple a fashion as is possible, the information that is most pertinent to digital compositing.

In an ideal world, we would be able to provide a simple table of different formats and the spatial resolution, color resolution, and aspect ratio for each of them. This is, unfortunately, an impossibility. First of all, there are so many different formats, and variations on these formats, that the task would be prohibitive. For any given format we often find that there is not really a definitive standard, but rather (at best) a group of standards, any of which you can choose and still claim to be following "the standard." This trend seems to be particularly prevalent in the video world.

Second, most of these formats represent images as **analog** data, and digitization methods will vary based on the hardware used for the conversion. Much of this hardware is manufacturer specific and is not subject to any particular standardization whatsoever. In other words, a piece of hardware can be built to sample an analog image at just about *any* resolution, and thus it is impossible to assign a specific resolution to a specific analog format. Only by knowing the characteristics of the hardware being used in your particular situation can you know with certainty the resolution of the format in question.

Due to the issues mentioned, we will tend not to give specific numerical values for the formats discussed, except as an aid to illustrating a concept or when a reasonably clear, simple standard exists. Appendix D has also been provided as an additional format reference. It attempts to diagram some common formats that are used when working with film and video, and gives a bit more detail about typical digital representations of these formats. Much of this information is highly susceptible to changing technology, which is part of the reason that it was placed in an appendix rather than in the main body of this book.

Ultimately, this chapter will talk about formats on several different levels, some analog and some digital. We will discuss the pipeline of imagery as it moves from the original recording medium through the digital realm (where we perform our compositing work) and back out again. Of course our primary concern (since this is a book about digital compositing, not about the myriad of different moving-image systems that exist in the world today) is how these sequences are used in the digital realm.

There are a multitude of different film formats and (depending on how you choose to define "format") probably an even greater number of video formats. Most of these formats are analog, but even when dealing with a source that is considered to be digital (such as D1 video), you'll find that the methods used to represent the digital data will be quite different from what we use to represent a frame within a computer. Fortunately, once an image has been taken from its original medium and format and converted into a digitized image that we are ready to composite with, the terms for specifying its format become much easier.

In fact, we usually only need to identify two specific parameters when detailing a digital image's format: the resolution (spatial, color, and temporal) and the **aspect ratio**.

ASPECT RATIO

We have already (in Chapter 2) discussed the concept of an image's resolution, which is simply the number of columns and rows of pixels in that image, the amount of data dedicated to color information for each of those pixels, and the number of these frames that are captured for a given period of time. The aspect ratio of an image provides additional information about the *proportions* of an image. This information can, in some situations, be even more important than the specific pixel resolution of the image.

The aspect ratio of an image is generally considered to be the width-to-height ratio of that image.[1] Note that when one is speaking of a *ratio*, the term is unitless. It will have the same value no matter what specific units of measurement are used. Consider the image shown in Figure 10.1. The aspect ratio of this image is 2:1. (When speaking, we say "two-to-one.") As mentioned, it doesn't matter what units we use to measure this image when determining its aspect ratio. If you get a ruler, you will find that the width of the image is approximately four inches and the height is half of that, or two inches. We would be correct in saying that

Figure 10.1   *Image with 2:1 aspect ratio.*

---

[1] But, of course, you can also find instances in which the aspect ratio is given as a height-to-width ratio instead. We'll consistently use width-to-height in this book, but don't assume that everyone else follows this convention.

the aspect ratio is 4:2, although in general we usually simplify everything by dividing both numbers by the smallest number so that we have a ratio that is relative to 1.[2] Divide both numbers in 4:2 by 2 to get 2:1. If we had measured the rectangle in centimeters instead of inches, we'd have an aspect ratio of 10:5, which again simplifies to 2:1. Usually, if we've already simplified the aspect ratio so that it is relative to 1, we don't bother including the ":1." Thus, a 1.85:1 aspect ratio will usually be specified as just 1.85.

If an image is already in digital form, then instead of measuring the sides with a ruler, we can simply divide the width of the image in pixels by the height, in pixels, to determine the aspect ratio. An image that is 2048 × 1024 will thus also have an aspect ratio of 2:1.

The aspect ratio of an image may seem like a redundant piece of information. After all, if we already know the width and height of our digital image, why bother to divide these to get the aspect ratio? The reason is that our digital images are usually just intermediate steps in the process of producing final imagery. That final imagery may not necessarily be formatted the same way that our intermediate images are. It may not need to be the same resolution as the intermediate resolution with which we've chosen to work. It may not even be a digital format, and thus the concept of a specific pixel resolution would be meaningless. More important, that final imagery may be intended for display via a method that distorts or modifies the width and height ratio of the source image. Consequently we need a unitless, media-independent method of discussing formats, and the aspect ratio will help to provide that.

Nonsquare Pixels

Although we've just finished telling you how to determine the aspect ratio of an image by dividing height into width, we will now look at some situations in which this may not give you the true aspect ratio of the format that you are using. This situation arises when your output medium does not display images in the same fashion as your intermediate compositing system displays them. More specifically, we are concerned with display systems that modify the width-to-height relationship of the images that we send to them.

When we give the aspect ratio of an image, we usually try to refer to the aspect ratio of the image as it will eventually be viewed. Both film and video have formats and situations in which the aspect ratio of the displayed image is different

---

[2] Once again, there are always exceptions. The aspect ratios for various video devices are more commonly given as whole-number ratios. Thus, the standard NTSC television aspect ratio of 1.33:1 is often referred to as 4:3, and the new HDTV specification calls for an aspect ratio of 16:9.

from the original digital image. We often refer to such systems as having **nonsquare pixels**. In this situation, "nonsquare" indicates that the width and height of the pixel are not equal. Its shape is rectangular rather than square. (Actually, it's probably *oval* rather than *round*, but nobody ever uses the term "nonround.")

This width-to-height relationship of a nonsquare pixel can also be represented as an aspect ratio. To distinguish it from the aspect ratio for the entire image, we call it the **pixel aspect ratio**.[3] On a normal computer's monitor (assuming it is adjusted properly), the width of every pixel is the same as its height, and we say that it has square pixels. Its pixel aspect ratio is 1:1.

Do not confuse the pixel aspect ratio with an image's aspect ratio. The aspect ratio of an image can be (and usually is) a completely different number than the pixel aspect ratio of the pixels that make it up. For instance, the generally accepted standard for digital video images (in the United States) is a pixel aspect ratio of 10:11. The pixels are slightly taller than they are wide. If the individual pixels are stretched, then obviously the entire image will be stretched as well. Thus, if we were to digitally create an image that has a perfectly round circle in the center of it and then send this image directly to D1 video without any additional modification, the circle would appear as an ellipse. For example, Figure 10.2a shows an original image created within the computer. It is perfectly round. Figure 10.2b shows what this image would look like if it were viewed on a video monitor. It is, in fact, stretched by 11/10ths vertically. Depending on the software and hard-

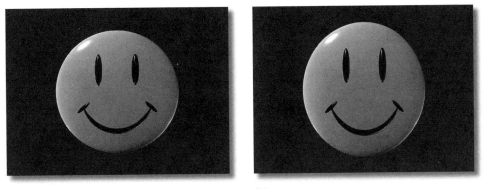

(a)   **(b)**

Figure 10.2   *Pixel aspect ratio. (a) Original image. (b) Image as viewed on a D1 digital video monitor with a pixel aspect ratio of 10:11.*

---

[3] Just as was the case with an image's aspect ratio, you will occasionally run across documents that give the pixel aspect ratio as a height-to-width ratio rather than width-to-height.

ware that is being used, you may need to manually scale your image before sending it to video in order to compensate for this discrepancy. Many systems will automate this step, however, so be sure you know how your particular setup behaves.

Some of the same situations can occur if we are working with film formats that involve optically distorting an image. Since images sent to film will no longer have identifiable pixels, instead of referring to these formats as having nonsquare pixels, we usually just call them **squeezed** formats. Formats that represent images with distorted aspect ratios are also commonly referred to as **anamorphic** formats. "Anamorphic" is a term borrowed from the art world that literally describes a distorted image that can be restored to its original shape. Historically, it involved an artist painting a wildly distorted image that would only look correct when viewed as a reflection in a specially curved mirror. In a later section of this chapter, we'll go into greater detail about some of the problems associated with anamorphic images when compositing them digitally.

DECIDING ON A RESOLUTION WHEN YOU HAVE AN ASPECT RATIO

Depending on your specific needs, the format of an image may be specified via resolution, aspect ratio, or both. If someone specifies that the images you should produce for a particular video game should have a resolution of 320×180 pixels, then you have enough information to do the work. But if you are going to be producing images for film, the only information that the client may give you is the aspect ratio of the images he or she desires. The reason for the lack of a specific resolution again has to do with the fact that film is a nondigital format, and as such it can be sampled, or digitized, at whatever resolution our hardware allows. The client may have little or no interest in the specific resolution, as long as the resulting image is acceptably sharp and has not suffered from any distortion of its proportions.

For instance, you may be told that you need to produce images with a 1.85 aspect ratio. It is then time to make a decision about the specific resolution that is necessary. This decision may be based on a number of factors, including practical considerations such as available disk space and processing power. Working at a resolution of 2048×1107 will produce an image with a 1.85 aspect ratio, but so will an image with a resolution of 185×100. However, if we were to transfer our 185×100 image back to film, we would probably be unhappy with the quality of the results, since we started with such a low resolution. It is almost as much of a problem if you decide to work at too *high* a resolution, since you will be confronted with unacceptable storage and computational requirements. Of course the decision about what resolution to use for a given aspect ratio is most often determined (or at least influenced) by the hardware that will be used to scan or output the images, since such devices typically have certain fixed resolutions that they use for the various film sizes available.

As we've said, once an image sequence is converted to a digital form, the format is easily understood. But the process of doing the conversion, and the decisions that need to be made during that conversion, bear further discussion.

FORMAT CONVERSION PIPELINE

Let's look at the various stages of the compositing process where an image's format is important. The flowchart in Figure 10.3 gives a basic pipeline that will occur for every image sequence that is to be used in a composite.

Step 1 is where the source imagery that we will be using in our composite is first created. These may be images generated entirely within the computer, such as rendered 3D imagery coming from a specialized animation package, or they may be images shot on film or video.

What happens next is determined by whether the source images are already in a digital format or if they were created via an analog method. If the source material is analog—a piece of film for instance—then we proceed to step 2. An analog-to-digital conversion occurs, and a specific digital format (a resolution and a bit depth) is chosen at that time. This step is the first situation in which we need to start thinking about image formats and aspect ratios. Video images may or may not already be in a digital format, depending on the hardware available, but either way we will probably need to do some sort of conversion due to aspect-ratio as well as resolution issues.

If the source images are already digital (having been created by a 3D animation system, perhaps), there may be no need for any further conversion. However, for whatever reason, we may still want to alter the format of this imagery—possibly to produce a new, lower resolution that will make better use of our available disk resources. In some situations, we may even need to go through an additional format conversion for images that were originally digitized from an analog source. This is potentially an undesirable thing, simply because it would have been more efficient to choose the proper format for the original analog-to-digital conversion instead of wasting the time it takes for a second conversion.

Other chapters of this book will provide slightly more information about step 4, so we won't discuss it here other than to note that it is certainly conceivable that not all the image sequences that are being used in our composite will be in the same format. This possibility will be discussed further in a later section.

Steps 5 and 6 reverse the processes from steps 2 and 3. The digital images are, if necessary, converted to yet another digital format—one specific to the eventual output medium. This step is the least likely to be necessary, since one will usually choose to work in a digital format that is the same as the desired output format. Finally, in step 6 (assuming our final images need to be in some analog format)

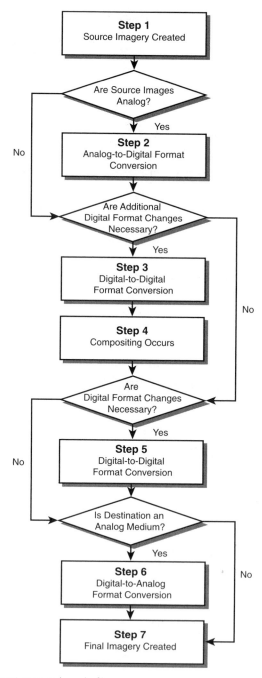

Figure 10.3   *The format conversion pipeline.*

the digital-to-analog conversion takes place. This new analog format may not necessarily be the same form as the original images.

We've gone through a scenario in which a number of different format changes occur. Remember that every digital-to-digital format change generally entails resampling the data and consequently will result in a slight loss of image quality. Avoid all unnecessary format changes wherever possible so that you will not suffer from this quality degradation.

The process of compositing is certainly much simpler if everything is created digitally and the intended final medium is also digital. None of the analog conversions are necessary, and a standard working resolution can be decided upon and maintained. Conceivably there will be *no* format changes necessary at all. The more complicated scenario occurs when our source and/or destination material is an analog medium, such as film. Not only do we need to deal with the analog-digital-analog conversions, but (particularly in the case of film) we will also probably need to be aware of a myriad of different physical formats that are in use throughout the industry.

Digital compositing is not the only discipline that needs to deal with format conversions. Conforming a feature film so that it can be viewed on video is a common example, one that can be particularly cumbersome if the original film footage was shot in some widescreen format.

The next section gives an example that follows the pipeline we've just detailed. Although it primarily uses a scenario based on film, it is suggested that you read through it even if you do not plan to do any film work yourself, since it touches on many format issues that are important no matter what the medium involved.

A Format Conversion Example

To get a better understanding of the format-conversion process and typical decisions that need to be made, let's run through the pipeline from Figure 10.3 while considering a piece of film as our source material.

The first question that one might ask about this film, particularly if one is dealing with the process of scanning the film into the computer, concerns the *format* of the film. Once again we must deal with the imprecision of the term "format." We already know that it was shot in a film format, as opposed to video. Let's also say that it was shot in a 35mm film format, the standard for feature-film work. Finally, to be as precise as possible, we find out that the film was shot in a 1.85 aspect ratio 35mm film format. We now have the information that we need for deciding how this film will be digitized.

Notice that this particular format, which would usually just be referred to as "1.85 format" (pronounced "one-eight-five format"), gives us a specific aspect ratio for our images. Not all formats have the aspect ratio so conveniently mentioned by name, and you would instead need to consult a chart such as that shown in Appendix D. The aspect ratio is mentioned for this particular format because the camera actually captures more image than is necessary—the extra image will simply be masked or blocked when the print is eventually projected for the screen. Specifying the format (and thus the aspect ratio) lets everyone know that the shot was filmed with a specific framing and that the extra image will not be used. Consequently, when we go to scan this piece of film, we can choose to scan only the area that will be shown in the theater. For the sake of this example, we will do just that, although in the real world we would probably decide to scan the entire frame of the negative just in case we need to use some of the extra image.

Figure 10.4 shows a frame of the film for our shot. You can see the full image that has been captured, as well as a box that is drawn to indicate the standard framing for a 1.85 format. If you measure the width of this box and divide it by the height, you will come up with a ratio of 1.85:1, as expected. The usefulness of the aspect ratio should be starting to become apparent. Film, like any analog source, has no inherent resolution in the purely digital sense.[4] You can subdivide

Figure 10.4   *Film with 1.85 format framing.*

---

[4] There are, of course, ways of measuring the "resolution" of a piece of film, but this quality is distinct from a digital resolution. A print or negative's resolution has to do with the fineness of the grain particles that are in the emulsion.

it as finely as you wish and you will always end up with new unique values. It is only when we sample it into discrete packets (i.e., pixels) that it is useful to define it in terms of its resolution. In other words, the digital resolution is determined only when we actually scan the film into the computer. Depending on the hardware we use, we can sample it at a fairly low resolution (such as that used when a telecine operation occurs), or we can sample at very high resolutions—4000 lines or more.

Let's say that we choose to sample the frame so that we end up with a resolution of 3656 × 1976. As we've indicated, this resolution is somewhat arbitrary, subject primarily to the abilities and limits of the available technology. You will notice, however, that the aspect ratio of our new digital image is the same as that of our original film image, 1.85:1. We could just as easily have chosen to scan at 1828 × 988, which would have given us a lower resolution but still kept the same aspect ratio.

Let's assume a worst-case scenario now: For whatever reason, someone decides that our resolution of 3656 × 1976 is not what we should use for the bulk of our work. Perhaps someone sat down with a calculator and realized that the amount of disk space that is available won't be enough to store our entire shot at this resolution. (A 3656 × 1976 image stored in the Cineon file format, for example, will take up approximately 29 megabytes of disk space *per frame*. As you can see, high-resolution film images can have significant storage requirements.) Consequently, the decision is made to convert all our images to a lower resolution. Let's try something more reasonable—something about 2000 pixels wide. We'll be conventional and use 2048 pixels. There's nothing particularly magical about using 2048 instead of simply 2000, unless you happen to have a compositing system that prefers such a number (yes, there are some that do), but it's somewhat of a convention to use computer-friendly numbers like 2048. Given our 2K width, and since we know that we need to maintain our 1.85 aspect ratio, we do a little math, divide 2048 by 1.85, and come up with a new resolution of 2048 × 1107. This gives us a friendlier image size as well, about 9 megabytes per frame. We've just gone through step 3.

We could just as easily (at least on paper!) have gone back to step 2 and rescanned the film instead, going directly to our 2048 × 1107 resolution. Whether one would choose to do so would probably be decided by real-world considerations such as the accessibility of the scanner or the time available. In this particular situation, one would almost certainly just reduce the already-digitized images, since it would be faster and the image quality would be comparable.

Now that we have our images converted to the digital format that we desire, we can spend time working on the actual composite, producing a whole new sequence of images. These new images will be the same format as the images that are being used to create them, 2048 × 1107.

Eventually it will be time to get our completed digital composite *back* to film. In order to make sure that our example covers as many scenarios as possible, let's say that the company that we were planning to use for our **film recording** (the process of getting digital images back onto film) has announced that it is getting out of the business and won't be able to help us. So we call up a different company, only to be told that they don't like to have images at 2048 × 1107 for creating 1.85 format 35mm film. They ask if we can convert the images to a resolution of 1828 × 988 before we send them over. We wish we had known about this sooner, since it means that not only are we going to spend time resizing a whole bunch of images, but also that we could have probably just done the entire composite at this lower resolution since we're dropping down to that resolution now anyway.

We go ahead and convert the images to the new resolution, which corresponds to step 5 in our pipeline, write them to a digital tape, and send them over to the film recording company. This company now feeds the images to their film recording hardware, which converts the digital images back to visible light, exposing them onto a piece of film negative. The image is properly placed within the film frame, and, if we care to take the time, we can go back and measure the shape of the resulting image to confirm that the width-to-height ratio is still 1.85 to 1.

Now that we have examined a specific example of how imagery may go through a variety of format changes during the compositing process, we'll spend a few sections getting an overview of some of the more common formats that a compositor may encounter.

FILM FORMATS

Although over the course of the past 100 years there have been numerous different film formats available, we will try to narrow this list down to a few of the most common. This section will not, as a rule, give detailed measurements for the formats—this is done for a few specific formats in Appendix D—but rather will attempt to give the reader a sense of how the different film formats are dealt with, the relative quality of the different formats, and any idiosyncrasies inherent to each format.

Most film systems today are designed to project images at a rate of 24 frames per second. There are a few exceptions to this, which we will describe on a case-by-case basis. The color resolution of a piece of film is, as with the spatial resolution, somewhat dependent on the hardware used to digitize the imagery. However, due to the large dynamic range of film, most systems are designed to scan at more than 8 bits per channel. The most common standard for scanning film imagery uses Kodak's Cineon specification, which utilizes a 10-bit nonlinear color space, as described in Appendix C.

Any given piece of film, as we've mentioned, can be scanned at a variety of different spatial resolutions, but these resolutions are at least partially determined by the physical size of the film that is being scanned.

The standard way to specify the size of a piece of film is by measuring its width in millimeters. This width is also known as the **gauge** of the film. By far the most common gauge for feature-film work is 35 millimeter, so we'll start our discussion with a look at this standard.

35mm Formats

Not only is 35mm the most common film format used for theatrical release, it is also, not surprisingly, the most common film format used for digital compositing work. As you will see, 35mm is not really a single, well-defined format. In fact, there are a number of different formats that fall under the general category of "35mm," and it is important to realize that the specific gauge of the film itself does not completely determine the size and shape of the image that is actually captured on that film.

The basic 35mm frame is shown in Figure 10.5. Every frame of standard 35mm film is bordered on each side by four of the perforations used to move the film through the camera. These perforations are often called "perfs," and consequently the 35mm format is sometimes referred to as **four-perf**. Along the left side of the film, between the perfs and the image itself, is a narrow area reserved for the soundtrack of the film. This is known as the sound stripe.[5]

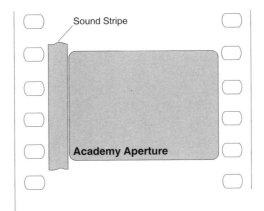

Figure 10.5 *Basic 35mm frame showing Academy framing.*

[5] The standard sound stripe is designed to store an *analog* soundtrack. To maintain backward-compatibility with the huge number of older projection systems in the world, the newer digital soundtrack methods were forced to find some other place to locate the sound information. There are a number of different, competing standards—some use the area between the perforations, while others use the margin of the film outside of the perfs. This particular bit of information has virtually nothing to do with digital compositing, and is presented solely for trivia's sake.

The area of the negative that is usually exposed when shooting standard 35mm feature films is indicated by the light gray rectangle in the diagram. Note that this framing, which excludes the sound stripe, has an aspect ratio of 1.37—it is generally referred to as the **Academy aperture**.

Imagery that is exposed with this framing will not necessarily be projected with the same framing. Instead, it will generally be masked for theatrical presentation to conform to one of the more popular projection standards. Since the Academy aperture framing is the most widely agreed-upon standard for 35mm work, we will try to point out how some of the different film and video sizes compare with the Academy frame in terms of absolute resolution. Appendix D also contains a chart showing this resolution comparison for a variety of formats.

Although the sound stripe area will be filled when the film is eventually projected, it is not something that necessarily needs to be protected when shooting the original negative. It is not uncommon, therefore, to remove the mask that blocks this area from exposure in order to capture a larger image. There is also some space above and below the Academy framing that can be used as well. Taking advantage of this extra area, which is called the **full aperture** (sometimes also referred to as the **camera aperture**), will result in a frame with an aspect ratio of 1.33. Simply by using this larger area, one is able to capture an image that is about 30% larger than normal Academy aperture. Certain formats make use of this extra area as an intermediate step before the final print is made, and it is not uncommon for visual effects elements to be shot "full-ap" to reap the benefits of a higher-resolution image. An example of the full aperture framing is shown in Figure D.1 of Appendix D, as well as for the rest of the 35mm formats we will be discussing.

1.85

An aspect ratio of 1.85 is by far the most common framing for movies that are shown in the United States. (In Europe, a 1.66 aspect ratio is much more common, and in the rest of the world it varies between the two standards.) Projecting an image that was shot with normal Academy aperture in a 1.85 format is simply a matter of placing a mask in the projector that blocks a small amount of the image—usually along the top. The cinematographer has planned for this framing from the outset, and thus will not have allowed anything important to occur in the top of the frame. A diagram of 1.85 framing was shown in Figure 10.4.

Super 35

The Super 35 format ignores the space normally reserved for the sound stripe and uses most of the full-aperture area of the negative to capture the desired picture. This picture will eventually be projected with an aspect ratio of 2.35, but only after some intermediate steps.[6] These steps are used to reformat the captured image into a different standard, usually Cinemascope (which we'll discuss in a moment), and consequently Super 35 should be considered primarily a format for acquisition, not projection.

Cinemascope

The **Cinemascope**[7] format (also known as simply **C-scope**) is an anamorphic format that has been designed to capture images that are squeezed by 50% along the X-axis. This squeezing is done in order to capture a wider field of view while still using as much negative as possible. We will be using the Cinemascope format later in this chapter to illustrate some of the concepts related to working with nonsquare pixels, and will discuss the process it uses to capture this squeezed imagery in more detail in that section. Cinemascope images are intended to be projected so as to produce an image with an aspect ratio of 2.35. However, due to the two-to-one squeeze of the captured images, the aspect ratio of a Cinemascope image on a piece of film is approximately half of that, about 1.2. The reason it is not *exactly* half has to do with the masking applied to the projected image to force it into a 2.35 aspect ratio.

There is another 35mm format that we will discuss in a moment, known as the **Vistavision** format. Due to the particular characteristics of this format, we have chosen to cover it in the "Specialized Film Formats" section instead, for reasons that will become obvious.

16mm Formats

Generally, at least as of the writing of this book, the various standard 16mm film formats are not used very often in digital compositing. This is probably due mostly to cost issues: If a filmmaker has the money to digitize and manipulate film footage, he or she is probably able to afford shooting in a 35mm format. Only time will tell if the migration of digital tools will get to the 16mm market before it is supplanted by standard or high-definition television as a platform for lower-end work.

---

[6] Technically, "Super 35" can refer to a variety of formats that use the full aperture for their exposure, but in practice, Super 35 is used almost exclusively to produce images that are intended for projection in a 2.35 aspect ratio.

[7] The term "Cinemascope" is actually the name of a specific widescreen anamorphic format that 20th Century Fox developed in the 1950s. However, it seems to have become a generic term for the 2.35 anamorphic format that is now primarily created using **Panavision** lenses.

16mm film *is* occasionally enlarged to 35mm for theatrical release, usually when a studio decides that a low-budget film is worth giving a wide distribution. In situations such as this, it is certainly possible that digital techniques might be employed to fix specific problems that may be unsolvable by other means, and it is conceivable that original 16mm negative will be scanned for compositing work. A more common use for 16mm film is as a source for television commercials. In this situation, however, the images are generally transferred directly to video via a telecine device. Thus, the resulting resolution and aspect ratio of the images produced will depend primarily on the video equipment you are using. Figure D.2 in Appendix D shows the size of the basic 16mm frame, relative to the other formats. It also includes a box indicating the size of a *Super 16* frame. The Super 16 format extends the frame into the standard 16mm sound stripe area, resulting in a larger image. Both of these formats are still quite a bit smaller than even the standard 35mm Academy framing, and will only be able to capture about 25% of the resolution.

Specialized Film Formats

There are a number of less common film formats that are usually reserved for special situations. These formats are generally designed to produce much higher-quality imagery via the use of a larger exposed negative. Large-format films require the use of cameras that are much bulkier, more expensive, and generally less reliable than standard 35mm cameras, and as such their use is limited. These larger formats will sometimes be used as intermediate steps in the production of a standard 35mm print, or they may be part of a "special venue" presentation that is capable of directly displaying large-format films.

Vistavision

Vistavision (or VistaVision) was originally developed by Paramount studios in the 1950s as a proposed new widescreen format. As mentioned earlier, the process actually makes use of standard 35mm film stock to capture imagery. However, in order to increase the resolution of the frames that are captured, specialized cameras that run the film *sideways* through the camera (instead of vertically) are used.[8] The 35mm frame now limits the *height* of the image instead of the *width*, and consequently the camera can expose an area of the negative that is more than twice as much as that exposed with standard 35mm film photography.

---

[8] The Vistavision negative is actually formatted in the same way that a 35mm *still* camera exposes its film.

Although it never really caught on as a mass-distribution format, Vistavision was used for a time as a method for capturing high-quality negatives that were then optically reduced to standard 35mm prints. Even this usage eventually became less and less common, and after the early 1960s Vistavision was effectively obsolete as a mass-market system. However, the lure of a larger negative was enough to inspire visual effects people to start using the format again, and consequently it is now used quite often as a method for capturing elements for visual effects compositing work, be it optical or digital. Figure D.1 in Appendix D shows a Vistavision frame. Compared with the standard 35mm Academy aperture, a Vistavision negative exposes about 2.7 times more area. The Vistavision format is often referred to as **eight-perf** because the area captured by a single frame spans eight film perforations.

65mm

A wide-gauge film that is run vertically through a special camera, 65mm is used not only for visual effects work but also occasionally as a source for films that will be presented in 70mm.[9] 65mm is also widely used as a format for a number of different special-venue situations. One of the most common of these is the **Showscan** method, which captures images at a rate of 60 fps instead of the normal 24, resulting in a dramatically improved image in which grain is nearly undetectable and flicker, or strobing, is virtually eliminated. Since a single frame spans five perforations of the 65mm negative, it is also known as "five-perf." A five-perf negative will capture an image that is about 3.6 times larger than the standard Academy aperture.

IMAX

Another system that uses a 65mm negative to capture its image is one created by the Imax Corporation. It runs the film horizontally through the camera and projector in the same fashion as Vistavision, producing an extremely large negative. Each frame spans 15 perforations of the 65mm film, creating a negative that is more than ten times larger than a standard 35mm Academy exposure. A size comparison can be seen in Figure D.2 in Appendix D. Although this format is

---

[9] You may see your local movie theater advertising a film as being "shown in 70mm." This is a specification for the *print* being shown, not the size of the original negative that was used when shooting the footage. Ideally a 70mm print was originally shot with some large-format negative, but there are no guarantees that this is the case. These days it is much more common that the original footage was shot with a standard 35mm format and then optically enlarged to fit onto a 70mm print. This results in a brighter, less grainy print, although it will still have less definition than something that was shot with a large-gauge negative.

most commonly used when capturing imagery for IMAX productions, the basic 65mm, 15-perf format is not really "the IMAX Format." Rather, IMAX is a complete system that includes image capture on 65mm, 15-perf negative, projection from 70mm, 15-perf prints, and carefully calibrated projectors, screens, and sound systems. Strictly speaking, one should only refer to "65mm, 15-perf" when describing this format, but colloquially it is simply called "IMAX."

Digitizing some of these special formats via a high-resolution scanner will result in images that require an extreme amount of data for every frame of the image sequence. This problem may be even further compounded by the fact that some of these formats are also used to capture stereoscopic imagery by using two cameras to photograph a scene. This stereo imagery essentially doubles the amount of information that is created for every frame.

VIDEO FORMATS

Video is, if anything, an even more ill-defined category than film, since there are an incredible number of different methods for representing, displaying, and storing video information. We will attempt to define some broad categories, as well as give some idea of the variability within those categories, without delving into an inordinate amount of detail about how video works. Again, there is a bit more information given in Appendix D for those who are interested.

Unlike film, where one can easily grasp exactly how the image data is stored by simply holding the medium up to a light source, video is a fairly complicated subject. Before we can even begin to discuss specific video formats, we need to define a number of additional concepts.

The important thing to remember about video is that even though it is an electronic format, it is still primarily (or at least historically) an *analog* electronic format. Thus, just as we saw with film, you will find that it is really the digitization hardware that will define the resolution you are working with, and this hardware can be very arbitrary in the resulting resolution it chooses for a particular video signal. There is slightly less variability in the possible resolutions than there was with film, in that the electronic video signal is only capable of representing a limited, fairly well-defined bandwidth. As such, there is an upper limit on how dense a sampling it makes sense to use. We will briefly describe, in as simplified a fashion as possible, an analog video signal so that these resolution limits can be better understood.

Lines of Resolution

Analog video can be thought of as a continuously variable signal that is used to build an image line by line. Since the line created by this signal varies continuously (providing color and brightness information), it is a true analog signal, with no inherent number of pixels associated with it. However, the number of these lines (known as **scan lines**) that makes up the full image remains fixed for any given format. In the case of the NTSC format, the standard in the United States, there are 525 lines in a single video frame. At this point, one would be tempted to assume that a digitized video frame should also have a vertical resolution of 525 pixels. One would be wrong. In fact, these 525 lines do not all contain image information. A good portion of them are used for other purposes, including things like closed captioning information and the time code. The portion of the video signal that *is* used for image information is known as the **active region**, and this is what we are usually interested in. This topic is discussed a bit more in Appendix D.

Ultimately, from a digital compositing artist's perspective, the video specification for the number of lines in an image is primarily important as a means to compare resolutions between other formats that use a similar signal.

Fields

Although we've just finished describing how a frame of video is composed of a number of scan lines, in actuality even this is a simplification. This is because those scan lines are not simply displayed sequentially, top to bottom, to produce an image. Instead, every *other* scan line is displayed first, creating an image that is the proper height, but with only half as many scan lines. Immediately after this image is displayed, the remaining scan lines are displayed, top to bottom, creating a second image composed of the alternate lines. In essence, we have two images displayed immediately after each other to produce a single frame. Each of these half-frames is known as a "field image," or simply a **field**. Each field is displayed for half the frame rate of the format with which we are dealing, so in the case of NTSC video (which runs at 30 frames per second), each field is displayed for 1/60th of a second. One of the primary advantages of showing 60 fields per second instead of 30 frames per second is that the resulting image has essentially no perceptible flicker.

Formats that use two fields to define a single frame are known as **interlaced** formats, and an image composed of two fields is known as an interlaced frame. Formats that do not use interlacing are known as **progressive scan** formats, since the scan lines are displayed progressively, without needing to double back to present a second field. Most computer monitors are progressive scan, and some of the HDTV formats we will discuss are progressive scan as well.

Most compositing systems are set up so that the user can ignore the interlaced nature of video. Typically, the hardware that converts the video stream into a digital RGB image will be able to automatically interlace the field images together to produce a single normal frame. But there may occasionally be situations in which one wishes to deal with the distinct fields explicitly, and it will depend on the capabilities of your individual system whether or not this is possible.

Packages with this ability will allow the user to **deinterlace** a frame into two half-height fields and work on the images individually. This process will of course produce twice as many images. Usually one can choose whether or not to simply treat them as vertically squeezed anamorphic images or just temporarily resize them to full height. The advantage of working with field images instead of full frames has to do with the increased temporal resolution. Motion artifacts, particularly for elements that move quickly across the frame (horizontally), are significantly reduced.

Figure 10.6a shows two frames of an animated sequence in which a ball is moving across the screen, left to right. The same animation rendered to fields is shown in Figure 10.6b. Remember that even though the field images appear to be squashed in our digital image format, they will be full height when displayed

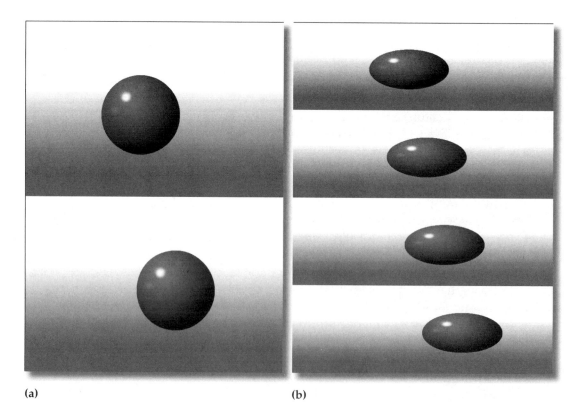

(a)   (b)

Figure 10.6   *Frames versus fields. (a) Two frames of an animated sequence. (b) The same animation represented as four field images.*

as a field image on a video monitor. As you can see, since we have twice as many images for a given time period, we can represent the movement more accurately. The result will be an animated element that has less flicker, or strobing, when viewed.

Once you have finished working with the field images, your system should allow you to reinterlace them to produce a new full-height frame. Figure 10.7 shows what these new frames would look like. This result might appear strange if you are looking at only a single frame, but remember that this is really an artificial way of viewing these images. They will appear perfectly correct when viewed at the proper speed on a normal video display system. In fact, if you were to examine a frame from video of a live-action ball thrown across the screen at the same speed, you would see exactly the same sort of interlacing characteristics.

Color Resolution

Video signals, particularly analog video signals, have historically been sampled at 8 bits per channel. This was primarily driven by the need to sample in real

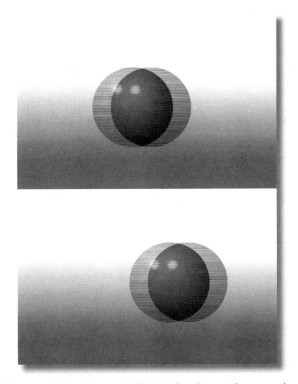

Figure 10.7   *Field images (from Figure 10.6b) interlaced to produce new frames.*

time, but the limited bandwidth and inherent noise in a video signal made this a reasonable bit depth to use. The standards for digital video have continued to evolve, and most specifications now provide the ability to sample at either 8 or 10 bits per channel. Working with video images that were digitized at 10 bits per channel is still fairly rare, but as the cost of 10-bit hardware drops, it will probably become more common.

Gamma

Anyone who has worked with video imagery from a technical perspective has probably been exposed to the concept of video's "built-in" gamma. The gamma correction that is inherent in a video image is actually a form of the nonlinear color space that we briefly mentioned in Chapter 2. It is primarily used as a way to maximize the available bit depth in an image, although it is also related to the way that a video display device (such as a television) converts a signal into an image. A complete discussion of this subject is far beyond the scope of this chapter, and you should consult the more detailed coverage that is given in Chapter 15 if you desire more information.

For the purposes of this section, it is sufficient to understand that standard video images include a gamma correction that is applied when the images are acquired. Typically this means that the video camera used to shoot a particular image applies this gamma correction before the image is written to tape. For all the different video formats we discuss (including HDTV), the standard gamma that is applied is 2.2.[10]

The fact that all properly stored video images have a built-in gamma of 2.2 means that if they are transferred without modification to a digital RGB image in a compositing system, they will appear to be too bright. You may need to apply a compensating gamma of 0.45 (1/2.2) to bring them back into the normal range. Don't do this blindly, however. Make sure that whatever hardware you are using to convert video signals into digital images isn't *automatically* applying the inverse gamma, which is becoming the common practice.

NTSC

Now that we've provided a bit of background on the basics of video, we can discuss the specific formats that are commonly used throughout the world. The most common of these is **NTSC**, the standard defined by the National Television

---

[10] Some of the standards documents for the PAL format actually specify a gamma of 2.8, although this generally seems to be ignored.

Systems Committee. It is the video standard in the United States, as well as in Canada, most of Central and South America, and a few Asian countries.

NTSC is designed to display images with 525 lines of resolution at 30 frames per second.[11] It is an interlaced format, so in reality it is displaying field images at the rate of 60 per second. With NTSC, the first field contains all the even-numbered scan lines, and the second field contains all the odd. This is referred to as the **field dominance** of the format. NTSC, as mentioned earlier, is a squeezed format, and a pixel that is converted to an NTSC image will have an aspect ratio of 10:11. The aspect ratio of the full NTSC frame is 4:3. See Appendix D for more information.

PAL

The **PAL** (Phase Alternation by Line) video format was developed by Germany and is used throughout Great Britain, parts of Europe, several African and Asian countries, and Australia. It is designed to carry images with 625 lines of resolution, displayed at a rate of 25 frames per second, or 50 fields per second. PAL is the opposite of NTSC in terms of field dominance, since field 1 contains all the odd-numbered scan lines and field 2 has the remaining even lines. The aspect ratio of a PAL image is also defined to be 4:3 (the same as NTSC), which, given the fact that the vertical resolution of the format is different, implies a different pixel aspect ratio. In this case, it turns out that any square pixels that are sent to a PAL monitor will have an aspect ratio of 59:54—they will be slightly squeezed vertically.

SECAM

SECAM is a less common format, developed by France and used in parts of Europe and Africa. Like PAL, SECAM is an interlaced system designed to run at 25 frames per second, carrying 625 lines of resolution. Unlike NTSC or PAL, SECAM is rarely used as a video storage format, or even as an intermediate format for editing. There is significantly less support for this format in terms of hardware, and generally most work in countries in which SECAM is the broadcast standard will use PAL as their primary format. The video signal will be converted to SECAM only when it is being broadcast.

HDTV

There is a fourth video "standard" emerging, known as high-definition television, or **HDTV**. Its primary distinguishing characteristic is the much higher resolution

---

[11] The official specification for NTSC playback defines the speed as 29.97 frames per second. Thirty fps is a fairly safe approximation for most purposes.

that it is capable of storing and displaying. The HDTV standard is actually yet another collection of standards, but fortunately HDTV is a much more computer-friendly format, since it is, by definition, a digital format. In theory, HDTV encompasses any video format with a resolution greater than standard video. Of course, as we've seen, "standard video" is a bit of a misnomer, so we've included a few specifics in Appendix D about what resolutions HDTV can encompass.

HDTV, being a collection of format descriptions, has provisions for either interlaced images or progressive scan. Most of the medium-resolution HDTV formats are progressive scan, but the high end of the specification also describes an interlaced HDTV format. HDTV is defined to be a square-pixel format, and has provisions for both 8 or 10 bits of color precision. It is considered to carry a built-in gamma of 2.2.

Of course, the fact that there are written specifications for a variety of HDTV formats is no guarantee that any of these particular resolutions will actually emerge as an *industry* standard. As of the writing of this book, worldwide HDTV broadcasts that are receivable by the general public are few, far between, and often incompatible. Only time will tell what true standard (or standards) will emerge.

OTHER FORMATS

Our final format category of "other" is, obviously, the least well defined. Certain media such as video games may have loosely defined standards concerning their working formats, but these are all as variable as the hardware on which they may run. The bottom line is that, for most of these "other" formats, there is no need for standard resolutions. Unlike film or video, these formats are all purely digital, and they are either flexible enough to be able to show images at just about *any* aspect ratio or resolution (as is the case with a standard PC) or are hardware-specific formats that are determined by the hardware's manufacturer. This is the case for video games, in which the game console itself will require the images to be in a very specific size, color depth, and file format. Most dedicated home-videogame consoles (such as those from Nintendo, Sega, or Sony) have a number of predefined resolutions that they support: 320×240, 640×240, and 640×480 are common, but there are quite a few variations.

Keep in mind that video games now tend to fall into the much broader category of **multimedia**, and even though the final images may be of limited resolution, the source material for this imagery can easily be from a higher-resolution format, perhaps even film. The color resolution of most video games, as well as most other multimedia applications, is, at best, eight bits per channel. More common is the use of indexed color in conjunction with a lower bit depth.

Understand that the reason for all these different formats, be they film, video, or something else (including the myriad of less common or obsolete formats that *haven't* been mentioned) is primarily historical. A number of different image capture formats have been proposed over the years, some of which became popular, others which did not.

It may seem strange that some of the 35mm film formats mentioned in this chapter involve a scenario in which a significant portion of the frame is exposed, yet never used. There are a few reasons for this. First, having a standard frame that covers several cases means that we can use the same equipment no matter what the intended format. The only difference will be that the cinematographer will be framing his scenes with a specific aspect ratio in mind.

Capturing extra imagery is also useful when transferring a film to video. The taller aspect ratio of standard television (1.33) means that we need a different framing. We can either zoom in on the 1.85 framing and then use **pan and scan** techniques to try to keep the important action in the scene, or we can shoot the original footage while also planning for the eventual video release of the film. The difference between the 1.33 aspect ratio of television and the 1.37 of the Academy aperture is fairly small, and requires less extreme measures to get an acceptable video framing. Finally, as we've mentioned, there are a number of situations in which you may choose to shoot with a format that is larger than your intended delivery format in order to have extra image information with which to work.

No matter what format you are given to work with as a compositor, it is important to always keep in mind the issues of resolution and aspect ratio. When working with multiple formats, it is dangerously simple to convert between two different resolutions. If these two resolutions do not have the same aspect ratio, however, you will end up with an image that is either squeezed or stretched by a certain amount.

WORKING WITH NONSQUARE PIXELS

If you are working with formats that utilize nonsquare pixels, there are some special considerations that you will need to take into account. To illustrate some of these concepts, we'll use the most common anamorphic film format, the Cinemascope format. Everything we'll discuss applies equally to squeezed film or video, but we've chosen the Cinemascope format for our example because its two-to-one squeeze is the most dramatic and thus illustrates the concepts quite well.

C-scope footage is shot using a lens that compresses the image by one-half along the *X*-axis. If you examine a piece of film that was shot with a C-scope lens, you will see that everything in the frame appears to have been squeezed so that it is half as wide as normal. When it comes time to project this strange piece of film in a theater, another special lens (that makes everything appear twice as wide as normal) is used, and the image appears correct once again.

When planning to digitally composite images that were shot in this format, there are a few different routes one can take. Initially, your elements will probably have been scanned exactly as they appear on the negative. We say that they have been "scanned squeezed," and if you look at a frame of this on your computer it will indeed appear squeezed. Now, it is possible that you may choose simply to do your work directly on these squeezed images. When dealing with less extreme squeezes, such as video, this is a common scenario. (The caveat comes when it becomes necessary to rotate a squeezed element—we'll discuss this in a moment.) Working with squeezed C-scope elements can, however, be visually distracting, and properly judging movement is a skill that may take some time to develop. (Horizontally moving objects will appear to be moving half as fast as they normally would, yet vertically moving objects are going at the proper speed. Diagonally moving objects are particularly hard to judge intuitively.)

In an ideal world, the best way to deal with these squeezed C-scope images would be to immediately unsqueeze them—that is, scale them nonproportionally to restore their proper aspect ratio. In practice this method has drawbacks, in that you either must halve your Y resolution (thereby losing 50% of the information you just scanned) or must scale your image by two times in the X direction (thereby doubling the amount of data to deal with, even though you haven't really created any extra sharpness or detail in your image).

The best solution is to find a compositing system that is capable of *displaying* the images as if they were in an unsqueezed format, while still *processing* the data in a squeezed format. Such a system uses either software or hardware to let you view the images as if they have been unsqueezed for all the tests that you are doing, yet still keeps and processes the images at their original resolution when producing the final composite. A well-designed system will be able to do this with little or no additional processing overhead.

Incidentally, we often refer to systems with the ability to do this temporary unsqueeze as being able to display nonsquare pixels. Don't assume that this means that the individual pixels you see on your computer's monitor will become squeezed or stretched. If you were to take a magnifying glass and look at these pixels, each would still appear to be properly proportioned. It's just that the system has applied a simple geometric transformation to nonproportionally resize the image so that it *appears* the same way as it will in its final form. The underlying image data has not been modified; it is only the display of these images that goes through this temporary process.

Most image processing and compositing operations will work just fine when applied to squeezed images. Simply layering one squeezed element over another is no problem, and things like color corrections will behave identically whether or not they are applied to squeezed imagery. But certain processes can be very problematic and will require special attention. Consider the issue of rotation.

Figure 10.8a shows the squeezed-image representation of a circular object placed in a standard Cinemascope frame. In this case, the extreme squeeze of this format has produced an image that is *much* narrower than it is tall. If we immediately send this image back to film and view it with the proper lens on our projector, it will appear round again, as shown in Figure 10.8b.

(a)

(b)

Figure 10.8   *Squeezed formats. (a) A circular object as viewed in a standard Cinemascope frame, producing an extreme squeeze. (b) The image as it will be projected.*

But let's say we wish to rotate this squeezed element by 90° before pasting it over a squeezed background. Figure 10.9a shows this rotated element, and 10.9b shows the result when we project it. We have suddenly generated an element that is drastically distorted, probably not the result we were looking for. To avoid

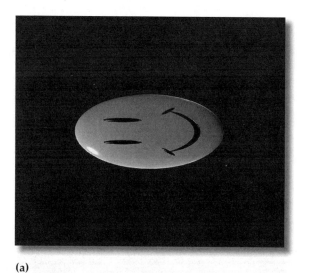

(a)

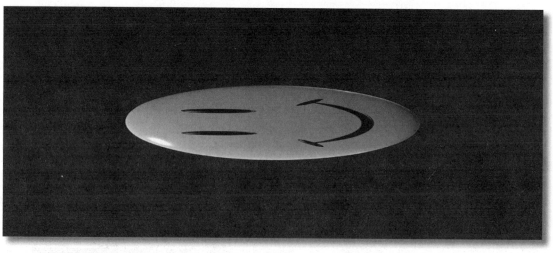

(b)

Figure 10.9   *(a) Circular, anamorphically squeezed object from Figure 10.8a rotated 90° without first unsqueezing it.(b) The object as it will be projected, showing unwanted distortion.*

(c)

Figure 10.9   *(c) The object as it should look when projected after a correctly performed rotation.*

this problem we would need to first unsqueeze the element, rotate it, and then resqueeze it along the *X*-axis. The result of this process would produce the image shown in Figure 10.9c.

Most spatial filters such as blurring will also need to be treated differently if you are working with squeezed elements. Thus, blurring a squeezed element by an equivalent amount in *X* and *Y* will result in an unsqueezed element that appears to have too much blur along one axis. If you have access to a blur algorithm that allows you to control both the vertical and the horizontal blur, you can adjust the relative amounts to compensate for any image squeeze.

The best compositing systems will usually be able to automate these tasks, allowing you to specify a working aspect ratio either for a specific operator (like rotation) or for the entire compositing session. The system will then automatically deal with the related issues, performing the unsqueeze/resqueeze process when rotating squeezed elements or transparently adjusting any other parameters for operations that require it.

Keep in mind that these issues can arise whether you are dealing with film *or* video. Because the amount of squeeze that is typical for video is much more subtle than for film, it is easier to overlook the fact that you are working with squeezed images. Many video systems automatically unsqueeze elements when transferring them from video to the computer and back, meaning that you will run into problems if you apply an additional unsqueeze. As always, be aware of the idiosyncrasies of your particular system.

COMBINING FORMATS

We've tried to give a very broad overview of the wide variety of formats that you may encounter. Depending on your particular situation, you may never need to deal with most of these formats. On the other hand, you may find yourself working on a composite in which you need to combine several different formats at the same time. Usually this doesn't present much of a problem, since the different images can just be scaled as needed. A mixture of squeezed and un-squeezed images will obviously require you to determine a working aspect ratio and then to conform everything to that standard. There may even be times when you wish to combine film and video in the same image. Chapter 13 discusses the process of creating elements and includes a section entitled "Choosing a Format," in which some of the factors that dictate format choices are presented in greater detail.

CONVERTING BETWEEN FILM AND VIDEO

Although this chapter gave a number of examples of how formats might be converted throughout the compositing process, there is a particular conversion that bears further scrutiny: the film-to-video conversion and its reverse, video to film. This conversion is problematic primarily because of the different frame rates that the formats in question use, particularly when converting between NTSC video at 30 fps and standard film at 24 fps.

In Chapter 6 we discussed some general-purpose methods for converting between different frame rates, but the specific conversion between film and video occurs often enough that a well-defined standard process has emerged. It involves taking a film frame and converting it to two fields of video, and then taking the next film frame and converting it to three fields of video. This alternating creation of two and then three fields in order to synchronize film timing to video (NTSC) timing is known as a **2:3 pulldown.**[12] A diagram of this process is shown in Figure 10.10.

Film frame A is used to create both fields of our first video frame. Film frame B is used to create both fields of video frame 2, and also the first field of video frame 3. Film frame C is then used to create the second field of video frame 3, and also the first field of video frame 4. Finally, film frame D is used to create the second field of video frame 4 as well as both fields of video frame 5. As you

---

[12] This is pronounced "two-three pulldown." You may also hear it referred to as 3:2 pulldown, which theoretically indicates that the first frame is converted to three fields and the second frame is converted to two. In practice the terms are usually used interchangeably.

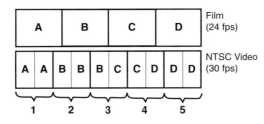

Figure 10.10 *The 2:3 pulldown conversion.*

can see, 4 film frames will make up exactly 5 video frames, and thus 24 film frames will make up 30 video frames.

Converting between film at 24 fps and PAL video (25 fps) can be done in one of two ways. The simplest method is to do a straight frame-for-frame transfer between the two, so that any given film frame corresponds directly to a certain video frame. This will obviously change the speed of any motion in the footage that is being transferred, but the speedup is only about 4% and is fairly subtle—subtle enough that the simplicity of the process makes it worthwhile. (Not to mention the fact that any movie that is transferred to video for television broadcast will be 4% shorter, giving more room for commercials!) But if a more accurate transfer is needed, a 25th video frame will need to be generated from the 24 film frames. Merely duplicating one of the frames would be visually noticeable, so instead two additional video *fields* are created, one from the 12th film frame and the other from the 24th.

These frame-rate conversions are usually accomplished by special **telecine** hardware that deals with both the digitization of the film *and* the pulldown. The process of going from video to film is much less common, but would follow the same logic for the speed change, in this case deinterlacing video fields in order to produce film frames. For the case of NTSC to film, the process is known as a **2:3 pullup**.

If film is being shot with the sole intention of transferring it to video, then the film camera can often just be adjusted to shoot at the appropriate frame rate, 30 fps or 25 fps, and any pulldown conversions can therefore be avoided. Many film cameras can actually be set to shoot at exactly 29.97 fps to perfectly match NTSC's rate.

Plate 24 *Image resulting from mixing 75% of Plate 18a with 25% of Plate 18b.*

Plate 25 *Masking to control brightness. (a) Mask image.*

Plate 25 *(b) Test image (Plate 18a) after being color corrected using Plate 25a as the mask.*

Plate 26 *Premultiplication. (a) Foreground image of a dog.*

Plate 26 *(b) A soft-edged matte for the dog.*

Plate 26 *(c) Foreground premultiplied by the matte.*

Plate 27 *Background image.*

Plate 28 *Premultiplied image (Plate 26c) placed over the background image (Plate 27) in a system that assumes all images are premultiplied.*

Plate 29 *Unpremultiplied image (Plate 26a) placed over the background image (Plate 27) in a system that assumes all images are premultiplied.*

Plate 30 *A doubly premultiplied image composited over the background. A dark halo is produced along the matte's edge.*

Plate 31 *The result of redividing a premultiplied image (Plate 26c) by its own matte channel.*

Plate 32 *The luminosity operator applied to Plate 26c. The matte channel for the foreground image was multiplied by 0.6 before being placed over the background.*

Plate 33 *Difference matting. (a) A clean plate of the background.*

Plate 33 *(b) The difference matte that is created by subtracting Plate 33a from Plate 26a.*

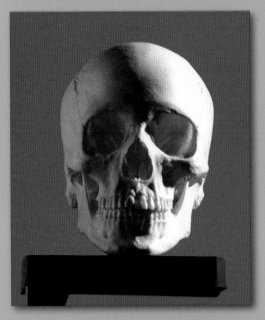

Plate 34 *Original bluescreen image.*

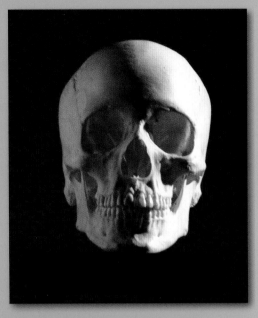

Plate 35 *The image from Plate 34 after applying spill suppression.*

Plate 36 *Plate 34 after matte extraction (reverse matte).*

Plate 37 *Data loss after applying two Brightness operators.*

Plate 38 *Candles shot from a close-up distance using a wide-angle lens.*

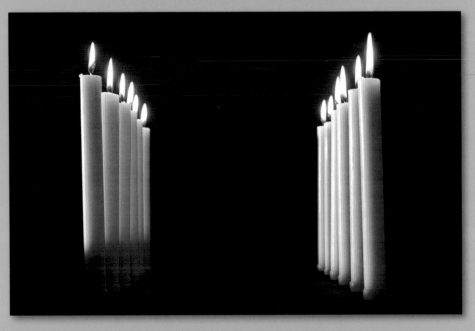

Plate 39 *Candles shot from farther away using a telephoto lens.*

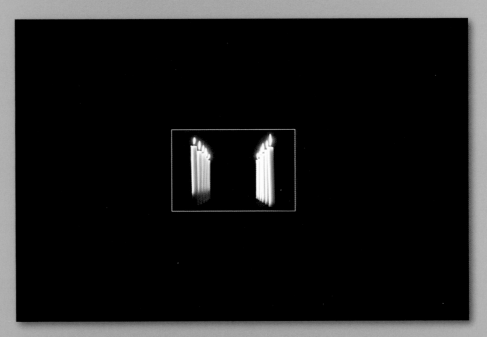

Plate 40 *Candles shot from the same position as those in Plate 39, but with the same lens as in Plate 38.*

Plate 41 *Depth of field. Only those objects within the depth of field are in focus.*

Plate 42   *Lens flares from a spherical lens.*

Plate 43   *Lens flare from an anamorphic lens (as seen when projected).*

Plate 44 *Focus. (a) A well-focused scene.*

Plate 44 *(b) The out-of-focus scene.*

Plate 44 *(c) A Gaussian blur of the original scene.*

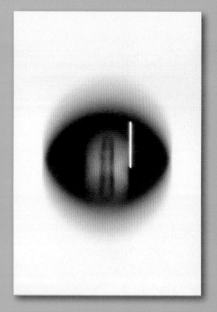

Plate 45 *Motion-blurred object.*

Plate 46 *Grain comparison. (a) Highly sensitive, low-light film stock (Kodak 5289).*

Plate 46 *(b) A slower-speed film stock (Kodak 5245).*

Plate 47 *The RGB channels of the film stock shown in Plate 46a. (a) Red channel.*

Plate 47 *(b) Green channel.*

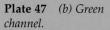

Plate 47 *(c) Blue channel.*

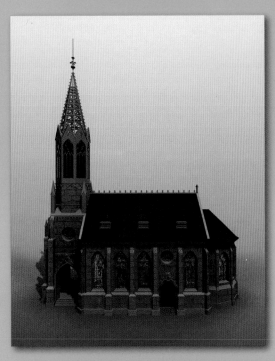

Plate 48 *Church shot from a high angle.*

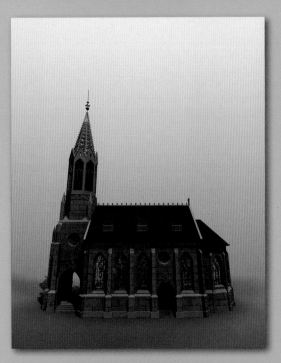

Plate 49 *Church shot from a lower angle.*

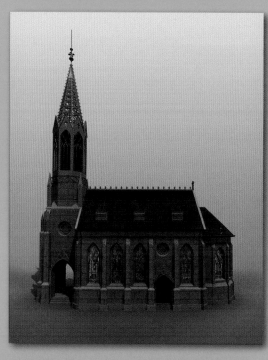

Plate 50   *The church from Plate 49 transformed to approximate the perspective shown in Plate 48.*

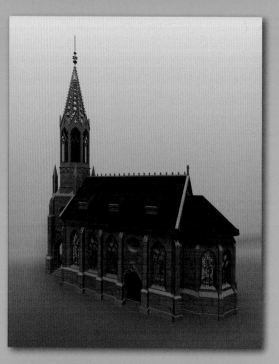

Plate 51   *The church shot from a different angle. Modifying this image to approximate the perspective of Plate 48 would be problematic.*

Plate 52 *Bluescreen integration. (a) The original bluescreen element.*

Plate 52 *(b) The element placed into the scene without spill suppression. Note the blue fringes on the subject, particularly in the hair.*

Plate 52 *(c) The element placed into the scene with simple spill suppression. Note that the color of the figure's shirt has also been changed by this process.*

Plate 52 *(d) The foreground and background element photographed together.*

CHAPTER ELEVEN

Quality and Efficiency

The intent of this chapter is to take a step beyond the basic processes involved in digital compositing and to start discussing how to apply all our tools to produce the highest-quality images in as efficient a manner as possible. In fact these two topics—quality and efficiency—are so co-dependent that it makes sense to discuss them together, in the same chapter.

As we did in some of the other chapters, we will be looking at a number of scenarios as if they were being accomplished with the use of a script-based compositing system. Certain methods may be less applicable for a system that does not support batch processing, but the basic concepts of efficiency with quality are still valid.

Even though we are taking the time to devote an entire chapter to the topic, we hope that you have already noticed a number of quality and efficiency issues that were raised in earlier chapters of this book. Everything from conserving disk space by using compressed file formats to using proxy images to speed intermediate testing will contribute to maximizing your resource usage.

QUALITY

In an ideal world, there would be time and budget enough to produce perfect composites for every job on which you work. After all, nobody gets into the business of digital compositing without having some kind of desire to do quality work. Unfortunately, the people *paying* for the work may not be as interested in the quality as they are with some other aspect, such as speed, quantity, or cost. The term "quality" is certainly subjective. Most compositing work allows for a great deal of personal aesthetics to be brought into the mix, and ultimately this book will never be able to fully identify exactly what constitutes a quality image. But there are certain absolutes of quality that *can* be identified. In particular, any technical artifacts or imperfections that are independent of artistic judgments will need to be addressed.

There are any number of these potential defects—aliasing artifacts, contouring, misaligned mattes, animation glitches, scene-to-scene discontinuities, mismatched colors, data clipping, and so on. Some of them (such as color mismatching) might bridge the categories of artistic and technical problems, whereas others are clearly a problem by any objective measure. The decision as to what is considered to be acceptable quality for a given job may ultimately be someone else's decision, but don't rely on others to find technical flaws for you!

EFFICIENCY

There is an old (rather cynical) adage that states that, given the categories of speed, cost, and quality, you can only have two of the three options. Fortunately, efficiency is an excellent way to cheat this rule and produce high-quality composites on time and on budget.

Efficiency is a matter of maximizing your available resources. No matter what your scenario, whether you are compositing a single frame on the PC in your basement or you are using dozens of CPUs to put together a 5000-frame composite for the next Hollywood blockbuster, your resources will always have a limit. The understanding of this limit, or, more properly, the understanding of the numerous limits that each piece of your compositing toolkit has, is the first step toward understanding where efficiencies can be introduced. Very few processes are inherently efficient, and it is up to the compositing artist to modify his or her methodologies so that he or she is able to produce work within the necessary time and budget.

Even though efficient working methods will save time and money, there is no reason why they should cause any loss of quality. In fact, many times we find that careful attention to producing an efficient compositing script will actually result in a higher-quality image than one generated from a hastily created script.

Methodology

In some ways it is impossible to teach someone exactly how to choose the best method for a given job, since every job is different. However, it *is* possible to discuss commonly observed problems and impart some sense of things that should be avoided. We will concentrate on things that can be done to make a script more efficient, while being as certain as possible that we are not degrading the image in any way. The discussion will include not only the actual compositing operators used, but also issues related to disk, CPU, and memory usage. Many times we can only give general guidelines, since certain things will depend on exactly what software and hardware you are using to complete your task.

For most of the discussions about efficiency, we'll be talking about methods to increase the productivity of the software and hardware that we are using. But determining the most efficient method for creating a composite involves not only weighing the amount of processing time the *computer* will need to spend on a particular composite, but also estimating how much of the *operator's* time will need to be spent to set up the process. Remember that the compositing artist has a certain cost associated with him or her, just as the computer system does. If you are creating the composite yourself, then you will be constantly making decisions that trade off the amount of time you will spend on a problem compared with the amount of time the computer will spend.

Many problems can certainly be solved by brute force. You may find that you can spend 20 minutes quickly setting up a process that will then take 8 hours to run on the computer. Or you could spend an hour setting up a much more elegant and efficient process that will only take the computer 2 hours to process. How do you decide which path to take? There is no definitive answer, of course. If it's the end of the day and you know that nobody will be using your computer overnight anyway, you'll probably choose the solution that takes less human time and more computer time. If, on the other hand, it's the beginning of the day and you need to produce imagery by that afternoon, the time spent setting up a faster-running process will be worth the investment. This may seem like common sense (and if you're an experienced compositor it had better be!), but it is always important to remember that just about any process will have these sort of trade-offs.

The ability to consistently make these sorts of decisions (often referred to as **production sense**) is something that generally only comes with a fair amount of experience, but we can certainly discuss a number of the issues involved. As mentioned earlier, we always want our quest for efficiency to be driven by our quest for quality. Consequently, let's start with a look at how even the most simple compositing process can be susceptible to drastic image-quality problems if one is not careful.

MINIMIZING DATA LOSS

There is a popular misconception that working with digital images means that one need not be concerned with decreased quality whenever a multitude of image manipulations are applied. This is such a pervading fallacy that it must be refuted immediately; in a large bold font:

"Digital" does *not* imply "lossless."

Certainly, digital compositing is a much more forgiving process than the optical compositing process, in which every step can cause significant generation loss. But even in the digital realm, data loss is generally something that can only be minimized, not eliminated (hence the title of this section). Just about *any* image processing or compositing operation loses some data. There are a few exceptions to this rule, such as channel reordering or geometric transformations that don't require resampling, but in general even the most innocuous operation will, at the very least, suffer from some round-off error. Unfortunately, whether this data loss will actually affect the quality of your composite is nearly impossible to predict in advance.

Whenever we begin a composite, we have a fixed amount of data available. All of the images that will be used are at the best resolution (spatial, chromatic, and temporal) that we are able to justify, and now the process of integrating them begins. Note that we talk about the "best resolution we are able to justify." What does this mean, and how do we decide such a thing? The bottom line is that we should try to work with the *least* amount of data necessary to produce a final result that is acceptable. Once again we're walking the fine line between having enough data to produce the quality we desire without having to process more pixels than is necessary. Choose too low a spatial resolution and you will have an image that appears soft and out of focus. Choose too low a chromatic resolution (i.e., bit depth) and you may start to see quantization artifacts such as banding and posterization. Even if the original source images appear to be of an appropriate quality level, once they are processed by multiple compositing operations these artifacts may show up.

The tempting solution might be to start every composite with very high-resolution images. But if our final result is intended for playback within a video game at a resolution of 320 × 240 pixels, we would be foolish to process all the intermediate steps at 4000 lines of resolution. Instead, we would probably choose to initially reduce all the elements to a resolution of 320 × 240 and then work directly with these images instead. As long as we pay attention to the various steps, we should be fine working with the lower resolution, and we will certainly have reduced the amount of time and resources necessary for the work. The trade-off decision about what resolutions are necessary must be made for every composite, although often it may make sense to standardize to a set of particular formats in order to reap the benefits of consistency and predictability.

There are no guarantees or formulas that let one definitively determine if a specific input resolution is high enough for a given composite. But not only will choosing an excessively high resolution cause a great deal of wasted man- and

CPU-hours, it *still* will not guarantee artifact-free images. It is actually quite simple to produce a compositing script that causes data loss even if the input images are high resolution and high bit depth. Consider the example shown in Plate 37, in which a brightness of 2.0 was applied to our original test image from Plate 3, and then a brightness of 0.5 was applied to the result. As you can see, a significant amount of data was lost. A graph of the result of this two-step operation is shown in Figure 11.1. Note that all the information in the brightest part of the image has been clipped to a uniform value of 0.5.

Any time we need to layer multiple operations on top of each other, we must be aware of what happens to the data in terms of overflow and round-off. In certain situations, some of the newer software may be smart enough to analyze multiple color corrections like this and consolidate these expressions into a global, more precise algorithm. (In the example just given, the two color corrections would cancel each other out.) This ability to automatically consolidate similar operators can make a huge difference in image quality and, in many cases, can even increase the speed of your compositing session because redundant operators are eliminated. As usual, the best advice is to test the behavior of the system yourself so that you know exactly what to expect. The ability of software to automatically deal with this sort of thing is very useful, but as you will see elsewhere in this chapter, an intelligent compositing artist can usually modify a script to avoid these problems in the first place and will be able to introduce efficiencies that an automated system cannot.

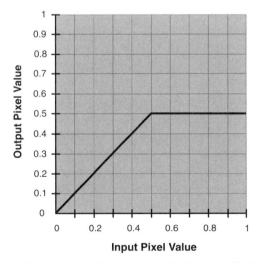

Figure 11.1 *Graph of the data loss caused by applying a Brightness of 2.0 followed by a Brightness of 0.5.*

Although the example was designed to show data loss when information is pushed outside the range of a normal image, similar loss can occur within the normal range if you are not working with enough precision. This possibility raises the issue of exactly how a given compositing system maintains the data with which it is working.

Internal Software Accuracy

Up to this point we have made the assumption that a compositing system that is given a group of 16-bit elements will actually composite those elements at that bit depth and produce a new 16-bit image. This is not necessarily a safe assumption. Many of today's systems still internally represent data at only 8 bits per channel. Even if they are able to "read" a 16-bit image, they may not be able to actually use all 16 bits and will immediately truncate the image to 8 bits. Any intermediate imagery will be produced at this lower bit depth, and the final image will also only be 8-bit. Thus, it is very important to know the internal accuracy of your compositing system.

Some software and hardware manufacturers claim that 8 bits per channel is enough information to accurately represent a color image and that there is no need to support the ability to process at greater than 8 bits per channel. (Coincidentally, the systems sold by these manufacturers all seem to be limited to this bit depth.) In many ways it is true that 8 bits per channel *can* almost always produce an image that is visually indistinguishable from a 16-bit image, particularly if the image contains the noise, grain, and other irregularities that are inherent in a digitized image from an analog source such as film or video. But rarely will we simply input an image and then immediately send it to its final destination. Rather, we will add multiple layers of image processing operations, color corrections, image combinations, and so on until we come up with our final result. It is during this multitude of additional processing that greater bit depth becomes useful. Each step will cause a minute amount of data loss (at least), and eventually this loss will start to manifest itself visibly if there is not enough color information available. Limited-bit-depth systems may be perfectly acceptable for simple composites without a large number of elements or processing steps, but once we need to push things to the extreme, they can rapidly fall apart.

Better systems will let you choose the accuracy that you wish to use when computing a solution. There may be times when you wish to work with only 8-bit accuracy to increase speed, and there may be times when you need the full 16 bits. You should be aware that some systems may make assumptions about the necessary bit depth. For instance, if your source image is only an 8-bit image, the system may assume that any further operations can also be done at 8-bits. The best systems will allow you to override this behavior, as certain things will appear much cleaner if computed at a higher bit depth. Even something as simple as a blur can introduce artifacts (particularly banding) if it is computed at only 8 bits per channel. In such a situation, you should be able to specify that the 8-bit image be temporarily converted to 16 bits for the purpose of the calculation, even if it will eventually be stored back to an 8-bit image. As usual, this sort of decision is something that you will need to deal with on a case-by-case basis.

Compositing systems are not necessarily limited to working at only 16 bits of accuracy or less. Some newer systems can actually go beyond this, representing the data that is being processed with up to 32 bits per channel. Unlike the jump between 8 and 16 bits, using 32 bits per channel is not done simply to increase the number of colors that can be represented. Rather, 32-bit systems are designed so that they also no longer need to clip image data that moves outside the range of 0 to 1. These 32-bit systems are usually referred to as "floating-point systems." At first, the ability to represent data outside the range of 0 to 1 may not seem to be terribly worthwhile. But the implications are huge, in that it allows images to behave more like they would in the real world, where there is no upper limit on the brightness a scene can have. Even though we will probably still want to eventually produce an image that is normalized between 0 and 1, we can work with intermediate images with far less danger of extreme data loss. For instance, we can now double the brightness of an image and not lose all the data that was in the upper half of the image. A pixel that started with a value of 0.8 would simply be represented with a value of 1.6. For purposes of viewing such an image, we will still usually represent anything above 1.0 as pure white, but there will actually be data that is stored above that threshold. At a later time, we could apply another operator that decreases the overall brightness of the image and brings these superwhite pixels back into the "visible" range.

The ability to calculate in a floating-point mode is usually an optional setting, which should be used wisely. Running in this mode will double or quadruple the amount of data that is used to represent each frame and will increase the amount of processing power necessary by an equivalent amount.

There are almost always ways to produce images of identical quality without resorting to the use of floating-point calculations. Instead, a system's floating-point capabilities should only be used whenever other methods are not practical. There may be an effect that can only be achieved in floating-point mode, or you may simply be confronted with a script that is so complex that you would spend more time trying to find a data-clipping problem than the computer would spend computing the results in floating-point mode.

Although compositing systems that support floating-point calculations are still fairly rare, they will almost certainly become the standard in a few more years as memory and CPUs become faster and cheaper. Eventually we may even have a scenario in which all compositing is done without bothering to normalize values between 0 and 1, resulting in a much simpler model and, as a side benefit, making large sections of this book obsolete.

CONSOLIDATING OPERATIONS

The purpose of this section is to discuss situations in which certain compositing scripts can be modified in order to eliminate unnecessary operators. Whether a given operator is necessary will not always be an objective question, but initially we will look at scenarios in which two operators can be replaced by a single operator without any change to the resultant image whatsoever.

For instance, let's take the extremely simple case of an image with a brightness effect added to it according to the script in Figure 11.2. In this example, we have applied a brightness of 0.5 to the original source image. Let's say that we look at the resultant image produced by this script and decide that we need the brightness decreased by another 25%. There are two paths we could take: Either we add a *second* brightness operator with a value of 0.75 (Figure 11.3a), or we modify our existing brightness tool and decrease it by an additional 25%. Doing the math, we take $0.5 \times 0.75 = 0.375$. This route is shown in Figure 11.3b.

Perhaps it is obvious that the preferred method would be to recalculate the proper numbers and modify the existing brightness effect. This will leave us with a simpler script, and the process should run quite a bit faster since it only needs to process one operation instead of two. This is a very simple example—once your script begins to have more than just a few layers, these sort of decisions can become much less obvious.

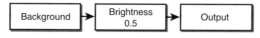

Figure 11.2 *A simple script for applying brightness to an image.*

Figure 11.3 *Two paths for modifying the image that results from the script in Figure 11.2. (a) Adding a second Brightness operator. (b) Modifying the original Brightness operator.*

Whenever one is creating a multiple-level compositing script, it is dangerously easy to add a new operator every time a modification is necessary. Before you add another layer to a script, stop to ask yourself if the layer is truly necessary, or if the same (or a visually similar) effect can be accomplished by modifying one of the existing layers. Compositing scripts have an uncanny ability to grow excessively, and unless great care is taken to simplify whenever possible, you will end up with a script that is not only incomprehensible, but also full of image-degrading problems.

Our ability to simplify the previous script relied on the fact that we knew that two Brightness operators could be "folded" together. Since the Brightness operator is merely a multiplier, this consolidation is straightforward. One cannot always assume that this is the case. Certain operators absolutely *cannot* be folded together to get the same result. For instance, two Biased-Contrast operators with different biases cannot be consolidated into a single Contrast operator that gives an identical result.

Many compositing systems are able to analyze scripts and automatically simplify the math before they run the process. On such a system, you might in fact *not* have any significant speed difference between these two examples. Such automatic optimization can only go so far, however, and to rely on it will inevitably produce code that is less efficient. Even the best optimization routines will probably be limited to producing images that are *exactly* what would be produced by the unoptimized script. A good artist, however, can look at a script and realize that two layers can be consolidated to produce an extremely similar, but not identical, image. The decision can be made to accept the slightly different image in the interest of a significant speed increase. But please, be careful not to compromise image quality in blind pursuit of the most efficient script possible!

Let's look at a slightly more complex example to discuss other areas that can be simplified. Consider the compositing script shown in Figure 11.4. We have a foreground element with several effects layered on it, and a background element with a few different effects on it. The first branch is then placed over the second.

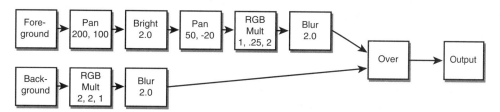

Figure 11.4 *A more complex script involving two source elements.*

Close examination of the script will reveal obvious inefficiencies. First of all, there is a Pan operator on the foreground element in two different locations, each offsetting by a certain number of pixels. These pixel offsets can be added together to produce a new, consolidated offset value, as follows:

$$(200,100) + (50,-20) = (250,80)$$

Also, we have both a Brightness *and* an RGB Multiply in our script. If you recall the definition of Brightness, you'll remember that it is effectively the same as an RGB Multiply, except that the same value is applied to all three channels equally. Therefore, we really have two different RGB Multiply operators, the first of which applies a multiplier of (2.0, 2.0, 2.0) to the image, and the second of which applies a multiplier of (1.0, 0.25, 2.0) to the image. These two operators can be multiplied together to consolidate their values, producing a new RGB Multiply of (2.0, 0.5, 4.0). Finally, the Blur operator on both images is the same value, so we can simply move it *after* the Over, so that it only needs to happen once, instead of twice.[1] We've just eliminated three operators, producing a faster, more comprehensible, and higher-quality script, as shown in Figure 11.5.

Now, let's assume that your supervisor takes a look at the sample test image your script produced and tells you that it looks twice as bright as it should. The tempting solution would be to simply apply a Brightness of 0.5 to the top of the script, after the Over, as shown in Figure 11.6. However, a much better solution, particularly in light of how much we're boosting the image in some of the earlier steps, is to go back and modify the RGB Multiply on both elements *before* the Over, again consolidating our correction into the existing operators. Thus, the script becomes as shown in Figure 11.7.

Figure 11.5   *Consolidation of operators to create a simplified version of the script in Figure 11.4.*

---

[1] Strictly speaking, this particular rearrangement will not produce an identical image. However, the trade-off in speed will be considerable, and in fact it is generally considered visually better to blur two elements together instead of blurring them separately and then combining them. Thus, this is a good example of a consolidation that would never be caught by an automatic system, but that would be obvious to an experienced artist.

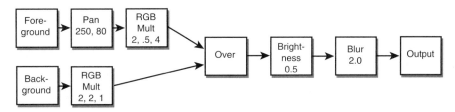

Figure 11.6   *The script in Figure 11.5 with an additional Brightness operator.*

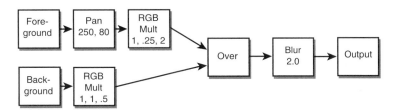

Figure 11.7   *The script in Figure 11.5 with consolidated operators.*

Obviously, not all scripts have such obvious places where you can simplify, but situations such as the one presented in this example will be quite common. What's more, when working on a large, multilayer composite, you should always keep an eye out for places where you can rearrange things to produce even greater efficiencies. Ideally this will be done before you fine-tune the composite, since this will give you more flexibility to change things without worrying about the effect on a "signed-off" element. Understanding the math behind various operators is important if you wish to make educated decisions on layer consolidation. Remember that the result produced by multiple operations will often be order dependent, and simply changing the order of two operators could radically affect the output image.

Recognize that there are always trade-offs for how long it may take to simplify a script compared with the time it may take to run the unsimplified version, but know that ultimately, if you are careful to think about efficiency every time you modify your script, you will be far better off once it grows to a huge size. Be aware of the entire process, not just the particular step with which you are dealing.

Incidentally, if you think that the relentless pursuit of simplified scripts is a bit too obsessive, consider the fact that even medium-complexity scripts can include dozens or even hundreds of different layers and operators. Again, refer to Plate 93 for an excellent example of a real-world script. Although large, it is actually a very clean script, produced by an experienced compositor. There is little if any room for additional efficiency modifications. Imagine how a script for a scene of this complexity would look if it had been produced in a more haphazard manner, without careful attention to issues of speed and quality! An overview of the process used to create this script is discussed further in Chapter 16.

REGION OF INTEREST

One of the most important things a compositing artist can do to increase productivity is to make sure that compute resources aren't spent on unnecessary calculations. We've discussed a few different ways to avoid excess computation, but one of the best methods is to utilize a **region of interest**. A region of interest (or **ROI**) is a user-specified rectangle that can be used to limit certain compositing calculations to within its boundaries (usually temporarily). Using the ROI to limit calculations is done primarily as an intermediate step in a composite, that is, when one desires to concentrate on tuning a particular area of the full image.

Very often you may find yourself in a situation in which you have balanced most of the composite to your satisfaction, but there is a small area that needs more work. By specifying a region of interest that surrounds only this small area, you are allowing the computer to deal exclusively with the pixels you choose. No extra CPU time will be spent to compute portions of the image that you do not need to modify. A well-implemented ROI can produce a huge increase in compositing speed. Complex composites may have a number of elements that fall outside of any given ROI, and the compositing engine will be able to completely ignore these elements when working only within the ROI. Ideally your software will let you interactively define and redefine the ROI as needed, but if it is not this flexible, or does not explicitly support ROI functionality, you may still gain similar benefits by precropping the elements to a region that features the area in which you are interested. You can tune your parameters with this lower-resolution image and then apply the values you prefer to the original uncropped composite. Be sure to go back and test the full image once you have tuned the area defined by the ROI, since there is a chance that something you did may have affected an area outside of the ROI.

Many of the better compositing packages are also able to use a similar calculation-limiting feature known as a **domain of definition**, or **DOD**. A domain of definition is usually defined within any given image as a bounding box that surrounds nonzero pixels. For instance, if you render a small CG element inside a fairly large frame, the rendering software may include information in the file header that specifies a rectangle that surrounds the element as tightly as possible. This DOD can then be used by the compositing software to limit calculations in the same way as the ROI. While both the DOD and the ROI are used to limit calculations, they are not the same thing. The DOD is generally an area that is automatically determined by a piece of software, based on the information in a specific image. The ROI, on the other hand, is chosen by the user and may be redefined as needed.

WORKING IN A NETWORKED ENVIRONMENT

While the bulk of the high-end film compositing work being produced these days is done at facilities with dozens or even hundreds of computers on a network, many smaller shops, even single-person operations, now have access to more than a single stand-alone computer system to help store data or process imagery. The physical connections between these machines will vary quite a bit, but there are certain guidelines that can help you deal with a group of networked computers as efficiently as possible. Generally, the network between any two computers will be much slower than the local disk drives on those machines.[2] As such, it usually makes sense to be aware of where your files reside. Although the goal of most good networks is to present a file system that behaves similarly whether files are local or remote, it is important to be able to distinguish between local and remote files. Ideally, if you are trying to get feedback on your composite as you are tuning parameters, you will have the source files local to the computer at which you are working. If this is impractical due to disk limitations on the local system, then you may find it worthwhile to make local copies of certain files that you are spending a large amount of time accessing.

A number of other considerations need to be kept in mind when working in a networked environment, but since they are not strictly compositing related, we will not go into much more detail. Suffice it to say that issues related to data sharing, concurrency control, and bandwidth maximization should all be considered.

DISK USAGE

The amount of available disk space is yet another limited resource with which you will need to deal. Throughout this book we've discussed a number of things that can help with managing disk space, including compressed file formats, single-channel images, and the use of proxies. But you should also be constantly looking for opportunities to discard data that is no longer necessary. If your source images started at a higher than necessary resolution, you may be able to immediately downsize them to your working resolution and remove the originals. Any tests that you generate that are outdated by a newer test should probably be removed as soon as possible.

---

[2] This is not *always* true, however. Well-funded facilities can afford to put high-speed networks in place that greatly diminish the access speed difference between remote and local files.

It will at times be important to estimate how much disk space will be used when a new image sequence is computed. This calculation is particularly critical if your system is creating images while unattended, since a suddenly full disk can have catastrophic consequences. You should always make sure that you have enough disk space available for a sequence before you create it. There are a number of ways to estimate this, but usually the simplest is to create a single frame and then multiply the amount of space it uses by the number of frames that will be in the final sequence. Be careful if you are working with compressed file formats, because the test frame that you generated may not be an accurate indicator of the file size for every frame in the sequence. Compressed files can vary considerably depending on content, and as such should only be considered as an estimate for what the average file size will be. If you are greatly concerned about this issue you may want to precompute several different frames throughout the sequence and see if there are major size differences.

You may also find yourself in a situation in which you have computed a low-resolution proxy image and now want to predict how much space the full-resolution equivalent will consume. Remember that the size difference will be proportional to the change in both the horizontal *and* the vertical resolution. A common mistake is to assume that doubling the resolution will result in a file size that is twice as large. In reality, doubling the resolution means that you are doubling both the X and the Y resolution, thereby producing an image that will be *four* times larger.

There is a maxim that "Data expands to fill the available space." Working with multiple image sequences is an excellent way to prove the validity of this statement, and you'll quickly find that your resources seem insufficient no matter how much space you have available. But efficient disk usage usually boils down to constantly monitoring the existing space and making sure that image sequences that are no longer necessary are removed from the system as soon as possible. Probably you'll want to back up most images to some form of long-term archival storage so that they can be recovered if needed. In an environment where disk space is at a premium, you may find that temporarily archiving files and then restoring them to disk as they become needed is an ongoing process instead of one that occurs only when a shot is completed.

PRECOMPOSITING

In any environment in which resources are limited, you may find that a trade-off can often be made between compute resources and disk resources. Consider the script again from Figure 11.7 earlier in this chapter. If we are thinking about this script as a batch process, we are assuming that there are two image sequences on disk (Foreground and Background) that will be read when we run the composite. Our five operations (the pan, two RGB multiplies, the Over, and the blur) will be applied in the proper order and a new image sequence (which we're calling Output) will be produced and written to disk. But there is nothing to prevent us from breaking this script into a set of smaller composites. We could, for instance, create a smaller script that only takes the foreground element and applies the pan and the RGB multiply. We would then write this new sequence out to disk and name it something like New__FG. This process is diagrammed in Figure 11.8. This new sequence is called a **preliminary composite**, or simply a **precomp**. To use this precomp, we now need to modify our original script to reflect the fact that we have a new element, as shown in Figure 11.9.

This technique might seem to be somewhat of a waste of disk resources, since it required creating an entire new sequence on disk, yet ended up with a script that still produces exactly the same result. If we only run our script a single time, then this evaluation is true. But the nature of most compositing work is that the same script (or sequence of operations) will probably be run several times, with only minor changes each time. Perhaps we're not sure about the quality of the blur that we're applying, and so we run the script several times, slightly modifying the blur parameters each time. Even though we're not actually changing the parameters for the other operators, we're still recomputing their result every time we run the script. By precomping our New__FG layer, we will not be recomputing the pan and the RGB multiply every time we run our script. In effect, we have traded some disk inefficiency for some gains in CPU efficiency. Our new script should run more quickly now that we have removed two of the operators.

Of course, the trick to all of this is deciding exactly when it makes sense to precomposite a portion of a script. Generally, you only want to precomposite something once you're reasonably sure that the operators that are being applied

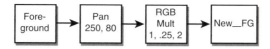

Figure 11.8 *Creating a precomposite for the foreground element of Figure 11.7.*

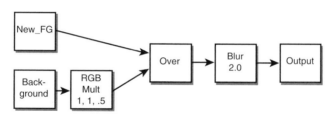

Figure 11.9 *New script that incorporates the precomposite.*

are not subject to change. If, for some reason, we realized that the pan we had applied to our foreground was incorrect, we would be forced to go back and rerun our precomposite before we could then rerun our main composite. There are no right or wrong answers when it comes to precompositing. Operations that are very compute intensive are good candidates for precompositing once you have a reasonable assurance that the parameters will not need to be modified.

Precompositing is also often used when a script grows too large for a piece of hardware or software to deal with it effectively. Extremely large scripts may require a great deal of memory. If the memory on a given system is limited, then you might want to break your large script into a number of smaller, more memory-friendly scripts. In a sense, most on-line compositing systems are really producing numerous precomps at every step of the process. By not having any batch capabilities, they are forced to precompute a new sequence whenever a new operator is added, and any modification to earlier layers will require manually retracing the same compositing process.

If you *do* decide to produce intermediate precomps, remember that they should be stored in a file format that has support for the quality that you feel you will need. It may be tempting to use a format that includes some lossy compression, or works at a lower bit depth, but doing so will potentially introduce artifacts that become more pronounced as additional effects are added to the imagery.

CHAPTER TWELVE

Learning to See

Although most of us spend our whole lives looking at the world around us, we seldom stop to think about the specifics of how the brain perceives what our eyes see. Most of the time it immediately reduces everything to some kind of symbolic representation, and we never even stop to consider issues such as how the light and shadows in front of us are interacting. But at some point in the process of becoming an artist, one needs to move beyond this. To quote the poet/novelist/scientist Johann Wolfgang von Goethe,[1]

> This is the most difficult thing of all, though it would seem the easiest: to see that which is before one's eyes.

Goethe's not the only one who is aware of this issue. Here are a couple more quotes on the subject

> I see no more than you, but I have trained myself to notice what I see.
> —*Sherlock Holmes, in Arthur Conan Doyle's "The Adventure of the Blanched Soldier"*

> Seeing is in some respect an art, which must be learnt.
> —*Sir William Herschel, the famous astronomer who, among other achievements, discovered Uranus and helped to prove the existence of infrared light*

---

[1] Although he is best known as the author of *Faust*, Goethe also published a book called *Theory of Colors*, which is an in-depth analysis of how the brain perceives color and contrast.

"Seeing" is definitely something that *can* be learned, (or learnt), and in fact is something that every artist from the beginning of time has had to learn. Digital compositing artists are no exception, particularly if they want to produce images that appear to be realistic and believable. Certainly digital compositing can be used to produce surreal or fantastic imagery, but as stated very early on in this book, one must still be able to believe that everything in the scene was photographed at the same time, by the same camera.

There are a number of excellent books that can help the artist to learn how to see. A couple of them are mentioned in the bibliography at the end of this book, and there are hundreds (if not thousands) of others that also cover the subject. But one must go beyond reading about it—one must practice it. Even if you don't take up sketching or painting, or even photography, you can always find time to better examine your surroundings, trying to understand exactly how the brain is interpreting the images it is seeing.

Ultimately, the more time you spend compositing, the more you'll learn about what things are important in order to fully integrate elements into a scene. There are a number of techniques (and several tricks) that can be used to trigger the visual cues the eye is accustomed to seeing. Every image is a complex mixture of light and shadow. In this chapter and the next (in which we discuss specific details about how the lights in a scene interact), we will provide information that is directly applicable to the process of creating a composite image.

JUDGING COLOR, BRIGHTNESS, AND CONTRAST

One of the most important things a compositor does when integrating elements into a scene is to balance everything in terms of color, brightness, and contrast. Different people's abilities to judge color can vary quite a bit, but it is *not* solely an inherited ability. Quite the opposite, in fact—having a good eye for color can be learned, generally through a great deal of practice.

Although the ability to judge color, brightness, and contrast is almost impossible to learn from a book, there are a few important facts that one should be aware of. The most important fact is that the perception of color (as well as brightness and contrast) can be significantly affected by outside influences. The classic example of this principle is shown in Figure 12.1. Although the inner circle is the same color in all three cases, it *appears* to be brighter when surrounded by a darker background. Scientists who study perception know this phenomenon as the "principle of simultaneous contrast." The same thing holds true with color imagery. A color will appear more vibrant and saturated when surrounded by complementary colors—red surrounded by cyan or green, for instance.

Judging the overall contrast in an element or a scene is also subject to the environment in which the scene is viewed. In fact, looking at a specific image

Figure 12.1 *Simultaneous contrast.*

while situated in a brightly lit surrounding environment will fool the eye into thinking that the image has more contrast than it really does. By the same token, images viewed while in a darker environment will appear to have less contrast.

To make things more difficult, there is even evidence that diet can also influence one's ability to judge color. In a series of experiments performed by the U.S. government during World War II, researchers attempted to provide Navy sailors with the ability to see infrared signal lights with the naked eye. Through the use of foods rich in a specific type of vitamin A (and deficient in another, more common type), they found that the subjects' vision actually began to change, becoming more sensitive to the infrared portion of the spectrum. The experiment eventually ended, however, with the invention of electronic devices that would allow the viewing of infrared sources directly.

Since the human visual system *is* so susceptible to environmental influences, one must do one's best to try to control that environment whenever judging color. Try to view different images in as similar a context as possible. If you are comparing two images on your computer's monitor, make sure that the surroundings, both on- and off-screen, are not biasing your judgment. Some people try to eliminate as much color as possible from their viewing area, to the extent of setting their screen background and window borders to a neutral gray. We have also mentioned that there are a number of digital tools for sampling the color of a specific pixel or a grouping of pixels. Knowledgeable use of these tools can be a tremendous help when trying to judge and synchronize colors between disparate plates.

Be aware too that the physical medium will greatly influence the color and brightness perception of an image. It can prove particularly difficult to judge how the color of an image on a computer monitor will translate when that image is sent to film. As mentioned in Chapter 9 when we talked about methods for viewing an image, you should be sure that whatever monitor you are using to judge color is calibrated to be as accurate as possible. But this will still only provide an image that is *similar* to what you will see on film. To aid the process of creating an accurately colored digital image, the use of a **wedge** is usually necessary. A wedge is a series of still images that feature incremental alterations to the color or brightness of a reference frame. Essentially these images are all slight variations around the artist's "best guess" in the digital realm. This series of images will be sent to film, and the final color and brightness can be chosen from the different options. The parameters that were used to create the chosen frame are then applied to the entire sequence, producing a final composite with the proper color balance.

THE CAMERA

Not only do we need to learn how our *eyes* perceive the world around us, but, since we will probably be producing images that are designed to mimic those shot with some kind of camera, we also need to learn how the camera perceives the world around it. In other words, not only does the compositing artist need to learn how to see, he or she will also need to learn how a camera sees.

One of the most important things that you should remember when using a camera is that it is only capturing a *representation* of a scene. The resulting image will, it is hoped, look a great deal like the original scene, but the information in this image is only a subset of the original scene. First of all, it is obviously a two-dimensional representation of a three-dimensional scene. Moving the position of your head when viewing the image or walking around it will not give you the same information that moving in front of the real scene would give, in terms of depth perception or of revealing objects that are occluded by other objects.

This image is also a subset of the real scene in terms of the amount of detail that is captured. The resolution of the real scene is effectively infinite—increasing the magnification or moving closer to an object in the scene will continue to reveal new information, no matter how far you go. The captured image, on the other hand, will quickly fall apart if it is examined too closely.

Finally, the captured image is very limited in terms of the range of colors and brightness that it has recorded. Areas of the scene that are above or below a certain brightness will be simply recorded as "white" or "black," even though there is really a great deal of shading variation in these areas.

These limitations are important to keep in mind as you are working with image data, as there may often be times when there is not enough captured information to effect the changes that a particular composite requires. This topic is covered in much greater detail in the early sections of Chapter 15.

In addition to the dimensional, detail, and range limits that are inherent in a captured image, you should also become familiar with any idiosyncrasies of the device that you are using to capture these images. Whether you are working with film or video, artifacts of shutter and lens must be analyzed and usually mimicked as closely as possible. If you are dealing with film (again, even if you are working on a sequence destined for video you will often find that your source elements were shot on film), you'll need to be aware of issues related to film stock, such as grain characteristics.

Even if you are not compositing live-action elements at all, most of these issues are still important. Just about any synthetic scene-creation process, from computer-generated images to traditional cel animation, will tend to use visual cues taken from a real camera's behavior.

DISTANCE AND PERSPECTIVE

One of the most significant tasks that a compositing artist deals with is the job of taking elements and determining their depth placement in the scene. Taking a collection of two-dimensional pieces and trying to reassemble them to appear as if they have three-dimensional relationships is not a trivial issue, and a number of techniques are used in the process.

Because the elements that are being added to a scene were usually not shot in the same environment, there are a number of cues that must be dealt with to properly identify the elements' distance from the camera—primary visual features that allow the viewer to determine the depth relationship of various objects in a scene. These features include such things as object overlap, relative size, atmospheric effects, and depth of field. One of the most important features has to do with the way that **perspective** is captured by a camera, and thus we will take a moment to discuss this in greater detail.

Much of this information will already be familiar to readers who are amateur or professional photographers. Basic photographic concepts are the same whether you are using a disposable "point-and-shoot" camera or a professional motion-picture camera. There is no better way to understand how a camera works than to experiment with one. Reasonably priced 35mm SLR cameras are available that allow the user to control exposure, speed, and lens settings. Consumer video cameras allow a great deal of control as well and have the advantage of nearly immediate feedback. Ultimately, your goal is to understand how a camera converts a three-dimensional scene into a two-dimensional image, and how it is that we are able to interpret the elements of this two-dimensional image as still having depth.

Perspective and the Camera

Perspective relates to the size and distance relationships of the objects in a scene. More specifically, it has to do with the *perceived* size and distance of these objects, and with the ways in which this perception can be affected. Compositors need to be aware of these issues, since they will constantly be manipulating distance and size relationships in order to integrate objects into a scene. Most of the information we will present in this section can be found in any good photography book, usually in much more detail than we will go into here. But its importance is significant, and so we will try to give a quick overview of the subject and leave further research up to the reader.

Examine Plate 38. Plate 38 was shot from a distance of about 16 inches, using a 24mm lens. Plate 39 was photographed from a much farther distance, about 4 feet, but using a longer, 85mm lens. Notice the difference in perspective between the two images. The apparent size and distance relationships among the candles in the scene are noticeably different—the candles seem significantly separated in 38 and much more tightly clustered in 39.

This difference in perspective is a result of the scene having been shot from two different *positions*. As we move toward or away from a given scene, the spatial relationships of the objects in that scene will seem to change, to be expanded or compressed. An extremely common misconception is that the perspective difference is due to the different lenses used to shoot the scene. While it is true that lenses with different focal lengths *were* used to shoot these two examples, it is best to think of lenses as simple framing devices that magnify a given scene by a certain amount. In this example, the scene in Plate 39 was magnified by an 85mm lens so that the objects in the scene fill about the same amount of frame as they did in 38. But the lens itself did not contribute to the perspective change. Look at Plate 40, which was shot from the same distance as Plate 39, yet with the same 24mm lens that was used in 38. In particular, look at the area with the box drawn around it and notice that the objects have the same perspective relationship that is seen in 39. The lenses are completely different, yet the *perspective* is the same. This may seem like a trivial distinction at first, but ignore it at your own peril, particularly if you are the person who will be shooting different elements for a scene. This topic is discussed further in Chapter 13.

Objects farther from a camera begin to lose their sense of perspective: Their depth relationship to other objects is deemphasized. Thus, when you use a "long," or telephoto, lens, you will notice that the scene appears flatter and objects start to look as if they are all at approximately the same depth. This effect is due to the distance of the objects that you are viewing. In contrast, a collection of objects that are closer to the camera (and thus would tend to be shot with a wide-angle lens) will have a much greater sense of relative depth between them. Look again at Plates 38 and 39, and notice the effect that distance has on the apparent candle positions. Those in Plate 39 appear to have much less variation in their relative distances. They appear more flat, and their apparent sizes are very similar.

Strictly speaking, whenever discussing perspective issues such as this, one should always talk about the camera-to-object distance. But, in spite of the basic principles involved, it generally tends to be much more convenient to classify shots by the length of the lens used instead of the distance of the scene from the camera. The focal length of a lens is a simple piece of information, whereas the distance to the objects in a scene can be difficult to ascertain. Thus, we say that scenes shot with long lenses (which implies that they were shot at a greater distance from the subject) will tend to be more flat and show less perspective, and scenes shot with wide-angle lenses (implying proximity to the subject) will tend to show more perspective. We'll generally use this terminology and risk propagating the myth that the lens itself causes the distortion.

Depth Cues

Now that we have an understanding of how the perspective of a scene is affected by the distance from the camera, let's take a look at some of the other visual cues that can be used to help position an object in space. We'll call these **depth cues**, and will try to break them up into a few basic categories.

Overlap

The most basic cue that one object is in front of another is for the first object to overlap, or partially obscure, the second. If you are placing a true foreground element into a background scene, this may be a nonissue, since your foreground will overlap everything else in the scene. But if your "foreground" element is actually located somewhere in the midground of the scene, you may need to isolate objects in the background plate that can be used to partially or occasionally occlude the new element. You may also simply add elements that are truly in the foreground.

Relative Size

Another cue that helps us to determine the placement of an object is the fact that the farther an object is from the camera, the smaller it will appear. This is simple and obvious in theory, but in practice it can be deceptively difficult to determine the proper size of an object when it is being put into a scene. This is particularly true if the object you are adding is not something whose size is familiar to the people who will be viewing the scene. Is that a medium-sized dinosaur that's fairly close to the camera, or is that a *really big* dinosaur that's far away?

In some situations there may be additional data (such as set measurements) that can help with the process of sizing an object, but all too often one must arbitrarily scale the element to what one hopes is an appropriate size. Learn to use other objects in the scene as clues to relative size and position. Even if there are no objects in the scene that are the same size and distance from camera as the new element, you can often look at several nearby objects and mentally extrapolate the proper scale for the new object.

Again, be aware of the overall perspective of the scene when doing these estimates. This will become even more important when you need to deal with objects that move toward or away from the camera. In this situation, you may even need to animate the scale of the object. The amount of scale change will be determined not only by the speed at which the object is moving, but also by the perspective in the scene. If the scene was shot with a long lens, the apparent size increase/decrease will be less extreme than it would be had it been shot with a wide-angle lens.

Motion Parallax

Motion parallax refers to the fact that objects moving at a constant speed across the frame will appear to move a greater amount if they are closer to an observer (or camera) than they would if they were at a greater distance. This phenomenon is true whether it is the object itself that is moving or the observer/camera that is moving relative to the object. The reason for this effect has to do with the amount of distance the object moves as compared with the percentage of the camera's **field of view** that it moves across. An example is shown in Figure 12.2. An object that is 100 meters away may move 20 meters in a certain direction and only move across 25% of the field of view, yet the same 20-meter displacement

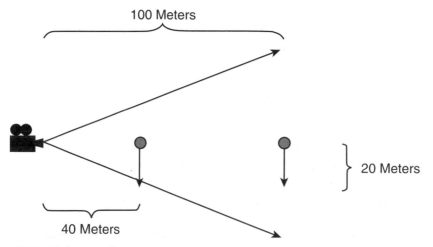

Figure 12.2   *Motion parallax.*

in an object that is only 40 meters away will cause the object to move completely out of frame.

Atmospheric Effects

One of the more subtle—and often ignored—depth cues has to do with the atmosphere in a scene. As an object moves farther away from the camera, the effects of this atmosphere will grow more and more pronounced. Atmospheric effects can include mist, haze, smoke, or fog, but even on the clearest days you will have atmospheric influences on objects in the distance. Air itself is not completely transparent, and any additional foreign gas or suspended matter will increase the opaqueness of the air.

Go look at some images taken on the surface of the moon, and notice how the lack of atmosphere makes even the most distant objects appear to have too much contrast. Shadows are far too dense, and in general it is extremely hard to judge the size and location of these objects. Even photographs taken from miles up appear to have been taken from a relatively low height, and the horizon seems far too near. Of course, part of this effect is because the moon, having a smaller diameter, *does* have a shorter horizon, but this alone does not explain the effect, or the difficulty in judging the size of objects in the distance. It is primarily the lack of atmosphere that fools our perceptions.

Consider Plate 94. Note the loss of contrast in the distant objects: The dark areas are brightened, and the image becomes somewhat diffused. In general, the darker areas will take on the color of the atmosphere around them. On a clear day, dark or shadowed areas on an object will take on the bluish tint of the sky as the object moves away from the camera (or the camera moves away from the object). This sort of effect becomes even more pronounced if the subject is in a fog or under water.

Depth of Field

If you pay attention to the photographed imagery that surrounds you, you'll notice that it is rarely the case that every element in a scene is in sharp focus. A camera lens can really only focus at a single specific distance. Everything that is nearer to or farther from the lens than this distance will be at least slightly out of focus. Fortunately, there is actually a *range* of distances over which the lens can produce an image whose focus is considered acceptable. This range of distances is known as the **depth of field**. Plate 41 shows an example of a scene with a fairly shallow depth of field. The camera was focused on one of the center candles in the row, and all of the other candles feature a greater amount of defocus as their distance from this in-focus location increases.

There are no hard-and-fast rules about what constitutes "acceptable focus." The method used to measure the amount of defocusing present in an image uses something known as the **circle of confusion**, which is the diameter of the circle formed when an idealized point goes out of focus. Different manufacturers may vary slightly in their calibrations, but a fairly common convention is that an in-focus image will produce a circle of confusion that is less than 1/1000th of an inch on a 35mm negative. In the real world, people depend on the manufacturer's markings on the lens, various tables (such as those contained in the *American Cinematographer Manual*, referenced in the bibliography), or (most commonly) their own eyes to determine the depth of field for a particular scene and lens setting.

Incidentally, don't make the mistake of referring to depth of field as "depth of focus." Depth of focus is a very specific term for the distance *behind* the lens (inside the camera) at which the film should be placed so that the transmitted image will be in focus.

The depth of field for a given scene is dependent on a number of different factors. These include the aperture of the lens, the focal length of the lens, and the distance from the lens to the point of focus. Most composites (at least the believable ones) will require the artist to deal with elements that exhibit various degrees of focus, and it is important to understand the factors that determine the focus range in a given situation.

Probably the best way to get familiar with how depth of field works is to do some work with a still camera, preferably one in which you have control over the aperture and lens length. If you work with images that have limited depth of field, you'll notice that the farther away from the camera the focus point moves, the broader the depth of field becomes. In fact, if you double the subject distance, the depth of field quadruples: Depth of field is proportional to the square of the distance. You'll also notice that if you use a zoom lens, the smaller the focal length of the lens (i.e., the more "wide-angle" the setting), the greater the depth of field. The depth of field is inversely proportional to the square of the lens's focal length. Finally, notice that the larger the aperture you use, the shallower the depth of field becomes.[2]

All this information might seem more useful to the person shooting the plate than it will be to you, the compositor, since you'll rarely be given enough information about a particular scene to manually compute the actual depth of field. But some of this knowledge might prove useful when you lack any other clues. Usually the primary depth-of-field clues that you will have available are the other objects in the scene, and these can be a guide for your element's degree of focus. If there

---

[2] In the example shown in Plate 41, the camera was about 4 feet away from the front candle. The lens was an 85mm, and the camera's aperture was set to f1.4.

is nothing in the background that is the same distance from camera as your foreground element, you will need to make an educated guess, which is when some of the information just discussed can be used. For instance, now that you understand about the relationship between aperture and depth of field, you can assume that a scene shot with less light was probably shot with a larger aperture, and consequently that the depth of field is narrower.

Stereoscopic Effects

There is a set of depth cues that we constantly deal with in our daily life, but that can't be captured by normal film and video. These are the significant stereoscopic cues that our binocular vision gives us. Although there isn't a huge amount of compositing work being done in stereo *yet*, it is certainly an area that is going to grow significantly with the popularization of virtual reality technology. A number of special venue and **ride films** have also been done in stereo, mostly using specialized projectors and polarized glasses to synchronize which eye is seeing which image. Chapter 16 describes such a film in greater detail.

Depth perception due to stereoscopic vision is based on the parallax difference between our two eyes. Each eye sees a slightly different image, whereby objects closer to the observer will be offset from each other by a greater amount than objects farther away. This effect is similar to the motion parallax described earlier, except that it occurs because the observer is viewing the scene from two different vantage points *simultaneously*. The brain is able to fuse the two images into a coherent scene, and at the same time it categorizes objects by depth based on the discrepancies between the two viewpoints.

Combining Depth Cues

Note that generally we will need to make use of several cues simultaneously in order to properly place an object at a specific depth. This is particularly true in the visual effects world, where one is often called on to integrate elements whose scale is something with which we're not normally familiar (such as a giant flying saucer hovering over an entire city). In situations such as this, you may find that certain cues such as relative size are almost meaningless, and things such as overlap and atmosphere take on a greater importance.

When you are adding multiple elements into a scene, be careful that their relative depth cues are consistent. Unlike the real world, in a digital composite it is possible to accidentally create a scene in which object A moves in front of object B, which moves in front of object C, which in turn moves in front of object A. This sort of contradiction can conceivably happen with several of the different depth cues.

In addition to the depth cues that we've just discussed, there are a number of additional visual artifacts that are characteristic of cameras and/or film. Several of these will be discussed next.

LENS FLARES

In the real world, when a bright light source is shined directly into a lens, you will get a **flare** artifact, caused by overexposure of the film and multiple reflections within the various components in a lens assembly. Notice the term "lens assembly." A standard camera lens is actually a *collection* of specially matched lenses, all brought together in a single housing. This construction is the reason a lens flare has multiple artifacts instead of just a single one.

Plates 42 and 43 show a couple of examples of what a lens flare can look like. Notice the diagonal row of artifacts in Plate 42. Each one of these is caused by one of the lenses in the overall lens assembly. You'll also notice that there is a noticeable hexagonal shape to some of the artifacts, which is caused by the shape of the iris that forms the camera's aperture.

The most important thing to keep in mind about these lens flare artifacts is that they are specific to the lens, not the light source. Because of this, they are always the closest object to the camera. Nothing will ever pass in "front" of a lens flare (unless you have something *inside* your camera body, between the lens and the film), and any elements that are added to a scene with a lens flare will always need to go behind the flare. Of course, the light source that is *causing* the lens flare may become partially obscured, but the result will be that the flare artifacts become dimmer overall, and conceivably change character somewhat, rather than that individual flare elements become occluded.

Since lens flares are a product of the lens assembly, different types of lenses will produce visually different flares. This is particularly true with anamorphic lenses, which tend to produce horizontally biased flares. Compare the two different flares shown in Plates 42 and 43. Plate 42 is from a standard spherical lens, whereas Plate 43 shows a lens flare that was shot using a Cinemascope lens. (This example was unsqueezed to show the way the flare would look when projected.)

The other thing to note with lens flares is that the different artifacts will move at different speeds relative to each other whenever the camera (or the light source) is moving. This is actually an example of motion parallax, caused by the different position of each element in the lens assembly.

Take the time to examine some real lens flares in motion. Notice that they are generally not "perfect," often featuring slightly irregular shapes and unpredictable prismatic artifacts, and tending to flicker or have varying brightness levels over time. These irregularities should not be ignored if you plan to add an artificial lens flare into a scene. The most common problem with most of the commercially available lens-flare software is that the packages tend to produce elements that are far too symmetrical and clean.

FOCUS

Earlier in this chapter we discussed depth of field and some of the issues related to how a lens focuses. What we want to discuss now are some of the actual *qualities* of an unfocused scene. Take a look at Plate 44, which shows a well-focused scene. Now look at Plate 44b, in which we've changed the focus of the lens so that our scene is no longer sharp. Note in particular what happens to the bright lights in the scene. They have not simply softened—instead, we have noticeable blooming and rather distinct edges. The characteristics shown will vary depending on the lens being used, as well as the aperture setting when the image was taken. As you can see, the defocused lights tend to take on the characteristic shape of the camera's aperture, just as we see saw in certain lens flares. This image is an excellent example of how much a true out-of-focus scene can differ from a simple digital blur. Plate 44c, which shows a basic Gaussian blur applied to Plate 44a, is provided for comparison.

Another effect that occurs when you are defocusing a standard lens is that the apparent scale of the image may change slightly. (Changing the focus of a lens actually causes a slight change in the focal length of the lens.) This scale change can be particularly evident in situations in which the focus changes over time. A common cinematic technique to redirect the viewer's attention is to switch focus from an object in the foreground to an object at a greater distance. This is known as a "rack focus." Since the scale change during a rack focus is somewhat dependent on the lens that you are using, it is hoped that you will have access to some example footage that can help you to determine the extent of this effect for the lens in question.

MOTION BLUR

When a rapidly moving object is recorded on film or video, it will generally not appear completely sharp, but will have a characteristic **motion blur**. This blurring or smearing is due to the distance the object moves while the film is being exposed (or the video camera is recording a frame).

The amount of motion blur is determined both by the speed of the moving object and by the amount of time the camera's shutter was open. Different devices are capable of using different **shutter speeds**. In a motion picture camera, the shutter speed is also specified in terms of the **shutter angle**, since the shutter itself is a rotating physical mechanism. The shutter rotates 360° over the length of a single frame, but can only expose film for a portion of that time. Generally, the duration of the shutter's opening is about one-half of the frame rate that was used to shoot the footage, and we would refer to it as being set at a 180° shutter angle. (This setting would correspond to a shutter speed of 1/48th of a second, assuming we're shooting at the normal film rate of 24 fps.) This is a very useful piece of information. It means that, for a moving object, the film camera would only be able to capture about one-half of the object's movement. Consequently, the size of the motion blur on a single frame of an object will be approximately one-half the distance the object has traveled in that single frame. Since a compositor will often be called upon to take a static object and give it motion within the frame, this behavior can be used to help determine the proper amount of motion blur to apply.

Be aware, though, that a 180° shutter angle is common, but by no means universal. Although most motion picture cameras can only have their shutter angle set in the range of about 50° to 200°,[3] video cameras do not have such limitations. Because they are not restricted by a mechanical shutter, many video cameras will allow the user to set shutter speeds at well over 1/1000th of a second. Slower shutter speeds (and consequently longer exposure times) will result in a larger amount of motion blur, whereas faster shutter speeds, particularly those available with video, will reduce or even eliminate motion-blur effects. Plate 45 shows a falling object captured by a film camera with a 180° shutter angle. The ball was falling at a rate that was fast enough to produce a noticeable motion blur.

Note that motion blur for images shot on film is symmetrical: The leading edge and the trailing edge of a moving object are blurred by the same amount. Contrary to popular belief, there is no in-focus leading edge with a trail of blur behind the object. This common misconception is probably the result of people looking at still images that were captured with flash photography, in which the shutter can be synchronized with the electronic flash to produce a trail.[4]

---

[3] Motion-control cameras are one of the exceptions to this rule, since they usually allow explicit control over the opening and closing of the shutter. There are also some specialized high-speed film cameras that treat the shutter differently, or at least are less reliant on the shutter since the exposure is determined more by a synchronized strobe.

[4] Either that, or it is the result of watching too many cartoons, which tend to depict motion by using a strong trailing blur.

CHAPTER THIRTEEN

Creating Elements

⌒

Visual effects photography, the process of creating the plates that will be used in a composite, is an art and science unto itself. So far we've been able to touch on only a few basic guidelines, but in this chapter we will try to provide a few more recommendations, while fully acknowledging that these will mostly be useful for fairly standard situations.

Although we'll spend a great deal of time discussing things that *should* be done during plate photography, let's make it perfectly clear that it's very likely that many of these things simply will not happen. Normally it is the job of the visual effects supervisor to see that plates are shot as well as possible, but the realities (and costs) of location shooting often make it difficult or impractical to ensure that every detail is covered perfectly. Frankly (and unfortunately), it really is sometimes cheaper to just "fix it in post," and the chapter following this one will go into greater detail about specific techniques that can be used to compensate for less-than-perfect elements.

This chapter is by no means an attempt to teach basic cinematography. We'll discuss issues specifically related to visual effects cinematography, and assume that the reader already has access to other resources that cover the essentials of standard cinematography. The information in this chapter will be presented for two reasons. The first, obviously, is to help anyone who will be photographing elements for use in a composite. But it is also presented for the benefit of those individuals who will be working on the digital side of the process, so that they can better understand the various problems that can come about during a typical plate shoot.

LIGHTING

Probably the most important thing that one must do when adding an element into a different background is to make sure that the new element appears as if it is being affected by the same lights that are illuminating that background. This process ideally starts when the background element itself is first being photographed, and takes the form of careful attention to the details of the lighting in the scene. Whether you are planning to integrate elements shot with bluescreen, synthetic CG images, or are just going to soft-split two plates together, it is critical that the different pieces look as if they were lit with the same lights. To this end, it is usually worth taking the time to create some kind of lighting diagram for the scene in question. This diagram may be nothing more than some basic notations about the placement of the main lights in a scene, or it may be a complete blueprint for the stage and all the lights (and cameras) that were used.

In particular, the following items should be noted when shooting the background:

- Identify the *location* of the various light sources in the scene. If you are on a set, you can (usually) easily identify the exact placement of every light that would affect an object in the scene. If you are shooting outdoors, identify the position of the sun (if in the daytime) or any artificial light sources that may be present. This information is necessary not only to help duplicate the same lighting on any subsequent elements, but also to help you keep track of the direction in which the shadows in a scene should be cast. Many times you will find that you need to recreate shadows from scratch, and you'll be thankful that you at least have some idea about the direction in which they should fall.

- Identify the *brightness* of the individual lights in the scene. There are light meters that can give numerical readings for each light's power output, but it may be acceptable to simply note the relative brightness of various lights—light A is twice as bright as light B, for instance. Again, if you are on a set, the various lights in the cinematographer's arsenal will probably all be well defined. Consequently, you can note that Light 1 is a 10K spotlight, light 2 is a 5K, and so on.

- Identify the *color* of the lights in the scene. Certain standard filters, or **gels** may be used to modify various lights on a set, and these can be recorded in your notes easily. Otherwise, subjective judgments will have to suffice.

- Finally, take note of the *quality* of the various lights in a scene. This measurement is by far the most subjective, and takes into account such things as how "hard" or "soft" a light is. Hard lights cast sharp-edged shadows and will produce high-contrast areas. Softer lights (which come from a broader light source) produce softer edges on the shadows and decrease contrast. If you're outdoors, consider your daylight quality and notice whether it is overcast or clear.

In the real world, light sources are not always idealized point sources. Not only can they be hard or soft, but objects between the source and the subject can cause irregularities and nonuniformity. This "dappled lighting" is something that you would see if you were standing beneath a tree, where the leaves all contribute to an uneven light pattern. On a stage, it is common to place shadow-casting objects in front of the light source to reproduce this type of look. These objects are known as **cukalorises**, or **cukes**. For instance, if you are planning to shoot an element that will be inserted into a scene taking place beneath a tree, plan on using something to simulate the necessary leaf shadows.

Although taking note of these four basic parameters—location, brightness, color, and quality—for each light source would seem to be enough to recreate any scene, in reality the lighting at any given location is much more complex. Not only do you need to consider the direct lighting in every scene, but you should also become attuned to what is happening with *indirect* lighting. This light can come from almost anywhere, but is generally defined to be light that is reflected, or "bounced," from other objects. This sort of thing is constantly overlooked, since it is usually fairly subtle and can be easy to forget about. But indirect lighting can, at times, significantly alter the look of a scene or the elements in that scene.

The most obvious case of bounce lighting is a light source reflecting from a mirror or other shiny object. But just about everything in a scene can provide bounce light to some extent or another. A white wall provides a great deal of fill light on a subject, and someone standing on a white sandy beach has a tremendous amount of light bounced back up on them from below. The color of the object off which the light is bouncing will affect the color of the light as well. A red curtain, whether the light is coming *through* it or bouncing *from* it, will tint that light with a reddish color, and therefore you should plan for any later element that might be shot for insertion into this scene to have a bit of red light illuminating it from the proper direction. Bounce light, unless it is coming from a very shiny mirrorlike surface, will be softer and more diffused than direct light.

Interactive Lighting

Many times you may find that the lighting in a scene changes over time. Do your best to keep track of inconstant or animated lighting (and the shadows that go with it!). Your background may contain a candle, or a towering inferno, or any number of other irregular light sources that you might need to keep track of. Be aware that duplicating this sort of inconstant lighting on all the elements in a scene can prove to be a difficult task. Ideally you want to synchronize things so that bright flashes occur at the same time on the background and the foreground, but with something that is completely random, such as flickering flames, this can be impossible. You may find that a combination of live-action lighting and some additional postprocessing work (which will be easier to synchronize with the fluctuating background) may give the best result.

When lighting effects are added to a scene—particularly lighting effects that fluctuate or are inconstant—they are often referred to as "interactive lighting." This is a broad term, encompassing a variety of different situations. In some sense, just about any lighting could fall under this umbrella, since it interacts in some way with the elements in a scene, but the term is usually used when referring to lighting effects that are designed to mimic a specific, uniquely identifiable light source.

So far we have been discussing our lighting scenarios as if all the lights in the scene exist only in the background and will contribute to the illumination of any new foreground element. But in many situations, the reverse may actually be true. A highly reflective object placed into a scene will obviously cause the lighting on nearby objects to change, but the more extreme case would be if the element that you are adding to the scene is something that is self-illuminating (i.e., a source of light). If this is the case, you will most certainly want to modify the background plate to account for this, particularly if the element you are adding is something whose brightness fluctuates significantly. The best example of this situation would be some kind of pyrotechnic element such as an explosion. Nothing makes an explosion look more "pasted on" than if it doesn't actually cause anything else in the scene to light up!

Although it is sometimes possible to simulate interactive lighting in the compositing process, it is generally more desirable to do so while shooting the elements in question. A simple compositing solution that could be used to add interactive light from an explosion into the scene might entail a general brightening of the background image, but this alone will usually look artificial since a real explosion wouldn't cause such a uniform effect. Instead, objects would cast shadows and the intensity of the light would fall off as the distance from the source increased. The best method would be to actually photograph the background scene with some sort of built-in interactive light that simulates the explosion. Of course, setting off a real explosion in the scene would be the most accurate method, but if you are able to do *that*, then you wouldn't need to do a digital composite! Instead of a full-sized explosion, something much more controlled, such as a flash-pot or even a manually controlled electric light, can be used. As mentioned earlier, the timing synchronization between foreground and background lighting can be difficult, and you may need to manipulate both foreground and background to obtain the best results.

MATCHED CAMERAS

Almost as important as ensuring that the lighting on the elements in a scene matches is the task of synchronizing the camera for all the elements. Usually this is the more simple task, since there are not quite as many variables to consider, but there are still a number of issues to be aware of. Let's again look at the case in which we initially shoot the background plate for the scene, and then later shoot the foreground element. The first thing you'll want to do is determine where in this background plate your foreground will eventually be located. You should have some idea about the size of the foreground element that you are going to add, and using this information we can start to decide on the camera placement and subject framing. We'll want to take the same sort of meticulous notes for our camera's setup as we took for our lighting setup, again so that we have enough information to recreate the background camera when shooting additional foreground elements.

- First of all, be aware of the camera's *distance* from the subject. This information is absolutely critical if you want the perspective on the composited elements to feel consistent. Try to get as accurate a distance measurement as possible. In many cases it is not necessary to be extremely precise, but at other times it may be quite important. Overall (as we've said many times before), you're better off having too much information than not enough. Incidentally, when measuring distance from a film camera, the convention is to measure from the *film plane*, not the front of the lens. This way, even if you have a different length or type of lens on the camera used for other plates, your measurements will still be valid. For convenience, many film cameras are marked somewhere on their body with a special symbol, a "ϕ," that indicates the position of the film plane. There is often even some kind of hook that can be used to attach a tape measure, since measuring camera-to-subject distance is something that the person controlling the focus on the camera will need to do as well.
- The next item of information that you should take note of is the *height* of the camera relative to the subject. Usually this is simply a matter of measuring the distance the camera is located above the ground, although if the ground is uneven or slopes drastically, you may need to try to obtain more detailed information.
- After this is done, determine the *orientation* of the camera, as it relates to tilt angles. Record not only how much the camera is tilted up or down, but

whether or not there is any camera tilt along any other axis. Camera orientation is usually recorded in terms of yaw, pitch, and roll, as shown in Figure 13.1.

- Make sure you have a record of what *lens* was used to shoot the scene. At the very least, get the focal length of the lens; there may be times when you want to record the aperture (measured in terms of its **f-stop** or **t-stop**) as well. Although there may not be much that you can do about it, you should be aware that the marked focal length on any given lens may not be terribly accurate. Different lenses from different manufacturers (or sometimes even from the *same* manufacturer) can vary by as much as 5 mm from their indicated length. Situations that require extremely precise measurements may require calibration tests on the lens, or at least an attempt to use the same lens when shooting the various elements in the scene.

- Finally, you should keep track of any other camera settings that might affect the synchronization of the shots. In particular, try to ensure that the same shutter speed is used so that any motion blur is consistent, and make sure that you are shooting all the elements at the same frame rate. There may be occasions when you choose explicitly to shoot at a different frame rate than was used for the other elements, for example, if you wish the various elements to move at different speeds. Shooting at a higher-than-normal frame rate can also be done if you are unsure about the exact timing you will want for your element. It is, in many ways, analogous to shooting with a larger-format negative, in the sense that you are capturing a higher resolution (temporal in this case) than you may eventually use.

Keep in mind that many of the camera parameters that we've just mentioned can actually change throughout the duration of a shot. Although the use of a locked-off camera will make the issues of camera synchronization much easier, as we discussed in Chapter 7, this limitation is becoming less and less acceptable to most cinematographers. If your camera does move throughout the shot, then every element will theoretically need the same camera move on it. Either plan on shooting the elements with a mechanical motion-control camera or be prepared

Figure 13.1 *Camera yaw, pitch, and roll.*

to do a lot of tracking in postproduction to try to duplicate or synchronize the different motions. Also mentioned in our tracking discussion from Chapter 7 was the use of witness points that can be placed into a scene to give the tracking software some well-defined points from which to determine camera motion. These points will be particularly important if there is nothing else in the scene that can be used to track the motion effectively.

Unfortunately, given the physical limitations that are inherent with plate photography, you may find that it is not always a simple matter to accurately create a foreground setup that perfectly matches the way that your background plate was shot. This is a typical problem one runs into when shooting on a stage or some other confined space where it would prove inconvenient to move the camera as far away from the subject as you would like. It may be tempting to simply use a wider-angle lens to compensate for the fact that you are closer to your subject. This is generally *not* a good solution, since the difference in camera-to-subject distance will cause a perspective discrepancy. It would be much better if you can come up with some other way to maintain the proper distance. Of course this may not be practical, in which case you will just have to live with elements that do not have perfectly matched perspectives. This may not be a huge problem, depending on the specific scenario. People tend to be less perceptive of perspective mismatches than they would be of a lighting mismatch, for instance. Additionally, Chapter 14 offers some suggestions that can sometimes be used to mitigate mismatches between elements.

There may be times when we can use the perspective/distance relationship to our advantage. An example of this is the situation in which you are shooting an element that will be fairly small in frame. Once you set up the proper camera-to-subject positioning, you can actually change to a longer lens and not cause a perspective switch. The reason for doing this is to capture a larger image of the subject, with greater resolution. (As we'll discuss in just a moment, the desire to capture elements with as much resolution as possible is a common occurrence in visual effects photography.) This particular trick means that you're putting the burden on the compositor to figure out the proper scale of the element, since changing the lens will increase the size of the object in frame. The correct scale should be easily determinable if you know the amount the lens length was changed, since the size change will be proportional.

THE REFERENCE STAND-IN

No matter how much attention you pay to faithfully duplicating the lighting and camera setups for your background plate, you will find that it is extremely difficult to produce a new foreground element that is an exact match for one that was actually shot in that background. Your new lighting setup will always just be an approximation of the original. To help the compositor understand exactly how the foreground element differs from what the element would actually look like if it had been shot in the scene in question, a reference **stand-in** can and should be used.

There are primarily two different types of reference stand-ins. The first type is a stand-in object or person that attempts to mimic as closely as possible the element that will eventually be placed into the scene. Consider the case in which you are shooting a background and will later insert an actor who was shot on bluescreen. Depending on how much control you have of the situation, it will be very helpful if you can get someone who is approximately the same size, and who is wearing similar clothing, to stand in the scene long enough to shoot some reference footage. The better your stand-in mimics the object that will eventually be inserted into the scene, the better off you will be when it comes time to create the composite.

But what about a situation in which you don't know exactly what is going into the scene (because nobody has made a decision yet, for instance) or in which the object that is going to be inserted into the scene is something that you cannot easily duplicate (for example, some strangely shaped and textured creature that will eventually be created via the use of 3D computer animation)? In these cases, it is often useful to photograph a simple object such as a neutral gray sphere in the scene.[1] This will at least give you some idea about the placement, intensity, color, and quality of the lights in the scene. This object (often called a **lighting reference**) will also be useful if there will be any 3D elements created for the scene, since it will allow the 3D artists to place a duplicate object into their artificial scene and light it to match. This should produce a 3D element that is more likely to be easily integrated into the background, although it will all come down to the compositor when it is time to marry the two elements together.

Of course there's usually no reason not to shoot *both* types of reference, since it shouldn't take long or cost much—at least not compared with the cost of having to fix a grossly mismatched element in post. Generally you will need only a few frames of footage on these reference stand-ins, so the amount of film used will be negligible. Keep in mind that this reference footage will be just as useful to the person shooting additional elements as it will be to the compositor. Even the simple gray sphere can be brought to the bluescreen set and, when compared with the reference clip, used to help with the lighting setup.

Stand-ins are useful for more than just lighting synchronization. If you place a properly sized reference object into your background, it will help to ensure that

---

[1] When shooting lighting reference for use by 3D artists, it is common to also shoot a shiny object, such as a large chrome ball, that can be used to analyze reflections in the scene.

the framing of the scene makes sense, and you will know how large the subject should be in the frame. At this point, you can also measure the camera-to-subject distance with more accuracy.

CLEAN PLATES

Whenever you are shooting an object that you intend to eventually extract or isolate from its background, it is often useful to shoot what is known as a "clean plate." We discussed this briefly in Chapter 5, when we used the clean plate shown in Plate 33b to help create a difference matte for our foreground object. Theoretically, everything is identical between the two plates, with the exception of the subject object.

There are a number of uses for such a clean plate, but they tend to fall into two primary categories. The first use would be to help extract a matte for an object, as we've already seen. This use goes beyond simple difference matting, and many times you will find that bluescreen methods can benefit dramatically from the availability of a clean plate for a given shot. This topic will be discussed momentarily, in the section on lighting and shooting with a bluescreen.

The second primary use of a clean plate is as a source of image information that can be used to selectively remove or replace some unwanted portion of the foreground element. For instance, a wiring harness that is suspending an object or actor in midair can be removed by strategically pasting areas of the clean plate over the area where the wiring harness is visible. The clean plate gives us image information that would otherwise have been obscured by the wiring harness and allows us to restore it to the scene. Replacing a portion of a scene with a clean plate can either be accomplished via standard compositing techniques or (probably more commonly) by having a digital paint artist carefully merge pixels from the clean plate into the main plate.

Obviously this sort of technique works best when there is a perfect match between the camera, lighting, and exposure on both plates. Consequently, clean plates tend to be much more common whenever the camera does not move throughout the shot (or if there is a motion-controlled camera involved). But even if the camera *does* move, it may be appropriate to shoot a clean plate. Tracking tools can be used to add motion to this clean plate so that it properly matches the original camera move, effectively producing a new element that can be used for the techniques just described.

FILM STOCK

If you are shooting on film, be aware of the film stock that you are using, since different stocks can have significantly different characteristics. For instance, every stock is balanced so that it will accurately reproduce colors only when illuminated with a certain type (i.e., color) of light. Most stocks are balanced either for daylight or tungsten lighting, and if you use the wrong stock for your lighting conditions, you run the risk of producing imagery with a serious color skew. Yet even if you shoot a subject using a stock that is properly balanced for the lighting conditions (or if you make use of colored filters to compensate), you will still not have a perfect color match. Ultimately, every film stock will have a unique response to light, and it will generally not match the response of a different stock. This is obviously a problem with visual effects work, where it is common to shoot a background element as an outdoor scene and then shoot the foreground element indoors, in front of a bluescreen. This situation almost always results in the need to manually color correct the foreground element by eye so that it fits better into the background scene.

Different-speed film stocks, even if they are balanced for the same lighting conditions, can also vary in their color reproduction. Higher-speed films tend to produce images that are lower contrast and have less saturation. What's more, the amount of grain that is captured by different stocks can vary considerably. Take a look at the images shown in Plate 46. Plate 46a is an extremely magnified section of a piece of film. This particular film (Eastman Kodak 5289) is a highly sensitive stock, well suited for use in low-light conditions, but it also is a fairly grainy stock. Plate 46b shows the same amount of magnification applied to a different, slower type of film. Notice the significant difference in the amount of grain that is visible. Although we have magnified the film in order to show the grain as effectively as possible, it should be noted that the grain difference between two different stocks can be very noticeable even without any additional magnification.

In general, the faster, more light-sensitive films tend to be grainier, whereas slower-speed films show less grain. This is only a rule of thumb, however. Don't assume that you can take two film stocks with the same rated sensitivity and produce images with matching grain characteristics. In fact, don't even assume that scenes shot on the same film will produce matching grain characteristics, since many other factors (such as exposure and development) will all affect the amount of grain present in a captured image. In practice this is usually not that much of an issue, and you can generally assume that similar stocks will produce similar grain, but you should be aware of the potential problems nonetheless. Incidentally, it is worth noting that the amount of grain can differ quite a bit between the different records (channels) in a film image. Plate 47 shows the red, green, and blue channels of Plate 46a. The blue record is characteristically the most noisy, the green record the least.

Unlike some of the other issues we've discussed in this chapter, grain is not necessarily something that you should strive to synchronize between all elements as you are *shooting* them. Instead, the amount of grain captured with an element (and consequently the decision concerning what film stock to use) will be determined much more by the type of work that is to be done with these various elements *after* principle photography, once they are in the compositing process. This precept is primarily because it is much easier to add grain to an element than it is to remove it. Grain is easily simulated digitally, and the user can precisely control exactly how much additional grain is to be applied to a scene. If, however, the element is already very grainy, then *removing* the grain can be nearly impossible. Any attempts to remove grain will almost always result in a slightly softer image. For this reason, visual effects photographers usually try to use the least-grainy film they can get away with for the given lighting situation. Part of the reason to shoot elements with larger-format film (as we'll discuss in a moment) has to do with the desire to minimize the relative amount of grain captured.

There certainly may be times when you *do* wish to shoot elements with the same amount of grain. A simple split-screen effect, which involves virtually no additional processing, is a classic example of a situation in which you want the grain in both your original elements to match as closely as possible.

FILTERS

Cinematographers use a variety of filters to obtain certain effects for the footage they are shooting. These filters (as opposed to the digital filters that we discussed in Chapter 3) are usually a glass or plastic material that modifies the color or quality of the light that is transmitted through it. While they can be useful for normal photography, they can cause a number of problems when photographing elements for compositing work, particularly for bluescreen shots. Color filters are placed either on individual lights that are illuminating the subject or are placed on the camera lens itself, causing the overall color of the scene to be modified. Obviously, colored filters would affect the color of a bluescreen element, potentially causing the process of extracting a matte to be more difficult than necessary. Less obvious, however, are the problems that can be introduced when using certain **effects filters**. These filters, when placed on a camera, are designed to introduce artifacts such as diffusion or flares into a scene. Isolating a bluescreen subject will be made more difficult if it was shot with one of these effects filters in place because the scattered light from the filter can easily contaminate the foreground element.

If you know that an element is going to be dealt with digitally, you will be better off shooting it with a normal, unfiltered exposure. Overall color corrections will be easier to tweak, and any additional effects (such as diffusion) that are necessary to match a background plate can be added during the compositing process. High-end filter manufacturers such as Tiffen are even starting to offer digital equivalents to their standard optical filters, making the process of synchro-nizing elements much less complicated.

CHOOSING A FORMAT

At first it might seem that choosing a format for the elements you plan to shoot would be a simple matter, given that the format in which you will eventually deliver the material is probably already determined. While it's true that format decisions for a particular production are often made even before the effects are considered, this does not necessarily mean that the effects elements will need to be shot in the *same* format. Even ignoring compositing, there are any number of examples in which the final, delivered format is different from the shooting format. Most television programs and commercials, in fact, are shot on film and then transferred to video. This is usually done to get a certain look, as well as to have some of the flexibility (such as an ability to shoot in slow motion) that video lacks.

When we are shooting elements to be used in compositing, one of the primary reasons to shoot with a different format is to gain additional resolution or (a byproduct of higher resolution) to reduce grain. Larger film formats such as Vistavision, 65mm or IMAX allow one to expose a bigger piece of the negative to the scene. Vistavision is more than twice as large as standard 35mm film; 65mm, and IMAX are even more so (see Chapter 10 as well as Appendix D for more details). With the larger negative, the grain size relative to the image captured is much smaller. If we scan and then digitally reduce the full frame from one of these large formats to our working resolution, we will have a nearly grain-free image. This result was particularly important when optical compositing was prevalent, since every optical generation introduced added grain into the scene. This reason alone was enough to rescue the large-format Vistavision cameras from obsolescence. Although increased grain is less of a problem with digital compositing, it still must be considered.

Shooting with a larger-format negative allows for flexibility in other areas as well. For instance, we can now zoom in to a portion of the image and not run the risk of revealing grossly magnified grain. A two-times zoom into a Vistavision frame will result in a grain size that is the same as that on a standard 35mm frame.

Of course there are a number of other factors that may influence your choice of format. Although from the compositor's perspective larger-format images are usually better, practical considerations such as the size or the availability of the equipment may prevail. Vistavision cameras tend to be more lightweight and compact than 65mm cameras, for instance, and have the advantage of using a more standard stock and processing, but they are also usually much louder when operating, making them less suitable for scenes in which sound must be captured.

Also, be aware that if you are shooting two different elements for a particular shot with two different camera formats, some of your measurements will need to be converted to maintain equivalency of depth of field, exposure, and field of view. For instance, a 50mm lens on a Vistavision camera will capture about the same field of view as a wide-angle 28mm lens on a regular 1.85 format.

Even if you are shooting with a standard 35mm camera, you may be able to capture additional resolution. Although most film formats do not actually require the entire frame area on the negative, there is no reason why you cannot use this area to capture additional image information. Make sure that your camera is not automatically masking out picture information merely to frame the format. Instead, shoot without any mask and plan on cropping the extra picture later, as needed. You can always remove unnecessary image in order to be efficient with your disk space, but will still have the ability to restore the additional information should it become necessary or useful.

It is also becoming more common to shoot larger-format *video* in order to capture additional image information. For instance, you may wish to shoot your elements using HDTV cameras instead of a standard-resolution video camera. This is sometimes done even when no visual effects will be involved, simply because the larger frames can be used to produce high-quality images in both the NTSC and the PAL formats.

Of course the fact that a larger-format image will give you more data is both good and bad. We've discussed the advantages, but the disadvantage is that you end up with images that require additional storage space and processing power to be dealt with effectively. As mentioned in the chapter on efficiency (Chapter 11), you should try to obtain as much data as is necessary, but no *more* than is necessary. This consideration will sometimes drive the desire to choose a *smaller-than-normal* format to capture an element that will be used within a composite. For instance, there may be times when it is appropriate to shoot video elements that will be added to a film scene. An obvious example would be an element that is intended to be used as a "burn-in" on a video monitor in a given scene. This scenario is not uncommon, and it should be obvious that there is no need to have a resolution greater than video if the result will need to look like video eventually anyway.

But video elements could also potentially be used if they are only going to fill a fraction of the frame. The resolution of a video frame relative to your film frame can easily be computed. If you are working with film images that have been scanned at a resolution of about 2000 pixels, then you really only have about three times the horizontal resolution of video. If you plan to add an element into the scene that will be less than one-third of the width of the frame, then using a video-resolution source would theoretically mean that you are not losing any resolution. Be *very* careful if you plan to do this. Although the spatial resolution of your video element may be acceptable, other factors may not. Remember that video has less color fidelity than film, so be sure that the lower chromatic resolution will not be a problem, and be sure that the video frame rate will not cause your element to appear to be moving at the wrong speed. Even if you ignore color resolution and frame rate issues, the bottom line is that video just *looks* different than film. Consequently you will probably need to process the video imagery quite a bit (adding grain, adjusting contrast, etc.) before it fits acceptably into the scene.

LIGHTING AND SHOOTING WITH BLUESCREENS

As with the rest of this chapter, this section is *not* intended to be a comprehensive discussion about how to light and shoot a bluescreen. The topic is significant, and there are so many variables involved that we will only be able to touch on some of the most basic issues. Continuing the precedent that was set in Chapter 5 (when we were discussing matte-extraction techniques), we will once again use the term "bluescreen" as a generic term for all uniformly lit, single-color backgrounds. Thus, unless otherwise specified, everything we discuss would apply equally well to a greenscreen scenario.

We've already covered the basic principles of how to synchronize lighting between different elements. Bluescreen elements are no exception to those principles. Lights should hit the objects in the scene from the same angle, have the same apparent intensity, and be of the same color as they are in the background. While this sounds easy in theory, in practice it is probably the most often violated rule in bluescreen photography, which may be due in part to the issue of duplicating outdoor lighting in an indoor setting. As mentioned, this is a common situation with bluescreen shoots, wherein the background is an outdoor scene and the foreground is shot later in front of a bluescreen on a sound stage. It is a particularly vexing problem since there is really no way to accurately duplicate the perfect single-source lighting that comes from the sun on a clear day. Another problem is the difficulty of judging the lighting on an element when it is placed in front of a bright blue background: The eye tends to see the background as a light source, even though it will be removed and neutralized in the final composite. Don't assume that the blue spill that is hitting the subject from behind will look the same as a normal backlight. In an ideal shooting scenario, the foreground object is lit first, and only after it is correctly matched to the background plate should you start to light the bluescreen backing.

To obtain the best matte-pulling results when using a bluescreen, the bluescreen itself must be as uniformly lit as possible. The brightness of the lighting should be consistent across the entire screen, with no hot spots, shadowed areas, or color differences. This almost always means that we will need to introduce additional lights into the scene to illuminate this backing. You should obviously try to direct the lights at *only* the backing, and avoid having these lights cast additional illumination on your subject, but in practice, this is not always easily achieved.

The blue backing itself may reflect additional light onto the foreground. This effect is known as **blue spill** and is a constant problem with bluescreen shots. Blue spill on the subject not only causes the lighting to be wrong, but also makes the job of pulling a matte off this subject much more difficult. Since the spill areas now have similar coloration to the blue backing we're trying to remove, most keying software will have a hard time distinguishing these heavily contaminated foregrounds from the bluescreen itself. It used to be a common practice to add some yellow lighting onto the subject in order to nullify any blue spill (yellow being the complementary color to blue). This practice has fallen into disfavor, however, since once again it is adding lights to the foreground element that were not present in the original photography of the background.

One of the most basic things you can do to prevent blue spill from contaminating the foreground is to ensure that the foreground is as far as possible from the backing. This is fine if you have a great deal of space, a very large backing, and the ability to light this large backing uniformly. If this is not the case (and it usually isn't), you'll need to be much more careful with lighting the scene.

The question of whether or not to light your bluescreen element so as to preserve shadows is *very* situational. A good matte-extraction tool should be able to bring a shadow along with the foreground image. But the shadow itself may not be appropriate, because the surface on which it is cast may not match with anything in the background plate. This topic will be discussed more in the next chapter, where we cover integration techniques.

Bluescreens are usually lit from the front, but there are also semitransparent screens that can be lit from the back. The choice is mostly determined by practical considerations: Rear-lit screens are generally more expensive and require more floor space to implement. But they can be very nice if you would otherwise have a hard time lighting your element without introducing unwanted light onto the backing.

The exposure (brightness) of the bluescreen relative to the foreground subject will vary depending on the subject itself, but the general rule of thumb is to expose the backing to a fairly neutral brightness. This will usually end up being about the same exposure as the foreground, although the latitude of most digital matting tools will often allow you to get away with a slightly underexposed bluescreen. This may make the matte slightly more difficult to pull, but will help to eliminate blue spill.

Of course, as with just about every aspect of the plate-photography process, there are always compromises that must be made. In the case of a subject on bluescreen, you will often be trading a perfectly exposed backing for more accurate lighting on the subject. This is usually a worthwhile trade-off, since there are a number of techniques that can be used to compensate for a nonuniform backing. But trying to compensate for an improperly matched foreground element can be next to impossible.

We have already discussed the utility of shooting a clean plate whenever possible. This step will be particularly useful when shooting bluescreens, assuming (as before) that your camera will not move during the shot. Packages such as Ultimatte support the ability to read an additional clean plate of the bluescreen (shot without any foreground subject) and will then use it to compensate for any inconsistent lighting on the backing or any imperfections in the screen itself. Clean plates, when used for this purpose, work best if the amount of grain present can be minimized. The typical method for accomplishing this is to shoot several identical clean plates and average them together to produce a less grainy result.

Earlier we suggested that you try to avoid the use of filters when photographing elements that will be used in a composite. This is absolutely critical when shooting bluescreen elements. Colored filters can affect the difference between foreground and background coloration, and effects filters (such as fog or diffusion filters) will cause edges to soften and light to bleed from background to foreground.

Bluescreen shoots should almost always be done with as neutral a camera setup as possible. This includes ensuring that no additional processing is being done on the image as it is being captured, as may be the case with a video camera. Many video cameras have a built-in **detail generator** that can be used to increase the sharpness of the image that is captured. While this can be useful for normal photography, it can cause a great deal of pain when working with a bluescreen element. If you recall, digital sharpening is simply a method of increasing the contrast around transition areas. Since the transition between foreground and bluescreen is usually much more dramatic than it would be between the foreground and the real background, the resulting sharpening of this edge will introduce an undesirable matte line around your foreground object. Always turn off this sort of processing when shooting on video or when transferring film to video via a telecine process.

Certain types of film stock can also introduce this type of problem. Some of the newer stocks that are designed for extreme sharpness will actually undergo a photochemical process that produces a similar edge artifact. Most film stocks also tend to be sharper in the blue and green records than they are in the red record, which can cause a slight magenta halo when working with a bluescreen.[2]

---

[2] At the time that this book was being written, Kodak was in the process of making available a new stock that is specifically designed for bluescreen and greenscreen photography. Kodak's SFX 200T claims to have a red record that is nearly as sharp as the blue and green records, yet does not introduce any additional edge enhancement into the image.

Bluescreen versus Greenscreen

Whenever the decision is made to shoot an object in front of a uniform background for the purpose of matte extraction, the first question that arises will usually be about the color that should be used for the backing. And usually this choice boils down to bluescreen or greenscreen. There are a number of different trade-offs involved in this decision, and we will discuss some of them here, but you'll find that there simply are no definitive answers for the bluescreen versus greenscreen debate.

The traditional backing for procedural matte-extraction shots is colored blue, and has been used at least since the 1920s as a method for producing traveling mattes for black and white photography. Greenscreens really didn't become popular until the 1960s,[3] and were initially much more common in the video world. This precedence probably occurred because video was a less expensive format in which to experiment, and consequently greenscreen's viability was proven sooner in that format. These days, both methods have been used countless times with both film and video to produce excellent composites, and the process of working with either color is straightforward and essentially identical. But there are certain factors that should always be considered when making the decision about which color to use.

By far the most important aspect of the decision has to do with the foreground subject itself, and any colors contained in it. Any similarity between a color in the foreground object and the backing will potentially introduce difficulties. Thus, if your foreground object has some saturated blue in it, you will probably want to use greenscreen. Conversely, if it has any bright green content, you should lean toward bluescreen.

The reason that red screens are seldom used is the heavy red content of most flesh tones. Since traveling matte shots usually involve people, this immediately makes the red screen a less desirable choice. You *will* sometimes find red screens used if the subject is not a person, and many model and miniature shots use a specialized red-screen process.

If there are no saturated blues or greens in your foreground, or if there are both, you will need to base your decision on other factors. A list of a number of these factors follows. As will become immediately evident, just about any argument in favor of a particular color can be countered with an argument in the opposite direction, and ultimately experience can be your only guide.

- Greenscreens will usually require less light than bluescreens to get an acceptable amount of illumination, in part because film and video are more sensitive

---

[3] Greenscreens really only became feasible with the development of "day-glo" green paints. Before this, it was not a simple matter to inexpensively produce a bright, saturated green surface.

to the color green than they are to the color blue. Using less light makes for a less expensive shot and will also help to reduce the risk of spill contamination.

- The most common spill-suppression technique used with greenscreen shots involves a partial substitution of the blue record into the green record. This technique is discussed in greater detail in Chapter 14, but the net result is that the substitution of the noisier blue channel into the green channel will increase the overall amount of grain in your resulting image. Thus greenscreen shots, particularly those that are already being shot with higher-speed film, can be prone to excessive grain problems. The problem is not nearly as great with video as it is with film, and greenscreen work is still quite a bit more common in video compositing. This issue is also much less of a problem with some of the newer, less grainy film stocks.

- On the other hand, the fact that the blue record is more grainy implies that any matte that is based on a bluescreen will be slightly noisier and more prone to holes than an equivalent greenscreen matte.

- Another consideration may be the specific color of the hair and skin that is being shot. Bright yellow hair will have a higher green component, and extremely black hair can appear almost blue. One school of thought also holds that darker flesh tones tend to have a slightly higher blue content, a fact that would tend to indicate that a greenscreen is more appropriate. This theory has never been rigorously tested, however, and the extreme variability between different individual's skins probably makes this a somewhat uncertain principle.

- Bluescreen shots may be more problematic if shooting outdoors, since the overall ambient light from a clear blue sky can give your subject an overall blue cast, which may make keying the subject more difficult. However, it also will be easier to get a purer blue color in your backing, whereas a greenscreen could be contaminated by this blue sky light.

- If your foreground element is to be composited into an unsheltered outdoor setting, the presence of a little bit of blue spill may be less noticeable than green spill, since it could be justified as coming from the blue sky. This would tend to favor a bluescreen setup. If, instead, your foreground element is to be surrounded by a large amount of green foliage, you may want to use a greenscreen. Thus, it is worth noting that sometimes the color content of the *background* may also be important in the choice of bluescreen versus greenscreen.

As you can see, there are a number of factors, many conflicting, that can drive the decision about what colored backing to use. Some cinematographers will even admit that they avoid greenscreens simply because they don't like the color and would rather spend the day standing in front of a calm blue screen instead of an unsettling green one! With all these different variables to take into account, it is not possible to make an overall recommendation regarding the choice of screen color. But there is one definitive recommendation that *can* be made, and that is to shoot as much test footage with your specific scenario as is reasonable. Not only should you test different screen colors (there are even a number of different *shades* of blue or green that are available), but you should also test various exposures on these screens. You'll also find that different software may be better suited to a particular situation, so you will probably want to do some tests with whatever different digital tools you have available.

SHOOTING ORDER

There can be very little general-purpose advice given for how to shoot elements, since such advice requires explicit knowledge of how the element being shot is going to be used. But there is an excellent rule of thumb for the order in which the various elements that will make up the composite should be shot: Always shoot the least controllable element in a scene first. Once this first element is captured, the other elements can then be adjusted to compensate for anomalies in the first plate. As usual, this is much easier said than done. Very often you will find that several of the plates will have things in them that are less than controllable. Usually when you are planning for a bluescreen composite, you try to shoot the background first, particularly if it is an outdoor scene, in which you have less control over the lighting due to time of day and weather. The foreground can then be synchronized to the desired take. But if you are putting a live actor into a miniature or 3D scene, it may make sense to shoot the bluescreen element first, particularly if there is a moving camera involved.

Of course, sometimes you may find yourself in somewhat of a dilemma, since you may need to shoot the foreground element first, without the luxury of knowing exactly how the background element will be lit. At times like this, you can only use your best guess. Be sure to keep track of what lighting *is* used when shooting the foreground, in the hopes that you can modify the lighting in the background to be as consistent as possible.

CHAPTER FOURTEEN

Integration Techniques

In an ideal world, the person responsible for shooting plates will light and photograph any foreground element in exactly the same way as its corresponding background element, and your job as a compositor will be miraculously simple. Don't count on this miracle happening very often. Instead, you will probably find yourself using a variety of different techniques to modify the foreground (or background) so that the two integrate as well as possible. Throughout the book we have attempted to describe how the various tools in question can be used to better integrate elements into a specific scene. This chapter is designed to round out this subject, address some of the most common issues, and provide some suggestions that aren't covered elsewhere. Of course, every shot has its own problems, and no book can cover every scenario. The true test of a good compositor is his or her ability to come up with efficient and creative solutions to issues that fall outside the boundaries of common, well-defined problems.

A number of the visual characteristics that we discussed in Chapter 12 ("Learning to See") will be mentioned again in this chapter in order to give suggestions about what kinds of methodologies can best be used to simulate these characteristics in a digital composite. Similarly, a number of the considerations we discussed in the last chapter as being important during the principal photography stage will now be referenced in our discussion of digital postproduction. In fact, you'll notice that many sections in this current chapter are direct counterparts to similarly named sections in these other chapters. If you skipped the last chapter because you thought you would never be involved with the actual photography of the elements, go back and read it now. It will give you a much better idea of what the foreground and background relationship *should* look like and will help to identify where the discrepancies exist. Knowing the problem is most of the way to finding the solution. Assuming that there is no longer the opportunity to reshoot anything to correct any faulty plates, it's time to start working on the integrated combination, using whatever tools you have available.

For the most part, we will not attempt to recommend specific tools or operators that should be used when dealing with a particular integration problem. There are too many tools and too many ways to use these tools for any kind of meaningful discussion to take place. Experiment with the tools you have available, and learn how they behave when using different types of imagery. For instance, although the Over operator is common to a large number of compositing packages, don't make the mistake of assuming that this is the operator that *must* be used when someone requests that a foreground be placed "over" a background. A number of different tools can be used to place an object into a scene, and many objects, particularly those that are semitransparent or self-illuminating, will be easier to integrate if something other than a standard Over is used.

As in previous chapters, we tend to discuss topics in the framework of a simple two-layer composite—a foreground over a background—and allow the reader to extrapolate to more complex scenarios. It should also be noted that properly judging whether an element is acceptably integrated into a scene will often require that you view the scene as a moving sequence, not as a single frame. The characteristics of a scene may change over the length of a shot, invalidating any tuning that was done for just a single point in time, and certain features, such as grain or motion blur, must be judged on a moving image. To finish off the chapter, a final section is provided that discusses how the idiosyncrasies of the digital image relate to the live-action issues we have detailed.

SCENE CONTINUITY

Up to this point, we've primarily discussed the integration of elements within a specific shot. But rarely will this shot exist in a vacuum. It is very important to keep in mind that not only should every element within a shot be consistent and well integrated, but also every *shot* should match or "cut" properly with the surrounding footage in the scene or sequence. In this context, **scenes** and **sequences** refer to groups of shots that are all part of the same narrative and that will most likely be viewed at the same time. A common problem in visual effects work is a shot that may be well balanced as an individual entity but, when viewed in the context of the entire sequence, stands out like a sore thumb because of problems with overall color timing, grain levels, or lighting. *Always* view your work in context before considering it to be finished.

Certain minor differences and inconsistencies between shots in a sequence can often be dealt with by using some kind of overall correction that is applied to the final shot. When working in film or video, this can even be done by the **color timer**, a person who is given the job of looking through the entire work and adjusting color and brightness so that continuity problems are minimized. The amount of change that the color timer can effect is not huge, so do not rely on this step! These changes will usually be limited to simple overall corrections such as color and brightness. If other things do not match—contrast or grain levels or blur amounts—the color timer will probably be unable to compensate.

For the rest of this chapter we will go back to discussing things from the perspective of a single shot, but always keep in mind that your work will also need to hold up when placed within the context of a multiple-shot sequence.

LIGHTING

As we have discussed, synchronized lighting between elements is probably one of the most important factors in a good composite, and unsynchronized lighting is certainly one of the most difficult problems to fix. Trying to tie together images whose lighting doesn't match can be a frustrating, seemingly futile, task. Of the four primary lighting factors (direction, intensity, color, and quality), having an element that is lit from the wrong location is usually the most difficult to deal with. If you are lucky, you may find that certain "easy" fixes may work. For instance, you may have a scenario with strong sidelight coming from the *left* in the background, and strong sidelight from the *right* in the foreground. Assuming there's nothing in the scene to give away the trick, simply flop (mirror along the *Y*-axis) one of the elements. (Remember, as long as you don't introduce a continuity problem with another shot, it is just as valid to change the background as the foreground.)

More complex discrepancies will require more complicated solutions. In the worst case, you may find it necessary to isolate highlights that occur in inappropriate areas and do your best to subdue them, while selectively brightening other areas of the subject to simulate new highlights. This isolation of certain areas is usually accomplished by using a combination of loose, rotoscoped mattes and some specific luminance keying for highlights or shadows. If the *overall* intensity or color of your lighting does not match, a more simple color and brightness correction, applied globally, may be sufficient.

The quality of the light in a scene can be difficult to quantify, but fortunately it is also less noticeable than some of the other mismatches. Distinctly mottled lighting can be dealt with via the selected application of irregular, partially transparent masks to control the placement of some additional light and dark areas. If the lighting in a scene, and on an object, is not consistent over time (including the presence of interactive light in the scene), you will need to do your best to conform your foreground's fluctuations to the background's. In some cases it may be as simple as adding a fluctuating brightness on the foreground that is synchronized to the background. In other situations you may need to have articulated mattes controlling the light so that it only falls on certain areas.

Taken to the extreme, very complex interactive lighting can be achieved by duplicating your foreground element as a neutral-color 3D model and applying CG lighting to it. This new element will include brightened areas that can be extracted and applied to the original 2D foreground element.

In a situation in which the foreground element is actually *producing* light, you'll need to remember that objects in the scene should cast shadows on each other and that the intensity of the light should fall off as the distance from the source increases. Assuming that this interactivity wasn't taken care of when the plate was shot, you should at the very least try to create some mattes to simulate shadows and use these to brighten the scene less (or not at all) in these areas.

SHADOWS

A common mistake made by novice compositors is to forget or ignore the fact that an object should cast a shadow (or several) on its environment. Any time you add a new element into a scene, you should think about how the lights in the scene would affect this new element, which includes the fact that the new object would block some of these lights, causing shadows to be cast. Whenever you apply these shadows, be sure to match other shadows in the scene in terms of size, density, and softness.

Part of the reason why shadows are so often forgotten can be attributed to the fact that many bluescreen plates are lit so as to intentionally remove shadows. Shadows that fall onto a bluescreen can make it difficult to easily extract the foreground object (particularly when using less sophisticated traveling-matte methods), and so they are often considered undesirable when lighting the setup. Whether there is a shadow available or not, many methods of extracting an object from its background do not allow this shadow to be brought along, at least not without additional effort.

Even if you *are* able to extract an object's shadow from its original background, it may prove useless due to the lighting of the scene or the shape of the ground where the shadow is cast. In many cases you may decide to create a shadow yourself. It is often acceptable to simply flip and scale the matte of the foreground element and use it as your shadow element. This method is fine if your shadow falls onto a fairly smooth surface, such as a floor. But if your shadow needs to be cast onto irregularly shaped terrain, you may need to create something more specific to the scene. Perhaps you can warp a flat shadow so that it fits, or you may need to go so far as to manually paint an appropriate shadow. Whatever you use, remember that it will need to change over time if your element (or the light striking your element) is moving.

Once we have the element (usually a matte) that we will be using to define our shadow, the most common way to actually create the shadow effect is to use this element as a mask to selectively darken the shadowed object. This technique will usually work fine, although if there are extremely noticeable highlights in the area that is going to be shadowed, you may need to explicitly remove them.

Remember that a shadow is not a light source, but the *absence* of a particular light source. Thus, two objects that cast a hard, distinct shadow onto a surface will not necessarily produce a darker shadow where those shadows overlap each other. Consider Figure 14.1. As you can see, the area where the shadows overlap is the same density as where they do *not* overlap, because both objects are obscuring the same light source—either object is enough to completely obscure the light. Even though their shadows overlap, there is no additional darkening needed in the

Figure 14.1   *Two objects casting overlapping hard shadows from a single light source will not produce a darker shadow where the shadows overlap.*

intersection. This might seem obvious on paper, but in a real-world compositing situation we could conceivably be manipulating the two shadow objects as separate elements, and thus the brightness decrease from the shadow masks could easily be inappropriately doubled if the layers were applied sequentially.

Soft, diffuse shadows will behave differently, since they are not blocking a particular light but rather are shielding an object from a more global, uniform source. This is the case with the lighting from an overcast sky. In this situation, not only will your shadows be much softer and only occur when objects are in closer proximity, but they can actually produce different densities in areas of overlap.

Multiple light sources will produce even more complex shadows. Theoretically, every light that is hitting an object will produce some sort of shadow, but this is often impractical to simulate within a composite. There may be a light source that is significantly brighter than the rest, and you can take your shadow cues from this alone, or there may be a need to add a few shadows, each the result of a particular source.

LENS FLARES

It is often desirable to introduce some sort of lens flare when creating a scene with bright light sources that were not present in the original elements. Be careful with this effect, as it has become somewhat overused in much of the CG imagery being created these days, but don't be afraid to use it where necessary, as sometimes it can play a very important part in making a scene look correct.

As mentioned earlier, a common problem with most of the commercially available lens-flare software is that it tends to produce elements that are far too symmetrical and illustrative. Instead of relying on these packages, you may wish to shoot real lens flares over a neutral (probably black) background (as was done to create Plate 43) and use these as separate elements. Or you may even hand-paint some flare elements that have a suitably organic feel.

Unfortunately, if you have a moving camera (or the light source that is causing the flare is moving relative to the camera), simply compositing a static lens flare onto a scene will not produce the proper characteristics. In this case, you will have to try to match the way a real flare would behave. There are a number of ways to accomplish this. You can shoot a real lens flare with a similar camera move or, even better, with a motion-controlled match-move. You can use a commercial lens-flare package that is able to automatically move the various flare elements relative to one another after you've tracked the light source's movement across the frame. Or you can simply manually create some visually appropriate motion for the various static flare elements. These techniques all have their good and bad points, depending on the situation. Remember that lens flares will usually have similar characteristics throughout a given scene. Examine the surrounding footage so that you can create a flare that fits with the other shots in the scene.

There may also be times when you have a background plate that already has a lens flare in it, and you need to composite a new object into this scene. In this case you'll need to come up with a way in which the new object can appear to be behind the flare. This task can be quite difficult, since the flare is almost always semitransparent. You may be able to key a basic shape for the flare, but you'll probably end up with some detail from the background as well. The typical solution is to apply additional flare over both foreground *and* background. While this will increase the apparent brightness of the flare, it will help to integrate the elements without showing an obvious difference between foreground and background.

ATMOSPHERE

When it comes time to add a distant object into a scene, you will almost always want to modify the element to simulate the effect of atmosphere. At its most basic, this modification can be as simple as decreasing the contrast in the element, but usually you'll be better off if you concentrate on the dark areas of the image. Distant objects can still produce hot highlights, but their blacks will always be elevated as they move away from the camera. They will also usually take on some characteristic color or tint, depending on the ambient light and the color of the atmosphere itself. You may want to use pixel and regional analysis tools to numerically determine the value of any dark areas in the background plate that would be at the same distance as your new element.

Atmosphere may also introduce **diffusion** into the scene, an effect that causes some of the light to be scattered before it reaches the viewer or camera. This effect can also be the result of certain filters that are placed on the camera itself. Diffusion is *not* the same thing as a blur or a defocus. Only *some* of the light is scattered, and there will still be detail in the image. Diffusion tends to cause a halo around bright light sources and will often also elevate the blacks. In the digital world, an excellent method that is often used to simulate diffusion is to slightly blur the image and then mix it back with the original image by some small amount, probably mixing brighter areas in at a higher percentage.

Thus far we have discussed only very uniform atmospheric effects. But if the atmosphere is something more distinctive—some well-defined tendrils of smoke, for instance—things can get more complicated. You will probably want to make it seem as if any new elements you are adding to the scene are behind, or at least partially within, this smoke. You may be able to pull some kind of matte from the smoke—based on luminance most likely—and use it to key some of this background over your new foreground element. This method will only work if your background is fairly dark and/or uniform. If the camera is locked off, try averaging a series of images together to create a new element. Averaging the smoke together will remove distinctive details and will give you something that can be used as a clean plate. This plate can then be used with difference-matting techniques to better isolate the smoke, producing a new element that can be laid over your foreground and will roughly match the existing smoke in the scene (one hopes). You'll probably find that once you've created the difference matte you'll want to clean it up a bit, possibly blur it, and so on. The good news is that in most cases the foreground smoke won't need to be an exact match for what's already in the scene to be able to fool the eye. Given this, it may be just as easy to get footage of similar smoke shot on a neutral background and layer that over your element. In a situation such as this, you'll probably end up wanting to put this new element over both foreground *and* background, though not necessarily at the same percentage. The major disadvantage of this solution is that, in order to make it seem like the smoke is well integrated, the overall amount of atmosphere in the scene will increase.

CAMERA MISMATCHES

If you recall, when shooting a foreground and a background as separate elements, we want to use cameras that are consistent in terms of location, lens, and orientation. Plates that were shot with mismatched cameras can be difficult to identify via a purely visual test, since the discrepancies are often subtle and hard to quantify. Once again the importance of good notes, which can quickly identify the existence of a mismatch, becomes obvious. Consider Plate 48, which gives an idea of the perspective in a scene when photographed from a certain position. Now look at Plate 49. We've moved the camera so that it is much lower than it was in the first image. Although the perspective is noticeably different for the two camera positions, the basic information that is present in the two images is fairly similar. If this building is a separate element, judicious use of certain geometric transforms may be able to modify Plate 49 so that it appears to have been photographed from nearly the same perspective as Plate 48. Consider the four-point distortion, or "corner-pinning," that is applied in Figure 14.2. If we place this modified element over the background (as shown in Plate 50), the apparent perspective feels much closer to the scene shown in Plate 48.

Using a two-dimensional transformation to correct a 3D discrepancy is known as a **perspective compensation**. Of course this was a fairly simple scenario, and we had the enormous advantage of having a reference image to help us determine the appropriate amount of transformation to apply. But at the very least, the example serves to illustrate that it is possible to at least partially compensate for elements with inappropriate perspective. Some specialized warping might be able

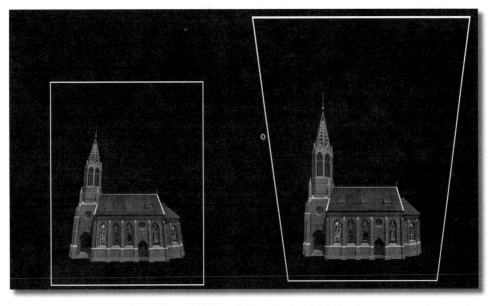

Figure 14.2 *The church in Plate 49 before (left) and after (right) using a corner-pin transform to approximate the perspective from Plate 48.*

to produce an even closer match, although the task would not be trivial, and you would run the risk of introducing artifacts that are more disturbing than the original problem. This sort of compensation can only be taken so far. Plate 51 shows the building from a much different angle. A whole new face of the building has been revealed, and obviously no amount of image manipulation would be able to transform Plate 49 into an exact match for this new image.

Since it is the camera-to-subject position, and not the lens, that determines perspective, two elements that were shot with different lenses will not necessarily cause a great problem. Assuming the camera was in the proper position, a different lens will usually result in nothing more than a scaling difference. As long as you have enough resolution to resize the element without introducing artifacts, your only problem will be determining the proper position and size for the element. While this is not trivial, it is usually far less difficult than having to compensate for perspective discrepancies. Of course, the chances are good that if the wrong lens was used, the camera distance was modified to compensate, and you therefore will be back to dealing with perspective issues.

As mentioned, the problems with a composite that includes these sorts of mismatches are hard to identify, but will still be noted by the subconscious expert. When questioned, people will say that the shot "feels wrong," that the elements just don't quite "fit" into the scene. If you don't have shooting notes that can help you to determine the nature or extent of the problem, you'll need to pay particular attention to any objects in either element that can give clues concerning what the lines of perspective are doing, in order to better align the two plates.

CAMERA MOVEMENTS

The nature of effects photography historically required that the elements of a composite all be shot with an unmoving, locked-off camera. While this made for easier composites, it didn't really make for interesting (or believable) cinematography. In Chapter 7 we looked at tracking tools that can help determine the move that a new element will require if it is going to be placed into a scene that was shot with a moving camera. Nowadays, this is at least as common as using a locked-off camera. Tracking can also be used to synchronize two elements that *both* have camera moves, even if the two moves are not similar. Understand, however, that two different moves implies that the camera-to-subject relationship will not be exactly the same for both plates. Some of the perspective compensations that we discussed in the last section may need to be applied to one or both of the elements in question.

Another method that is often used to introduce camera movement into a shot is to add the move *after* the composite is complete. In this situation, all the elements would ideally have been shot with an unmoving camera, and the composite would initially be put together as a locked-off shot. Once the shot is finished, an additional digital pan could be applied, giving the sense that a camera was moving across the scene, following some piece of pertinent action within the frame.

The camera move need not be a sweeping pan or zoom. Instead, you may find it necessary to add some sort of minor camera bounce or shake to your shot to match surrounding footage. A subtle move such as this will often be enough to take the curse off an otherwise static shot, hiding the artificiality of its origins. There may even be times when a defect in the shot that would be fairly difficult to correct explicitly can be covered by a strategically placed camera shake. Obviously there would need to be some sort of justifiable motivation for such a shake, but assuming it is warranted, this ploy could save a great deal of work.

If the move that needs to be added to a shot is fairly large, then you may need to work at a larger-than-normal resolution so that the push-in won't cause unwanted softness. If the move is small, then a slight push-in will probably be unnoticeable even if you are already working at the same resolution as the rest of the surrounding shots.

The shot from the film *Speed* that is discussed in Chapter 16 makes use of some of these tricks, adding a two-dimensional pan to an otherwise locked-off shot in order to heighten the excitement and action in the scene.

FOCUS

The most common method for simulating an out-of-focus element in a digital environment is to use some kind of blurring algorithm. While this is often perfectly acceptable, it is really a compromise solution. As we discussed in Chapter 12, a true defocus has a number of well-defined characteristics—characteristics that go beyond the look obtained by using a simple blur. Ideally, your compositing package will provide you with tools to help simulate a more accurate defocus, including some facility for highlight blooming, scale changes, and even depth-of-field effects.

If you need to add depth of field to an existing scene, you may be able to use a gradated mask to selectively defocus objects that are farther in the distance. If your scene is a synthetic, CG image, a Z-depth image (discussed more in Chapter 15) may be used to determine the amount of defocus each area will receive.

It may seem obvious, but remember that an out-of-focus object should have an edge softness that is appropriate to the overall softness of the object. Creating an appropriate edge tends to be most problematic when pulling a matte on a soft or motion-blurred object, since the thresholding used by certain keyers may produce a harder-than-normal edge. Either work on your key some more or (if you can get away with it) just add a bit of additional blur to your new edge.

If you need to add an element into a scene that features a rack focus, you should plan on spending some time synchronizing the timing of your new element's defocus. Since there are no real tools for measuring the "amount" of defocus in a generic scene, the compositor will need to visually match the timing of the focus change as closely as possible. This can be difficult: Individual frames may appear to be matched properly, but once the effect is seen in motion, the illusion may fall apart.

MOTION BLUR

If you wish to place a moving object into a scene, and that movement is something that *you* created (either as a 3D element or with a 2D transformation), you should plan on motion blurring your element. Most high-end systems allow motion blur to be added to a 2D move or rendered with the 3D element. If your system does not provide a true motion-based blur, you may have to resort to using some kind of directional blur or smear. It may not be quite as accurate (the tool may be unable to create a blur that curves along the object's path, for instance), but in many cases it will be enough to fool the eye.

As mentioned in Chapter 12, different types of cameras and camera settings can greatly affect the amount of motion blur that is captured with an image. While cameras will always have a limit to the range of shutter speeds they can use, most software that is designed to simulate motion blur will have no such restrictions. At times this may be useful to create a desired special effect, but usually you should do your best to analyze any reference material you have for the scene in question so that your depiction can be physically accurate and consistent.

Remember that motion blur will be more extreme for elements that are closer to camera, since (according to the principle of motion parallax mentioned in Chapter 12) they will appear to be moving more quickly. Don't expect to be able to apply the same motion-blur parameters to two elements that are at different distances from the camera.

If your original element already has some motion blur associated with it, be aware that changing the movement of this element will introduce a visual discrepancy that may be perceptible. For instance, adding vertical movement to an object that only has horizontal movement (and horizontal motion-blurring) would produce imagery that might appear somewhat strange. While there are certain algorithms that can sometimes *remove* motion blur from an element, they are not common and are limited in their scope. Ultimately, your only choice may be to apply additional motion blur that properly matches the new move and hope that the effect isn't too damaging to the already-blurred image.

FILM GRAIN

We've already discussed how visual effects photographers who are shooting on film will tend to try to capture most imagery with as little grain as possible, under the assumption that it can be added in post as needed. This practice generally means that each element will need an appropriate amount of grain added before it is placed into a scene. Conceivably, an overall grain pass can be applied to the finished composite, assuming that all the source elements were equivalently grainless. Forgetting to add grain to an element is an extremely common mistake when integrating rendered 3D images into a scene, causing the CGI element to appear far too "clean" for the rest of the image. (Incidentally, a little bit of grain added to a CG element can also do a wonderful job of eliminating the contouring or banding artifacts associated with limited-bit-depth CG images.) Even two different live elements may not have the same amount of grain, owing to different film stocks, exposure levels, development processes, and any operators that may have been applied.

A number of compositing processes can add to or enhance the grain in an element. Sharpening, for instance, can dramatically emphasize the grain in an image, as can a large contrast adjustment. If you plan to digitally enlarge an element, be warned that your grain will enlarge as well, possibly giving the image a blotchy look. Postproduction work on bluescreen (and, even more so, greenscreen) elements will often use processes that can affect the amount of grain in the result—an issue that is discussed later in this chapter.

Be aware of processes that *remove* grain as well. The most common process would be any sort of blur algorithm, but various other filters, such as the median, can also cause a decrease in the amount of visible grain in the treated element. When using these operators on a background that originally contained grain, you will probably need to add grain back into the element after you have performed the operation. In a real image, since the grain is a function of the film and not the lens, even the most out-of-focus image will still have the same amount of grain in it.

There are times when some element in a scene may not really need to be a sequence of images, since there is nothing moving in the element. If you decide to use a repeated single frame as an element, you will still probably have grain in the scene, only it will not change over time. This will almost always be even more noticeable than not having any grain at all. If possible, you should try to acquire a very short sequence of images instead of a still frame and then loop this sequence repeatedly to achieve the necessary shot length. This solution assumes that you can obtain a sequence that doesn't contain any object motion that would betray the trick being used. You'll ideally want to use at least 16 frames or so to make sure that persistence of vision can't detect the repeating grain patterns.

Another common solution, particularly if you can only get two or three identical frames, is to average these frames together to produce a single, grainless image. Moving artificial grain can then be reapplied as needed. This technique is preferred if you need to enlarge the element in question, since you can add your grain *after* the enlargement so that it does not appear to change size.

Tuning grain to match another image is a highly subjective process. Try to notice both the size and the density of the grain particles, as well as the amount of color and brightness variation. Ideally, whatever software you have for introducing grain will allow you to control these various parameters. Many packages now include the ability to specify a particular film stock and will automatically apply what it considers to be the proper grain characteristics to match that stock. Be very cautious when using such tools, since there are so many factors beyond the specific film stock that can affect grain. Automatic tools won't know about any abnormal exposure or development that might have been used, nor will they know to compensate if the element in question already has some grain present. For that matter, you can never be certain that the information about the stock to which you will be matching is accurate. The bottom line is that you should never apply an automatic grain-generation tool without visually checking the result to see if it is appropriate.

If your compositing system does not have the ability to create grain explicitly, you can always take some raw film stock, give it a slight exposure (a process known as **flashing**), and then scan the result to use as a grain template. A sequence of these images can be looped and combined with your grainless images to introduce the proper grain. Be sure to use a film stock that is appropriate for the situation, and realize that the same warnings we gave about using prepackaged grain generators apply in this situation as well.

Grain should be judged by looking at moving sequences, not just still frames. In a single image it will be much more difficult to judge the quality of grain, particularly if the scene contains a great deal of random detail, since it may not be obvious if a particular spot is from detail or grain. Grain should also never be judged when looking at a proxy image. Any filtering that is done to resize an image for proxy use will greatly affect the grain, sometimes increasing it (particularly if using a fast, rough filter) and sometimes decreasing it.

Finally, remember that grain is one of the most important issues to consider when examining scene continuity. In the days of optical compositing, a cut to a shot with noticeably more grain was almost a dead giveaway that there was a visual effect involved. These days, it's even conceivable that you could provide a shot that has too *little* grain to match the surrounding shots.

BLUESCREEN INTEGRATION

Most of the issues that we have already discussed will continue to be applicable when working with a bluescreen element. As with any element that relies on a procedurally generated matte, make sure you examine how the edges you have created behave over time, examine overall lighting integration, and so forth. But there are a few additional items that need to be mentioned that will only be an issue with bluescreen shots.

As we have already discussed, the process of placing a bluescreen element into a new background involves several steps. The matte-extraction step has already been described, and can actually be done via a variety of different methods. But equally important is the color balancing step, which will almost always require explicit spill suppression on the foreground element. No matter how carefully the foreground character was lit, there will always be a bit of blue colorization that comes from the backing. Fortunately, there are some excellent, well-defined tools for removing it that will generally not compromise the overall balance of the image. Many of these tools are proprietary and are only found integrated with certain software packages. As such, they will not be dealt with here. But the most common spill-suppression technique comes once again from a traditional optical compositing method. It is considered to be part of the color difference method, and we have already discussed it briefly when we looked at this method in Chapter 5.

If you recall, the spill-suppression step of this process involves the selective substitution of one channel into another. In the case of a bluescreen, we selectively use the green channel as needed. The most simple version of this step compares the blue and green component for every pixel in the image. Whenever the blue component exceeds the green component, the value of the green component is also used to replace the current blue value. An example of this is shown in Plate 52, where Plate 52a shows our original bluescreen element. This element was intentionally shot with a bit of blue spill, particularly in the mannequin's hair, to emphasize some of the issues we need to discuss. Hair, especially blonde hair, is widely recognized as one of the most difficult things to composite when working with bluescreen imagery. If we extract a matte for the mannequin and place it directly into the background scene (as shown in Plate 52b), you can still see quite a bit of blue contamination on the foreground. But if we apply a spill-suppression technique before the composite is performed, a more pleasing (but hardly perfect) result is obtained. This is shown in Plate 52c.

For comparison purposes, take a look at Plate 52d. This is *not* a composite—the mannequin was actually photographed standing in front of the background. Examination of fine details (such as the hair) as well as the overall color balance will give you some idea of the issues that can arise when attempting to produce a composite that properly matches with reality. As you can see, the channel substitution that we used will easily neutralize blue spill areas, causing them to become a gray tone. Of course, this technique will usually not be able to distinguish the difference between blue spill and blue objects, with the result being that certain things that should remain blue will be inadvertently affected. The typical solution is to either explicitly isolate such elements (via specific procedural or manually generated mattes) so that they are not affected by the spill suppression, or to manually color correct them back to the appropriate tone.

This channel substitution will, in some situations, have some additional drawbacks as well. One of the more significant drawbacks occurs primarily when working with greenscreens. The same logic we used to suppress blue can be used to suppress green, merely by substituting green for blue and blue for green in the spill-suppression equation. Thus, anywhere the value of the green channel is greater than the value of the blue channel, use the value from the blue channel instead. But this technique can be more problematic with greenscreen because of the relative amount of noise that is present in the various layers of motion picture film. The blue record is significantly more grainy than the green channel. Look again at the various images shown in Plate 47 for a good example of this feature. As you can imagine, using a larger amount of this noisier blue channel to replace the green channel can increase the overall amount of grain by a noticeable amount. Whether or not this effect will be a problem is very dependent on the situation. If you are using slower, less grainy film, or if you have very little green spill to suppress, you may not need to worry. If you are shooting on video, the noise difference between the two channels is usually negligible, so you also will typically not have a problem. But certain shooting scenarios may create enough of these problems to make bluescreen the preferred technique.

DIGITAL INTEGRATION

It may seem a bit odd to find a section specifically targeted to digital integration at the *end* of this chapter when, at least theoretically, the entire chapter should have been covering this topic. But if you look again at the preceding sections you will find that our discussions generally viewed the integration process from a real-world perspective. Element matching was looked at in terms of lights and shadows, atmosphere and cameras, and the digital aspect was not heavily stressed. This was intentional, since it provides a very familiar method for understanding the issues involved, but in reality the digital compositing artist is working with none of these things. The only objects that are truly being dealt with are pixels, channels, and other collections of data. This data is used to *represent* objects and lights, but at some level the representation is inaccurate, or at least limited. This section will concentrate on some digital-specific methods for integrating elements, rounding out the suggestions that were provided earlier in the chapter.

Although we have talked about the importance of matching the lights and shadows in a scene, in the digital realm all we have to work with are the numerical measurements of these lights and shadows. Instead of adjusting a light on the set, we will be confined to working with image processing operators that can adjust brightness, contrast, and color. Even if all the elements that are to be integrated into a scene were shot with identical lighting setups, the resulting digital image files may not be properly matched. Many of the conversion steps that the images go through as they are digitized can introduce inconsistencies, including color or brightness shifts. At some point the issue of how the elements were created becomes less important, and you will need to concentrate on synchronizing the digital values as these elements are added to a scene.

Consider the case of the darkest areas in an image. These areas are usually referred to as the "blacks" of the image, and may be found where there are heavy shadows, or merely in areas where the object that was photographed is extremely dark. Rarely are the darkest parts of a photographed scene completely black, and if you want to add something to that scene you should make absolutely certain that the darkest parts of your new element aren't any darker.

Mismatched black levels are one of the most common problems you will find with composited imagery. This is due in part to how difficult it can be to accurately judge relative brightness in the darker areas of an image. The problem is compounded even further by the fact that you will often be viewing the images in a fashion that is different from how they will eventually be displayed. As mentioned in Chapter 9, your computer's monitor (even if it has been carefully calibrated) can still only give an approximation of what the final image will look like on film or video. Subtle black-level mismatches that your CRT is unable to display may become suddenly noticeable when the image is transferred to its final format. Even if you *do* have the opportunity to view your images in what you think is their final format, don't assume that you have nothing else to worry about. Ultimately you can never be certain what will happen to your images once you are finished with them. For instance, it is a very common practice to slightly boost the brightness of film images when they are released on videotape, due to video's much lower contrast ratio. Suddenly, areas that looked to be of uniform blackness can reveal hidden detail, including compositing artifacts!

Fortunately, there are some very simple methods that can be used to help judge how well the black levels are matching. The first, and easiest, is to simply boost the brightness of the composited image you have created. This will obviously be a temporary step, since you presumably have already created an image that is the proper brightness, but it can quickly reveal problems that would otherwise be undetectable. By taking a few moments to create an image that is much brighter than necessary, you will move the darkest areas into a range where slight tonal variations will be far more noticeable. There are a few different ways that you can accomplish this temporary brightness shift. You can certainly just apply an additional brightness to the image itself, creating a new image for viewing purposes. On the other hand, it may be easier to adjust the brightness of your computer's monitor instead. Make sure that you can easily return to any calibrated settings that may have been in place on this monitor! Many software packages will even allow you to load a specialized look-up table that will be applied to every image that is displayed. This method is usually best, since the table can be quickly turned on or off as needed.

Most compositing tools will also include the ability to digitally sample values from different regions of an image (see Chapter 9). By carefully sampling appropriate groups of pixels from areas that should be equivalently dark, you will be able to obtain a numerical confirmation that the levels match to within an acceptable threshold.

Although we have only discussed black-level matching so far, the concepts obviously extend beyond this. Many of the same issues hold true for the brightest parts of a scene, and care should be taken that the white levels match as well.

Typically there is less of a problem with compositors not matching their highlights, partially because, even with darker images, whites can often reach 100%.

Ultimately, of course, you will be matching a variety of different values between elements. Colors and contrast ranges may all need adjusting, and although there may be some analysis tools that can help you to determine numerical correlations between specific areas, your final decision will always be based on your own aesthetic judgments.

CHAPTER FIFTEEN

Advanced Topics

Throughout this book we have looked at a wide variety of topics related to digital compositing. For most of these discussions, an attempt was made to provide a reasonably complete coverage of the topic given the limited amount of space available. To be sure, this entailed a fair amount of simplification in certain areas, particularly when you consider the fact that many of the chapters in this book could easily be expanded into complete books themselves.

This chapter will now take the time to go into a bit more detail about certain things that were only alluded to in earlier chapters, including concepts that the average compositor may not need to deal with regularly and that are somewhat more advanced in their application. Certain other topics that are related to, but not necessarily an integral part of, digital compositing will also be covered in this chapter.

BEYOND BLACK AND WHITE

One of the biggest mistakes that the digitally trained artist can make comes from trying to think about the real world in digital terms instead of trying to view the digital world in real-world terms. As we stated in Chapter 12, it is important to recognize that a camera is only capable of capturing a limited *sample* of any given scene. This sample contains far less information than the scene itself, and consequently there are great limitations on how much manipulation can be done with it.

Consider the image shown in Plate 53a. It features a scene with two obvious light sources. If you compare the image of the two light bulbs, you will see that the centers of both bulbs have the same apparent value. Both are "white," the maximum brightness that the film was able to capture. But in fact, these two lights are actually quite a bit different—the bulb on the left is a 100-watt bulb, the bulb on the right is only 25-watts. Theoretically, the higher-wattage bulb is putting out about four times as much light. Plate 53b confirms this fact. The camera's aperture has been decreased so that the overall exposure of the scene is significantly reduced. The difference between the two light sources now becomes obvious, since the lower exposure prevents the lower-wattage bulb from overexposing the film. There is detail visible in the center of the bulb. The 100-watt bulb, however, is still bright enough to expose to white.

This example underscores the fact that the terms "white" and "black" refer to very arbitrary concepts and are really only valid within the context of whatever system is being used to capture the image. They are also tied to whatever is being used to *display* the image. For instance, on a computer or video monitor, "black" can be only as dark as the CRT is when no power is being applied to it. Look at an unplugged TV and you'll realize that the screen is really not that black at all—more like a dark gray. By the same token, a "white" object on a monitor may look much less so if you compare it with an identical object being viewed in bright sunlight.

A great number of digital compositing processes are built on the concept that black is represented by a digital value of 0, and white is represented by a digital value of 1. While this is, indeed, a very useful conceit, it does not accurately represent the way that the real world works, and there are times when we need to disregard this simplification. There is an inherent danger in making the assumption that the white or black areas in two different images can be treated as if they were equivalent values. Often you will find that white and black pixels should even be treated differently from the rest of the pixels in the *same* image.

Consider again Plate 53a as compared with 53b. If we attempt to modify 53a digitally to produce an image that matches 53b, we can produce an image like the one shown in Plate 53c. As you can see, although this has reduced the wooden character to an acceptable match, the areas that were white in the original have also been brought down to a darker value. Our digital tool is obviously not doing a very good job of mimicking what happens in the real world. Although the use of other digital tools and techniques may be able to do a slightly better job of preserving the brightness of the white areas in the image, we still have a problem with the detail in the center of the 25-watt bulb. If all we have to work with is Plate 53a, we will *never* be able to accurately recreate the image that is shown in Plate 53b, since the information in this portion of the scene has exceeded the limits of the system used to capture it.

Areas that exceed the exposure limits of film or video are a common problem even when there is no digital compositing involved. Trying to photograph a scene with a bright blue sky while still being able to see detail in areas that are shadowed can be a nearly impossible task. If you use an exposure designed to capture the color of the sky, the shadow areas will probably register as completely black. But if you increase the exposure in order to see into the areas that are shadowed, the sky will become overexposed and "burn out" to white. Digital compositing tools are sometimes used to solve just this problem. By photographing the scene twice, once for the sky and once for the darker areas, an **exposure split** (or **E-split**) can be used to combine the two images into the desired result.

In some ways, overexposed areas should not be thought of as being white at all. Rather, any region that is at the maximum level of the system in question should really be considered to be *above* white. This is sometimes referred to as **superwhite**. Although we have no way of measuring exactly how much above white the area really is, there are a variety of compositing situations in which the concept of superwhite (or superblack) can be put to use. In Chapter 12 we described how an out-of-focus image of a very bright light source will look significantly different from a simple blur applied to an in-focus version of the same scene. Some of the reasons behind the difference should now be a bit more obvious. Applying a basic blur to the in-focus image will merely average the "white" pixels (pixels with a value of 1.0) across many of the adjacent pixels. But these white pixels should actually be much brighter than 1.0, and consequently the amount of illumination that is spread by the blur should be increased as well. Because the bright areas in our digital image are limited to a value of 1.0, the amount of light that is spread is limited as well. In the real scene, the light source has no such artificial limits imposed on it, and there will be enough illumination coming from it to overexpose the entire range of its defocused extent. Instead of the soft-edged blob that is produced by our digitally blurred image, we have a noticeably defined shape.

It is not at all uncommon to treat superwhite areas of an image differently when dealing with them in a digital composite. These areas may be specific light sources, as shown in our example, or they may simply be the part of an object that has a very strong highlight. For example, to better simulate the behavior of an out-of-focus light source while still using an ordinary blur tool, we might isolate anything that is a pure digital white into a separate image. Once we apply our blur to both images, we can add the isolated superwhite areas back into the scene at a greater intensity. This technique will help to simulate the fact that the real light source was far brighter that what our image considers to be "white."

White Point and Black Point

Another technique that is often used to better deal with the whites and blacks in an image involves choosing a slightly smaller range of values to represent our "normal" black-to-white span. In this situation, a specific, nonzero numerical value is defined to be black, and another value, not quite 1.0, becomes white.

For instance, we might arbitrarily define black as having a digital value of 0.1 instead of exactly 0. Similarly, we might say that white will be considered to be anything at or above the digital value of 0.9. We call these values the **white point** and the **black point** of the image. By treating these points as if they were the limits of our brightness range, we effectively create a bit of extra room at the top and bottom of our palette. The values that fall outside the range defined by our white and black points are, once again, often referred to as superwhite or superblack. Understand that the process of choosing a white point and a black point does not necessarily change the image itself. Initially they are simply values that we need to be aware of. It is only when we actually convert our digital image to its final format that the white and black points have an effect on the image.

Let's say we are sending our image to an analog video device. In this situation, instead of the normal mapping that we usually apply when sending images to video, the conversion is done so that any pixel in our digital image that has a value above or equal to our white point will be displayed at the full brightness that the video device is capable of. In effect, our white point is now truly "white," at least within the limits of our video system. The same thing will be true for the black point: All pixels at or below this value will be as dark as is possible. A diagram of this conversion is shown in Figure 15.1.

In a way, the use of a white and black point when working with image data provides some of the benefits of a floating-point system (as discussed in Chapter 11) without the need for the additional computational resources that such a system would ordinarily require. Of course there are disadvantages as well, including the fact that the bulk of our compositing work is being done with a slightly smaller range of values (the range between the white point and the black point). This constraint will reduce the number of colors that are available to work with, and consequently may be more likely to introduce certain artifacts.

One of the biggest problems that must be dealt with when using artificial white and black points is how to accurately view these images. Since we know that our

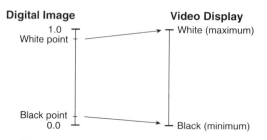

Figure 15.1 *Mapping white and black points to an analog video display device.*

white point will eventually be displayed as pure white, ideally we could implement a method so that the images reflect this as we are working with them. This is best accomplished via the use of a specialized look-up table that is applied to our display device. At the end of Chapter 14 we discussed how such a viewing LUT can be used to temporarily boost the brightness of an image to better judge the values in the darker areas. With our current scenario, the LUT would be used continuously whenever we are working with these particular images. As before, this LUT does not affect the values in the image itself, merely the way that they are being displayed. The net result is that the white point will actually appear to be white, since it is being mapped to the brightest value that our computer's monitor is able to display. At the same time, the black point will be mapped to the darkest value that is possible.

The real usefulness of a white or black point comes when we are actually able to capture a greater range of brightness values than we will eventually need to display. Such a situation occurs in the film world, where the negative that is created in the original photography has a much greater sensitivity range than the prints that will be produced from it. This feature is what allows so much flexibility in the printing process: The extra range in the negative means that the brightness of the print can be increased or decreased by fairly significant amounts without losing detail in the bright or dark areas of the image. We can take advantage of this in the digital realm because it is the negative that is used when we digitize the image.[1] The full brightness range will be captured even though we won't necessarily be able to see all of that range when a final print is made. Careful testing should be performed with the system that is being used to scan and output the film in order to determine the optimal white and black points that should be defined.

At the risk of complicating this discussion even further, it should be noted that some video systems actually already have built-in white and black points. Values above a certain threshold are considered illegal and will be automatically clipped to an acceptable level, as will values that are too low. Intermediate systems may make use of this fact, using certain out-of-range values for special functions such as keying.

NONLINEAR COLOR SPACES

In Chapter 2, we looked at a few different methods that can be used to reduce the amount of storage space a given image will consume. Most of these compression

---

[1] Even though we scan the negative, we immediately invert the values digitally so that the image appears to be a normal "positive" when we are working with it.

schemes, while mathematically quite complex, can be used quite easily, without ever needing to understand their inner workings at any great level of detail. But there is one final compression technique that requires a bit more education before it can be effectively employed. This technique involves the use of nonlinear color spaces.

Conceptually, the best storage format would be one that keeps only the useful information in an image and discards everything else. Of course, what actually constitutes the *useful* data in an image is difficult, if not impossible, to determine precisely. Certain assumptions *can* be made, however, and if these assumptions are accurate then great data reductions can result. We already discussed one such assumption in Chapter 2 when we looked at JPEG encoding, which assumes that color information is less important than brightness information. But JPEG is a fairly lossy format and rather unsuitable for high-end work. Another fairly drastic method that could be used to reduce the space requirements for an image's storage would be to simply reduce its bit depth. Reducing an image from 16 bits per channel to 8 bits per channel will halve the size of the image, but obviously throws away a great deal of potentially useful information. If, on the other hand, we properly modify the data before discarding some of the least-significant bits, we can selectively preserve a good deal of the more useful information that would otherwise be lost. In this situation, our definition of "useful" is based (at least partially) on the knowledge of how the human eye works. In particular, it is based on the fact that the human eye is far more sensitive to brightness differences in the darker to midrange portions of an image than it is to changes in very bright areas.

Let's look at an example of how this principle can be applied when converting an image to a lower bit depth. We'll look at the extremely simplified case of wishing to convert an image that originated as a four-bit grayscale image into a three-bit file format. Once you understand this scenario, you can mentally extrapolate the process to real-world situations in which we deal with greater bit depths. If our original image starts as a four-bit grayscale image, we have 16 different gray values that we can represent. It should be obvious that converting this four-bit image to a three-bit storage format will require us to throw away a great deal of information, since our three-bit destination image has only 8 different grayscale values. The most simple conversion would be merely to take colors 1 and 2 from the input range and convert them to color value 1 in the output image. Colors 3 and 4 would both become color 2, 5 and 6 would become 3, and so on. This mapping is shown in Figure 15.2.

A graph of this conversion is shown in Figure 15.3. The horizontal axis represents the value of the original pixel, and the vertical axis plots the resulting output value for the pixel. The dotted line shows the generalized function that would apply no matter how many color values we are dealing with. As you can see,

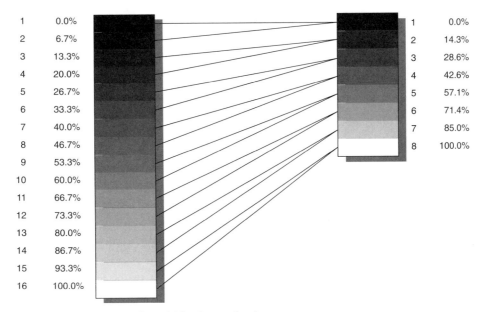

1	0.0%
2	6.7%
3	13.3%
4	20.0%
5	26.7%
6	33.3%
7	40.0%
8	46.7%
9	53.3%
10	60.0%
11	66.7%
12	73.3%
13	80.0%
14	86.7%
15	93.3%
16	100.0%

1	0.0%
2	14.3%
3	28.6%
4	42.6%
5	57.1%
6	71.4%
7	85.0%
8	100.0%

Figure 15.2   *Linear mapping of 16 colors to 8 colors.*

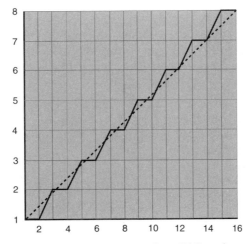

Figure 15.3   *Graph of the linear color conversion. The solid line shows the actual mapping; the dotted line shows an approximation of the function that would accomplish this conversion.*

this function is completely linear, and this conversion would be called a "linear encoding" of the image data.

The disadvantage of this linear method is that it ignores the fact that the human eye is less sensitive to differences in tone as brightness increases. This principle is difficult to demonstrate with only 16 colors, particularly with the added complexity of how the various brightness levels are reproduced on the printed page. But consider if we had 100 evenly spaced grayscale colors to choose from, ranging from black (color number 1) to white (color number 100). You would find that, visually, it is almost impossible to distinguish the difference between two of the brightest colors, say number 99 and number 100. In the darker colors, however, the difference between color number 1 and color number 2 would still remain noticeable. This is not merely due to the human eye being more sensitive to particular brightness levels, but also to the fact that the eye is more sensitive to the amount of *change* in those brightness levels. In our 100-color example, a white value of 100 is only about 1.01 times brighter than color number 99. At the low end, however, color number 2 is *twice* as bright as color number 1.

Since brightness differences in the high end are less noticeable, a better way to convert from 16 colors to 8 colors would be to try to consolidate a few more of the upper-range colors together, while preserving as many of the steps as possible in the lower range. Figure 15.4 shows an example of this type of mapping. In this situation, any pixel that was greater than about 80% white in the source

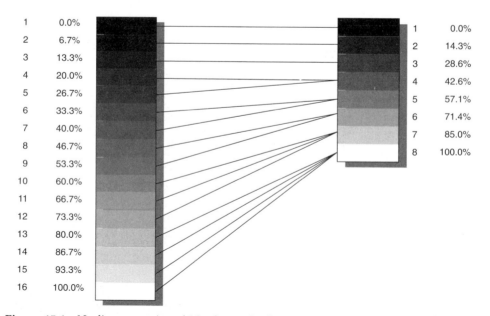

Figure 15.4   *Nonlinear mapping of 16 colors to 8 colors.*

image will become 100% white in the destination image. Pixels that range from 60% to 80% brightness become about 85% white, and so on. Figure 15.5 provides a graph (solid line) of this mapping, as well as an approximation (dotted line) of a function that would accomplish this conversion. As you can see, the function is no longer a straight line, and consequently this would be considered a *nonlinear* conversion.

Because this conversion actually modifies the colors in an image, it produces a result that is visually different from the original image. If we were to view this new image directly, it would appear to be far too bright, since we've shifted midrange colors in the original image to be bright colors in our encoded image. To properly view this image, we would either need to reconvert to its normal representation or modify our viewing device (i.e., the video or computer-monitor) so that it simulates such a conversion. An image that has had its colors modified for storage purposes is said to have been converted to a different **color space**. In this case, since a nonlinear function was used to produce this conversion, we say that the image is stored in a **nonlinear color space**.

In general, we tend to work with digital images in a linear color space. The concept behind linear data storage is simple and intuitive. It essentially assumes that the relationship between a pixel's digital value and its visual brightness remains constant, or linear, across the full gamut of black to white. In reality this is a *very* slippery concept, since one of the issues that we're discussing relates to how a pixel's brightness is *perceived* by a human observer. To fully understand this topic we would need to delve into a huge range of issues relating to everything

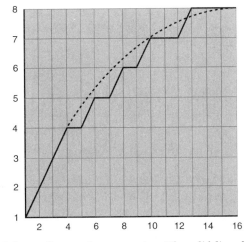

Figure 15.5 *Graph of the nonlinear color conversion. The solid line shows the actual mapping; the dotted line shows an approximation of the function that would accomplish this conversion.*

from the physical characteristics of film emulsion to CRT phosphors to the entire human visual system. However, for simplicity's sake we'll assume that an image is stored and represented in a linear color space (or "linear space") unless otherwise specified.

The primary reason for using a nonlinear color space to store an image is the same as for any other compression scheme—the desire to store information as efficiently as possible. But the conversion of an image from a linear to a nonlinear color space is not, in itself, a compression technique. All we are doing is taking an input color and mapping it to an output color. There is no explicit mathematical compression as in the run-length or JPEG encoding schemes that were discussed in Chapter 2. It is only when we convert the image to a lower bit depth that it is actually compressed, and significant amounts of data are then lost. Thus, it is useful to think of this conversion as a two-step process. The first step is simply a color correction, nothing more. The result of this color correction is that certain color ranges are consolidated so that they take up less of your color palette, thus leaving room for the other, more important ranges to keep their full resolution, even when reducing the number of bits used to store a given image. But until we actually store the data into a file with a lower bit depth, very little data is lost, and the process is essentially reversible. Of course, it is usually not very worthwhile to apply this color correction *without* lowering the bit depth, since the color correction by itself does not actually reduce the file size. A 16-bit image stored in a nonlinear color space will be the same size as a 16-bit image that is stored in a linear color space.

The second step of the conversion is where we decrease the bit depth, and consequently discard a great deal of information. Once we truncate our 16-bit file to 8 bits, the image that has been converted to a nonlinear color space will have a distinct advantage over its linear counterpart: It is using its 8 bits to hold more important information. When it comes time to linearize the data to work with it (and you will almost always want to do so), we will need to convert it back to 16 bits of precision. But once this is done, the nonlinearly encoded image will have lost far less of the visually critical detail than the image that remained in linear space throughout the bit-depth changes.

Working with Nonlinear Color Spaces

If we had an unlimited number of bits per pixel, nonlinear representations would become unnecessary. However, the usual considerations of available disk space, memory usage, speed of calculations, and even transfer/transmission methods all dictate that we attempt to store images as compactly as possible, keeping the minimum amount of data necessary to realize the image quality we find acceptable.

Unlike most of the more traditional compression techniques, however, it is very easy to view (and work with) nonlinear images directly. And because nonlinear encoding is really only a color correction, *any* file format can be used to store nonlinear data. This is one of the most confusing issues that arises when working with images that are stored nonlinearly. There is effectively no foolproof way to determine if an image is in a linear or nonlinear color space, other than to visually compare it with the original scene. Consequently, it is very important to keep track of how your images are being used and exactly what operations or conversions have been performed on them. Certain file formats may be *assumed* to hold data in a certain color space, but a format by itself cannot *enforce* a particular color space.

Nonlinear encoding is useful in a variety of situations, and whether you work in film or video, you will probably be dealing with the process (at least indirectly). Although it may be possible to remain fairly insulated from the topic given the increased sophistication of software and hardware systems, you should still understand where and why the process is used and needed. Let's look at a couple of situations in which it is typically employed. We'll start with the video world, where this nonlinear conversion is known as a "gamma correction." We looked at the gamma function a bit in Chapter 3. If you compare the graph for the gamma operation (from Figure 3.5) with the simple nonlinear encoding function that we demonstrated in Figure 15.5, you can see that the basic shapes of the curves are quite similar.

Typically, video images are captured and stored with a built-in gamma correction of 2.2. This correction is part of the image capture process, when analog images that enter the camera's lens are converted to numerical data and stored on videotape. In a sense the camera is performing a nonlinear conversion between the infinite color resolution of the real world to the limited bandwidth of a video signal. The visual result is that the image is made brighter, but the important issue is that the high end has been compressed in order to leave more room to represent low-end colors. Standard video display devices are actually nonlinear in their response, so if we send these images directly to video, the monitor will, by default, behave as if an inverse correction had been applied, thereby producing an image that appears correct. But if we want to view these images in the digital world so that they appear to have a brightness equivalent to the original scene, we will need to compensate for this gamma correction.

There are two ways to perform this compensation. The first is to simply apply another gamma correction, the inverse of the original, to restore the images to a linear color space. In this case, a gamma of 0.45 (1/2.2) would be used. This is the process (or at least part of the process) that we would use if we plan to actually work with the images and combine them with other linear-space images. We'll discuss this further in a moment. But if we simply want to view the images, it may be easier to adjust the viewing device (the computer's monitor) so that it is darkened by a gamma of 0.45.[2] This adjustment will display the images at the proper brightness without the need to preprocess every frame. As we mentioned earlier, certain flipbook tools will make it even easier, allowing you to load a specialized color table that modifies the way that images are displayed on the system's monitor.

For film images, a more complex nonlinear conversion is often used, which takes into account various idiosyncrasies of how film stock responds to varying exposure levels. The most common file format used to store film images is the **Cineon** file format, which includes a specification for conversion into a nonlinear "logarithmic color space." A logarithmic curve is again similar to the curve shown in Figure 15.5. The Cineon file format is discussed in a bit more detail in Appendix C, and an example image using Cineon encoding is shown in Plate 54.

Although you may have chosen to store images in a nonlinear format, you will almost always want to convert these images back to linear space before working with them because of the way in which color corrections will affect an image that is stored in a nonlinear space. Consider the image shown in Plate 55, which is an example of a simple color correction in which the red, green, and blue channels have been multiplied by constant values of 1.2, 1.2, and 0.8, respectively. The left side of the image was corrected in linear space, and comparing any pixel with the original image will show a red value that has been reduced by 20%. The right side of the image, however, was first encoded into a nonlinear color space (in this example we used the Cineon specification), and *then* the same multiplication was done. Once the color correction was applied, the image was restored to linear space. As you can see, a fairly slight color correction in linear space has become rather drastic when applied to a nonlinearly encoded image. In particular, notice how the midtones have changed quite a bit more than the darker areas of the image. This problem can be particularly vexing when working with bluescreen elements—attempts to reduce blue spill may result in undesirable shifts in flesh tones, for instance. Even the simplest image-combination tools can produce different results when they are used on nonlinear images.

Although there are certainly operations that do *not* have this problem (geometric transformations work equally well on images that are stored in any color space,

---

[2] Although we state that you should "darken your monitor by a gamma of 0.45," this does not necessarily mean that you should explicitly set your monitor's gamma at 0.45. Rather, you will need to first determine what monitor settings are needed to give your monitor a linear response and then add the adjustment on top of *that* setting. Different systems will have different (often poorly documented) controls for adjusting the monitor to respond linearly to a video signal, and consequently there is no way that we can tell you exactly what setting should be used.

for instance), in general the compositing artist would do well to heed the following warning:

> Color correcting or compositing images that are stored in a nonlinear color space can easily produce unpredictable results. *Always* linearize your images before manipulating or combining them.

WORKING WITH 3D ELEMENTS

In a number of places throughout this book we have mentioned issues that come up only when working with synthetic, computer-generated 3D elements. There are a few final items to be discussed, including some that relate to or can be considered as part of the more advanced topics that are covered in this chapter.

The bulk of the general lighting and camera guidelines that we've discussed apply equally well to the completely synthetic elements that are produced from a 3D animation and rendering package. Usually the artist actually has *more* control over a 3D environment than a real-world one. Synchronizing camera and lighting setups will still be important in this environment, and even though different software may have different conventions for how to specify these setups, there is almost always a way to translate these settings into real-world units. The 3D artist should thus be able to faithfully recreate the original background scene's environment and produce imagery that will integrate easily.

As we've mentioned elsewhere in this book, there are a number of features that distinguish images that were created with a 3D system from those captured via more traditional photography. The most obvious is, of course, the availability of an explicit matte channel—a tremendous aid to the compositing process. Another useful feature, the Z-buffer, will be discussed in detail in the next section. But there are also a few additional idiosyncrasies with CG images that need to be noted. First of all, remember that an image from a 3D rendering package has been produced by a *simulation* of a camera, not the real thing. As such, real-world characteristics such as lens distortions or film grain may not be included and will need to be added during the compositing process. Remember too that the brightness range of a CG image may be different from a live-action image. Very often a scanned film image will never have any digital values below a certain threshold, yet a digital image may actually have values down to zero. Integrating the two will require that the contrast range in the CG image be adjusted, boosting the blacks so that they match with the live-action plate.

When working with 3D elements, there will always be situations in which one can choose to either modify the rendered element in the composite or to modify the color and lighting parameters in the 3D scene and rerender the element from scratch. Deciding which route to take may be dictated by practical considerations such as the amount of time available, but even assuming that these things are equal, the decision should still be on a case-by-case basis. Within the 3D environment there is a much greater amount of control over how an object is lit than there is once it has been rendered into an image. Unlike in 2D, where changing the apparent direction of a light source can entail a great deal of effort, in the 3D world one can easily move and modify lights at will. Thus, any significant changes in lighting direction will usually require a rerender. Changes in the overall color balance of an element, on the other hand, may be something that is done just as easily in the composite. Rarely is the decision a trivial one, and often you will find that the best method is to attempt the changes first in 2D and then revert to the 3D solution as needed. Some of the more sophisticated software packages on the market will actually offer the user a hybrid 2D/3D solution, wherein certain parameters that would normally only be available in a 3D package are stored in a specialized image file. Using such a system, the compositing artist can directly manipulate such things as the relationships among the ambient, diffuse, and specular illumination on an object. This integration between 2D and 3D will continue to become more common as time goes by.

Working with 3D elements may also present some additional logistical problems, particularly if your 3D elements are being created by someone else. When dealing only with a collection of live-action plates, you know that the elements you are given will remain the same for as long as you are working with them. When integrating 3D, however, the situation may not be quite so stable. It is very common for the development of a particular 3D element to be something that is happening concurrently with the integration of that element into a scene, a process that has both benefits and drawbacks. The benefits are that it will give both the compositor and the 3D artist the ability to address problems by rerendering as necessary. There may even be times when a compositing script can be made more efficient by removing certain operations (such as a color correction) and applying a compensating operation to the 3D element itself as it is being rerendered. Of course the significant downside to this process is that the compositing artist may spend a great deal of time balancing a particular element into a scene and then suddenly be confronted with a radically changed new element provided by the 3D artist. The only way to avoid this is to ensure that the communication between the 2D and the 3D artists is thorough and timely.

With the growing popularity of completely computer-generated movies, television shows, and theme-park rides, there is now a good deal of compositing work being done without *any* live-action elements involved. Although it is possible for an entire CG scene to be rendered as a single finished shot, experienced 3D artists will still tend to render more complex shots as a series of discrete layers and then composite these layers together into a final scene. This methodology allows the 3D artist to avoid time-consuming rerenders of large scenes when there is only a problem with a specific element. Instead, only the element in question will need to be redone, usually saving a great deal of time and resources.

Z-Depth Compositing

There is yet another useful technique that can sometimes be used when dealing with synthetic CG images, a method that gives the compositing software additional information about the spatial relationships among objects in the 3D scene. This technique is known as **Z-depth compositing**.

Whenever a 3D database is created for the purpose of rendering a CG image, every object in the scene will have a specific color, material, and illumination assigned to it. When it comes time to render a scene from this database, each pixel in the image that is generated will correspond to a certain point on one of the objects in the scene. But there is more information in this database than just the color and lighting description of the scene. The *spatial* relationships of the objects in this scene are also very well defined. Every object in this virtual scene has a specific location in virtual space, and the 3D software is obviously able to determine these locations with great accuracy. Z-depth compositing (or sometimes just "Z-compositing") uses a special image that is explicitly created to quantify these spatial relationships, thereby incorporating depth information into the compositing process. In addition to the standard color image that is rendered for a scene, software with Z-depth functionality allows you to turn on a special mode that can render a second type of image. As with a matte image, this new type of image requires only a single channel to represent its data. But instead of using pixels to represent transparency information for the corresponding point in the color image, each pixel specifies the spatial location for each point.

The image that is generated is known as a **Z-depth image**, based on the typical axes that are used to measure space in a 3D coordinate system (X is horizontal, Y is vertical, and Z is depth). Depending on the tools you are using, this Z-depth image may be kept as a separate file, or it may be integrated with the color image as an additional channel. When integrated, it is referred to as the **Z-channel** or **depth channel** of the image. Consider the image shown in Figure 15.6a, a simple synthetic scene. Figure 15.6b is the corresponding Z-depth image for this scene.

We can choose to represent spatial information in a few different ways, but in general we are interested in the specific distance any given point is from some fixed reference point. This reference point may be an absolute location in our 3D space—usually the origin—or it may be relative to a given object, usually the camera. For the sake of this discussion we'll consider the case in which we are only interested in the distance from the camera. Areas in the image that are closer to the camera are represented with darker pixels; those that are farther away are brighter.

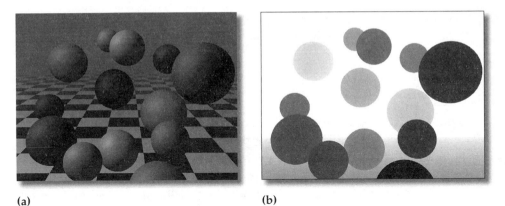

(a)   **(b)**

Figure 15.6   *(a) A simple 3D rendered scene. (b) The Z-depth image for this scene.*

This depth image can be useful in a variety of ways. At its most simple, it can be combined with the original image in order to add some depth-based atmospheric effects that increase with distance. But most software will allow us to use much more powerful tools in conjunction with the Z-depth image. Since we now have accurate information about the depth of the various objects in the scene, the process of determining occlusion can be automated. In a simple scene this ability may not save us a great deal of time, since we could have already generated a matte for the various objects and have manually determined the foreground/ background relationship between anything new that we want to add to the scene. But if our scene becomes more complex, automated Z-depth compositing can be incredibly useful. Consider a second image such as Figure 15.7a, which is also an image with a large number of objects in it at a variety of distances from the camera. If we have Z-depth information for this image as well (Figure 15.7b), the software can automatically determine the proper foreground/background relationships for each of the different objects in the scene. Figure 15.7c is the result of our Z-composite of Figures 15.6a and 15.7a. This same step, had it been done manually, would have required a great deal of time to individually determine which objects should overlap.

It is important to recognize that there are several limitations to Z-depth compositing. The most obvious is that this Z-depth information is generally unavailable for any live-action elements (more on this in a moment), and thus Z-compositing is typically useful only when combining CG elements. But even within a wholly synthetic scene there are limits to the accuracy of this Z-depth information. Earlier we mentioned that each pixel in the Z-image will correspond to a point on a particular object. But this is not always the case. If we have a partially transparent object in the scene, the pixels for this object in our color image will receive color

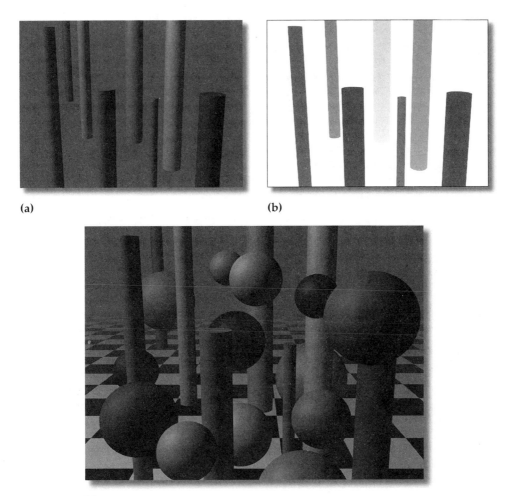

(a)

(b)

(c)

Figure 15.7 *Z-depth compositing. (a) A second 3D rendered scene. (b) The Z-depth image for this scene. (c) The Z-composite of Figures 15.6a and 15.7a.*

information from both the foreground (semitransparent) object as well as from any object that is behind this object. How do we assign a depth value for such a pixel? The short answer is, we can't, at least not usefully. We could choose to use the depth values of the foreground object (which is usually what is done), but if we tried to use this depth value to add a new, more distant object into the scene, our Z-compositing software would automatically put this new element behind the first object. But the first object, being partially transparent, is already showing a bit of the original background behind it. Thus, the foreground object would appear to be in front of the new element, but would still be revealing a bit of the original background.

An example of this problem is shown in Figures 15.8 and 15.9. Figure 15.8a shows our scene, and Figure 15.8b shows the depth information for this scene. As you can see, the semitransparent sphere is fairly close to the camera, and the checkered wall is farther away. Now, let's attempt to compose the object shown in Figure 15.9a into this scene. The depth information for this object is shown in 15.9b. Based purely on the depth information, a Z-composite would produce the final image shown in Figure 15.9c. As you can see, the result is unacceptable. The final image *should* look like Figure 15.9d, where the new object is still visible through the foreground sphere. Unfortunately, there is really no way to fix this problem, short of rerendering the scene as an integrated whole or rendering all

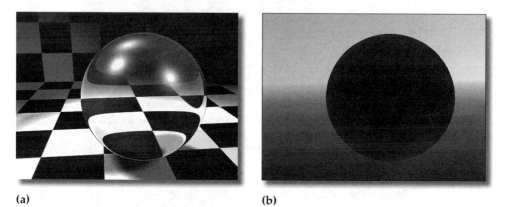

(a)   **(b)**

Figure 15.8 *(a) Scene containing a semitransparent object. (b) The Z-depth image for this scene.*

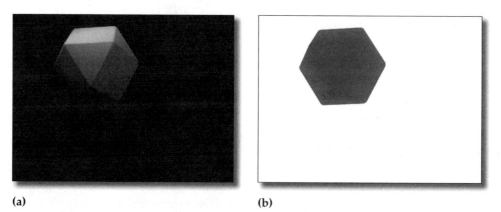

(a)   **(b)**

Figure 15.9 *(a) The new element. (b) The new element's Z-depth image.*

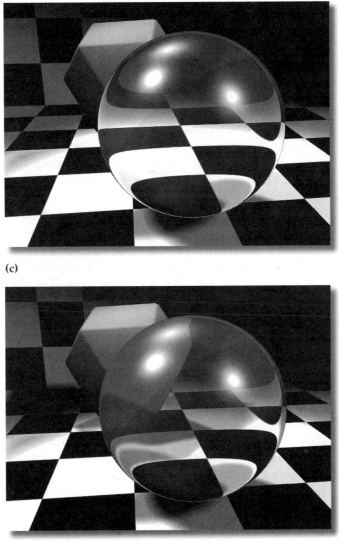

(c)

(d)

Figure 15.9   *(c) An unsuccessful attempt to composite 15.9a into Figure 15.8a based purely on depth information. (d) Proper integration of the new element.*

the elements individually. Consequently, it is generally safe to say that Z-depth compositing will be problematic and in some cases even useless if there are transparent objects in the scene with which you are working.

Unfortunately, even if there is no *explicit* transparency involved, the edges of certain objects can sometimes cause a problem because most 3D objects are actually rendered with antialiased edges, which effectively introduces a small amount of transparency in these areas. A pixel that is precisely on the edge of an object will get part of its color from the foreground object and part from the background. This will always present a problem unless your object was rendered in front of a neutral (or black) background and you have an additional matte channel to define the transparency of these edges. Even if your foreground object is overlapping something at a different depth, the background information that is mixed with the foreground edge may not be terribly noticeable, particularly if your foreground object is in very sharp focus. Often a bit of additional edge processing can help to alleviate any artifacts that are introduced. In general, though, it is safe to say that whenever there are problems with Z-depth compositing, they usually involve either transparency or object edges.

Another inherent problem with the Z-compositing process is the fact that there are no standards for exactly what depth or distance corresponds to a particular brightness value in the Z-image. In fact there really *cannot* be any standard, since two different scenes may have wildly different distances from the camera. Usually when Z-depth images are rendered, one specifies a particular depth range that will be represented, and all pixel values in this image will be normalized for this range. But this range might be the equivalent of only a few meters of depth in one image, whereas another image may have depth values that would be measured in thousands of miles. It is not uncommon to spend some time normalizing two different Z-depth images to each other before they can be combined.

Precision and bit depth is also an issue. If your system is only using 8 bits to represent the Z-depth values, then you will only have 256 different depths that can be identified. Sixteen-bit Z-depth images will be better, but the best systems use floating-point values, which provide for much higher precision as well as far more flexibility for the range of depth values that are used.

As we stated earlier, Z-depth compositing is primarily used with computer-generated images, since this is the only type of image for which accurate depth values can be automatically generated. But it *is* possible to occasionally make use of these techniques even when live action is involved. Most commonly this is done by arbitrarily assigning a constant depth value to a particular live-action object and then integrating it with a synthetic element. If we create a Z-depth image for our live-action element, we can choose an overall depth for that object. Assigning a medium-gray value for the Z-image of our live-action element would cause the Z-depth compositing software to automatically place this live-action element about half-way back in our 3D scene. In certain situations, it may even be worthwhile to hand-paint a more detailed Z-depth image for a particular object. This will, of course, require someone who is skilled enough to determine the relative depths of the different objects in the scene, but the time savings may be worth the effort.

Research is being done on allowing Z-depth information to be automatically extracted from live-action footage. Stereoscopic photography inherently contains some depth cues, and even a single camera view can give some information if it is moving enough to introduce parallax shifts. Sophisticated software algorithms are able to analyze such imagery and can often produce useful depth information for the scene. As the availability and reliability of these tools increases, expect to see more and more use of Z-depth compositing in conjunction with live-action footage.

RELATED 2D DISCIPLINES

In the very first chapter of this book, we alluded to the fact that there is 2D work that does *not* fall into the category of digital compositing. We will round out this chapter with a look at a few disciplines that share many things in common with pure digital compositing but should usually be considered as separate fields. The following processes share some conceptual similarities with digital compositing, and you will find that they are often used in conjunction with digital compositing as part of the overall process of producing a finished set of imagery.

Morphing

In Chapter 3 we briefly looked at tools that can be used to warp, or distort, an image. Elsewhere, in Chapter 4, we covered some image-combination tools that could be used to dissolve between two different images over a period of time. Although both of those processes are used quite often by themselves, there is also a combination process that uses *both* techniques to implement a very specialized transition between two different images. This process is known as **morphing**. Morphing, in theory, is really quite simple, although the process of creating a good morph can be quite time-consuming. It is essentially a two-step process, although the steps will not necessarily occur sequentially. Morphing is considered a specialized transition not only because of the complexity of the tools that are used, but also because it really only works effectively if the two elements that are involved in the transition have some reasonably similar characteristics in common. It was developed, and is still primarily used, as a method to make it appear as if one object were physically transforming into another.

The first step in the process is to identify which key features in the first element will correspond to features in the second. Consider the example images shown in Figure 15.10. Let's attempt the classic morph scenario, in which we wish to make the skull appear to transform into the smiley face over a series of frames. For the first step of the morph, warping tools are used to generate two new sequences of images. The first sequence consists of the skull being warped over

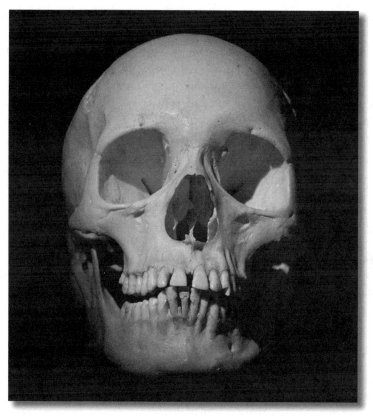

(a)

Figure 15.10   *Morphing. (a) The starting element.*

a period of time so that its shape is as close as possible to the second image. Selected frames from such a sequence are shown in Plate 56a. At the same time, a second sequence is generated that consists of the second image being warped so that it ends up looking as much as possible like the first image (Plate 56b). Note that we are attempting to synchronize key features, such as the eyes and the mouth, as well as the overall shape of the two objects. Once these two new sequences are generated, the second sequence is reversed, so that it *starts* with the distorted image shown in the final frame of Plate 56b and ends with the original smiley face. The two sequences that have been produced are usually designed to be the same number of frames.

Now that we have the two sequences, the final step is to simply dissolve between the two over a period of time. If everything works correctly, the result should be a visually pleasing transition between the two. Although the final warp

(b)

Figure 15.10   *(b) The ending element.*

steps shown in Plate 56 do not look particularly attractive by themselves, the dissolve transition will, one hopes, cause these excessively distorted images to be mostly obscured by their less-distorted counterparts. Selected frames from the final morph transition are shown in Plate 57. In reality, the dissolve step is usually more than just a uniform mix between the two plates. Rather, the same controls that are used to define the warp parameters can also be used to selectively dissolve different areas of the image at different times. Thus, the dissolve for the eyes might occur early on in the morph, while the mouth from the second plate might not be revealed until the end of the morph.

Although this example is a very typical use of morphing technology, many of the morphs being done today are not nearly as noticeable. For instance, a morph can be used to transition from a famous actor to his stunt double just before a dangerous stunt occurs, giving the impression that the actor performed the stunt instead of the double. These "hidden morphs" are becoming more and more common, and probably most morphs being done today, at least in high-end work, are of this less explicit type.

There are a number of additional factors to consider when creating a morph, but the process is primarily one of careful attention to timing and detail. Very few elements will have correspondence points that are completely obvious, and most morphs will require additional compositing or paint work to produce a perfect result. It should also be mentioned that the warping process is prone to a number of different artifacts. Warps that occur quickly should really be motion blurred, just as any other moving item would be, for instance. Unfortunately, very few packages actually support motion-blurred warps. There is also the issue of image resolution: Heavy warps can distort parts of an image to the point at which there is not enough resolution to compensate. Warping is effectively a localized scaling, and a large distorting warp therefore entails the same resolution requirements as a large zoom-in would require.

Digital Painting

The term "painting" still evokes the image of a brush and a canvas. Although there are digital tools that mimic this paradigm (usually with a stylus and a tablet), digital painting is far more than just a method for drawing colored lines into an image. In fact, digital paint programs offer a huge range of tools, many of them similar or identical in function to the compositing tools that we have discussed throughout this book. Even the most basic paint packages will allow the user to color correct an image, to apply geometric transformations, and to composite separate layers into a single scene. What's more, the "brush" that is used in digital painting is really nothing more than a series of composites that are applied along the path on which the brush moves. The effect will be limited to the extent of the brush size, and may be applied with soft edges around the periphery of the brush's path, but the operations should all be familiar. Simple painted brush strokes are usually just some kind of image processing, ranging from color correction to color replacement, but the brush can also be used to apply everything from blurring to localized warping.

Ultimately, the primary distinction between compositing and painting tends to boil down to whether or not the tools can be applied in an automated fashion to a sequence of images, instead of to a single one. Even this division is not foolproof, since there are a number of paint packages (most integrated within a compositing system) that can record a brush stroke on a single frame and then reapply that same stroke over a sequence. The attributes of the brush itself can even be animated over time. This sort of **procedural paint** functionality effectively allows single brush strokes, or groups of brush strokes, to be treated as individual layers in a composite. The strokes themselves are commonly recorded as splines so that their shape can also be manipulated to change over time.

Having a good paint program that can be used in conjunction with a good compositing system will prove to be invaluable. It can be used not only to create rough or detailed masks, but also to touch up any problem areas. Very few composites will be perfect, and the use of some final paint work to finish the image is a common practice. In fact, most of the situations that bring paint tools into the compositing process involve the need to explicitly correct problems, as opposed to actually creating new imagery. Often a bit of simple touch-up painting, even if it must be done to a sequence of images, will be far less time-consuming than attempting to redo the compositing process to fix the problem areas.

The use of digital paint tools is not restricted just to fixing artifacts of the compositing process, however. For instance, there is a whole class of work known as **wire removal** that is particularly well suited to a combination of painting and compositing techniques. Unlike the traditional compositing scenarios, in which the goal is to *add* objects to a scene, paint tools often prove more necessary when the need arises to *remove* objects from a scene. Many times a photographed scene will inadvertently contain unwanted harnesses, ropes, or wires that were used as part of a stunt or a practical effect. It is not always possible or cost-effective to fully hide these items from the camera, and consequently digital tools may be employed to remove them from the scene. Since the process seems to be most often used to remove wires, the term "wire removal" has to a certain extent grown to be a generic term for the removal of undesirable stage elements from a scene. "Rig removal" is another common term that is broader in its scope. Certain vendors offer compositing and paint software that includes tools specifically designed to aid in the wire-removal process.

This type of fix-it work can range in complexity from something that may only take a few minutes to accomplish (if it is merely a matter of removing something from a few frames of a sequence) to shots in which complex and/or time-consuming techniques must be employed to achieve the desired result. In fact, certain wire-removal shots can end up being the most expensive shots in a film. These types of shots are almost always finished off with painting techniques, with careful attention to any areas that exhibit temporal artifacts when played at speed.

Digital techniques make it possible to remove things that would never have been considered feasible before. In one of the most extreme cases, a major motion picture featuring Arnold Schwarzenneger was approaching completion when it was discovered that a fictional electronics company whose logo featured prominently in the film had a name that was extremely similar to a real-world company. The real company was upset at the unflattering portrayal of the fictional company and was concerned that the public could confuse the two. The decision was made by the production to go through the entire film and digitally replace the company name and logo in every scene in which it appeared! This work certainly involved a good deal of traditional compositing steps, such as tracking the logo as it moved through various shots and compositing a new logo over the original. But there were also a huge number of shots in which the company name was painted out, frame by frame. Obviously this was an expensive, time-consuming project, although without the use of digital paint tools, the work could probably not have been done at all.

Editing

The editing process concentrates on the assembly of shots and scenes into a final product. As such, it tends to be primarily concerned with decisions about the length of individual shots and the order in which they will appear in a scene. But the editing for any given project will generally start before any compositing can begin and will continue after the final composite is delivered.

Modern editing, be it with film or video, tends to make use of digital image-manipulation devices that are conceptually quite similar to digital compositing systems. Elements are digitized into the system (albeit not necessarily at a very high quality level) and can then be quickly reordered, compared, trimmed, and otherwise adjusted in order to better visualize how the final shot will look. The editor can make timing decisions by cutting the beginning or the end of a shot or by adding or dropping frames at regular intervals, in exactly the fashion that was described in Chapter 6. Transitions between scenes can also be dealt with by the editor, who may want to control the duration and timing of a dissolve, for instance.

Not only will the editor need to determine the length and placement of every composited shot, he or she will also need to determine which elements should be used for this shot. As such, it becomes very useful for an editor to be able to previsualize a composite while the elements are being chosen. To this end, many digital editing systems include rudimentary compositing tools for performing split-screens, simple bluescreen composites, and so on. Once again, the distinction between compositing and editing is becoming difficult to define, and many compositing systems now combine the features that are necessary for both disciplines into a single package.

Of course no matter how much previsualization is done before the compositing work starts, there is always the chance that the edit will change after the shot is delivered. In order to give the editor a bit more flexibility, it is not uncommon for composites to be designed so that they are a bit longer than necessary. This goal is usually accomplished by having the editor specify that extra frames at the beginning and end of each element should be digitized along with the rest of the shot. These **handles**, usually less than a dozen frames at either end, will provide the editor with some additional room for adjustment once the composited shot is delivered.

CHAPTER SIXTEEN

Case Studies

This final chapter will now examine a number of digital compositing examples that are taken from the real world. We will attempt to give a sense of the diversity of work that is being created using digital compositing methods, and will discuss how the various concepts that we have presented in this book were used to create this work.

JAMES AND THE GIANT PEACH

In Chapter 1, we used a number of elements from the film *James and the Giant Peach* to help define some basic digital compositing terms. This section will now describe the process that was used to actually prepare and composite these elements into the final shot shown in Plate 1. As mentioned, the elements for this scene are a combination of miniatures and synthetic CG imagery.

The creation of the shot began with photographing the model of the peach itself. As you can see in Plate 2a, the peach was shot in front of a bluescreen so that it could be easily extracted and placed into its new environment. Careful attention was paid to the way that the peach was lit, since not only did it need to be appropriately lit for bluescreen extraction, but it also needed to match the other shots in the sequence in terms of lighting direction. The sequence features several shots in which the sun is visible, and all the shots in the sequence were planned in advance so that the location of the sun and the way the objects in the scene were lit would be consistent. The peach in this shot is a model measuring about 1 foot in diameter. The characters standing on top of the peach are puppets that moved via **stop-motion animation**. This technique involves photographing the shot a single frame at a time, then repositioning the puppets by a minute amount before the next frame is shot. This process is repeated for the entire length of each shot; consequently, filming can be extremely time consuming. For a typical 5-second shot, filming can take days to complete, particularly if there are several characters in the scene, as in our example. The peach itself was also moved throughout the scene, in order to give the impression it is being restrained by the cable that runs into the mouth of the giant mechanical shark.

You'll notice that the peach was shot very large in frame, even though the element would be much smaller in the final composite. This was done to ensure that the compositor would have more than enough resolution for this element. There was no need to predetermine the scale of the peach in the original photography, since this could easily be done during the compositing process. The exact location of the peach and the framing of the shot did not need to be decided upon until the other primary elements in the scene (the shark and the water) were more completely realized.

The peach was extracted from the bluescreen using a combination of proprietary and off-the-shelf software, coupled with some spline-based garbage mattes. Spill suppression was primarily accomplished with the simple equation that was given in Chapter 5.

The background sky plate was also photographed on a stage as a separate element. It was a large piece of canvas and the clouds were airbrushed on by a scenic artist. The plate was shot locked off, and several identical frames were photographed so that they could be averaged together in order to eliminate film grain.

The rest of the elements in the shot are 3D computer-generated images. The obvious ones are the shark and the water, but there are a number of additional ones as well. The water was procedurally generated using some custom software that was written specifically for the show. It actually consists of 3 different layers: the basic water, the foam that caps the top of most of the waves, and a slight layer of spray that is emitted from the tips of these waves. The splash that can be seen in the bottom right corner of the frame was also created as a separate 3D element. The shark was rendered as a single image, as shown in Plate 2b, but the steam and smoke that comes from the shark's gills and dorsal fin were created as separate elements, as was the cable that runs between the shark and the peach. The movement of the shark and the cable were animated to match the movement of the peach described earlier.

The shot was assembled in the following manner. First, the peach and the sky elements (which had been digitized directly into the Cineon color space when they were scanned) were converted to a linear color space. This would allow these plates to properly match with the CG elements. The sky plate was then given a slight animated move over the duration of the shot. This move is extremely small and subtle, designed to give the impression that the clouds are moving slowly across the sky. The water was added over the sky background, and some additional atmosphere was added near the horizon with the use of a simple gradient. The animated foam and spray elements were added to the scene as well.

Several tests were done to determine the proper placement of the peach, and it was then scaled and added into the scene. Obviously, spill suppression and color correction were performed in order to better integrate the peach into the shot. A couple of additional elements—a shadow element and a reflection element—were created to help with the peach's integration into the scene. Both of these were generated by creating a quick stand-in element for the peach in the same 3D environment in which the water was being created. This stand-in did not need to be terribly accurate or detailed, since it was only being used to create shadows and reflections, but it did need to be approximately the same size and color as the "real" peach. These two new elements were composited into the scene as well, adjusting their values until a visually pleasing result was obtained.

Essentially the same process was used for the addition of the shark to the scene. The shark itself was placed into the scene first. (Other shots in the sequence made use of Z-depth compositing for situations in which the shark was farther in the distance.) Once the shark was in the scene, a rendered shadow was added and the densities adjusted. Some initial tests were done with a shark reflection as well, but all the other elements that were being added obscured it to the point at which it was not worth the effort, and so it was removed. Other shots in the sequence did make use of these rendered reflections. A rendered line of foam and splashes was added to the areas where the shark intersected with the water, and a larger splash was created that synchronized with the action of the shark's fin slapping the water. Finally, the smoke and steam were added to the scene, after several adjustments were made to their transparency.

The last step in the process was to introduce some synthetic film grain into the scene. This grain actually needed to be added to all the elements in the scene. The CG elements obviously did not have any grain on them originally, and we have already mentioned that the grain was explicitly removed from the sky via multiple-frame averaging. But even the peach had become effectively grainless due to the amount of scaling that was applied to it. This scaling had the effect of averaging the existing grain together, reducing its noticeability significantly. Thus, the grain was applied as a single pass to the finished composite.

SPEED

Visual effects are often used to increase the perceived danger that is present in a specific stunt. For the film *Speed,* a bus carrying a load of passengers needed to appear to jump over a huge gap in an elevated freeway that was under construction. Plate 58 shows the completed effects shot in which this was accomplished. The bus, traveling at high speed, has just driven off the edge of the concrete and is soaring through empty space. In reality, the bus that was used in the stunt *did* jump off the edge of a road and fly through the air for a good distance. However, the danger was quite a bit less, since the ground was really only a few feet below the bus. A short ramp was built that duplicated the look of the gap's edge, and then the stunt driver was able to launch the specially reinforced bus over the edge.

Plate 59 shows the original plate that was shot for this scene; you can see that the road actually continues beyond the edge of the ramp. The task of the compositor was to replace this road with a huge drop-off. To accomplish this, an artist created a digital matte painting of the ground below, detailing it with terrain and equipment that would be typical for a construction site (Plate 60). As you can see, the painting is designed to replace as little as possible. Fortunately, the scene was actually filmed atop an elevated highway, so the background off the edge of the road has an appropriate sense of depth and distance.

The plate was shot with this sort of replacement in mind. The camera angle was chosen so that the bus didn't actually cross over the road at any point. This setup allowed the painting to be placed only over the road and made it unnecessary to extract a matte for the bus. Shot with a locked-down Vistavision camera, the background plate was scanned at a high enough resolution that there was plenty of room to animate a slight camera move into the final sequence. The move was created to simulate the motion that a cameraman might have introduced were he or she actually filming the scene. This included a less-than-perfect attempt to follow the bus as it is moving through frame. The pseudo-camera actually takes a moment to catch up with the bus immediately after it jumps, for instance.

Of course the painting, being a single frame, had none of the grain that was in the rest of the shot, so animated grain was added to the sequence of images that were produced from the painting. As is usually the case with adding grain to an element, it is essentially unnoticeable, but its absence would have been immediately apparent. A few pieces of computer-generated debris were also added to the final scene—unidentifiable objects that were heavily motion blurred and whose primary purpose was to cross over the split line between live action and matte painting. Such a trick helps to mask the split between the two and gives a better sense that everything is really part of the same scene.

Although the bus itself did not cross over the area that was to be replaced by the matte painting, some of the dust that was thrown into the air did. This caused a noticeable edge to appear at the juncture between the live action and the painting wherever the dust was heaviest. This problem only lasted for a few frames at the end of the shot, so the easiest solution proved to be a simple manual paint fix. The dust had very little character—it was mostly a haze that caused the apparent color of the roadway behind it to shift toward a brownish tint. By hand-tinting the appropriate area of the matte painting for the 10 or 12 frames at the end of the sequence, the noticeable split between painting and live action was easily hidden.

STAR TREK: INSURRECTION

The next shot we will discuss is from the ninth installment of the *Star Trek* film series. Three of the final frames have been reproduced here, shown in Plates 61, 62, and 63. This was a short, simple shot, and will be an excellent opportunity to look at some of the issues that can accompany even the most basic effect.

In this shot, the character Worf is swinging a weapon to fend off an attack from a flying mechanical drone. The challenge of the scene was to make it appear as if the drone, which would be created primarily as a CG object, were actually interacting with the objects in the scene. A frame from the original photography is shown in Plate 64. This frame corresponds to the final frame shown in Plate 61. As you can see, the original element featured a large box instead of the flying drone. This box is a pyrotechnic device, rigged to explode when it is hit. Before the computer-generated drone could be inserted into the scene, this box would obviously need to be removed from all of the frames that precede the explosion.

To facilitate this removal, a clean plate was shot that matched the main element. Although this is not a locked-off shot, all of the camera movement was captured by a motion-control device. The identical move from the main plate was reapplied when the clean plate was shot, resulting in a nearly perfect match between the two sequences. There were a few minor misalignments that became evident when the two plates were examined carefully, which were due to a slight wobble in the motion-control rig. These problems were easily dealt with by tracking a reference point in each sequence and comparing the differences. The compositor was then able to split in the clean plate whenever the box needed to be removed. The split line was defined with a hand drawn, soft-edged matte. The process was not completely without problems, however. As the box was struck, the cable that was supporting it swung around behind the actor and re-entered the frame. This cable (with a small piece of the box still attached) was partially visible through the smoke from the explosion. Obviously the smoke was not a part of the clean plate, so the replacement of the areas where the cable was seen required some additional hand-painting on a frame-by-frame basis. The painter was able to use information from frames before and after the cable became visible to selectively replace the cable as needed. Fortunately, there were only a few problem frames, and so the work went relatively quickly.

As usual, all of the plates for this element would be color-corrected in order to match with a color reference provided by editorial. If you compare Plate 64 with Plate 61, you will notice a significant color difference between the two. Normally the clean plate would also have the same color correction applied to it as was applied to the other elements, but in this situation those adjustments needed to be modified slightly because the element was photographed about 30 minutes after the main elements—enough of a time difference to cause the outdoor lighting to change slightly.

Once the box was removed from the scene, integrating the drone was relatively straightforward. The CG element had been rendered with attention to lighting in the original plate, so the lighting cues were appropriate to the scene. Slight color modifications were made once it could be viewed in the scene, and animated grain was added that would match with the grain in the main plate. The CG element was created so that it would fly into pieces at the appropriate moment, and these pieces were manipulated in the composite so that they took on the color of the explosion.

The frames for this shot were photographed with an anamorphic lens, resulting in images that were squeezed by 50% horizontally. The compositor who worked on the shot maintained this anamorphic squeeze throughout the compositing process, in order to keep the full detail from the original element while not introducing any additional data by resampling to an increased width.

The shot itself is fairly short—only 69 frames long—which is only about three seconds of screen time. When the footage was digitized, an additional five frames at the beginning and end of the shot were also scanned. These handles were included so that the editor who was assembling the final picture would have some flexibility to lengthen the shot or choose a slightly different frame range. This is a common practice when producing visual effects shots. The extra cost of scanning a few more frames is negligible, and usually there is very little (if any) extra work that needs to be done to add the effect to these extra frames. If the shot does, for some reason, require significant additional work to complete the handle frames, that work is usually not done until the editor decides on exactly which new frames will be used.

CON AIR

A climactic scene toward the end of the film *Con Air* features a C-123 Provider plane crash-landing onto the crowd-filled Las Vegas strip. In order to create this scene believably, a variety of different visual effects techniques were used. Although many of the shots in the film were created using a large-scale, 280-foot-long miniature of the Strip, there were a number of shots that required a model of the plane to be composited into a live-action background. For the final image shown in Plate 65, the main element was shot on location in Las Vegas. A locked-down Vistavision camera was used in order to get as much information as possible while avoiding the need for any complicated camera match-moving.

Once this background was available to the effects crew, work could begin on creating the proper plane element to place into the scene. Using the same fifteenth-scale C-123 miniature that appears in several of the other effects shots, a motion-controlled movement was programmed for the plane, mimicking the motion it should have if it were actually sliding down the street toward the camera. Once the basic movement was completed, the motion-control system allowed multiple different lighting scenarios to be photographed, all with exactly the same motion and timing for the plane. For example, a plate was shot that featured the plane in front of a bluescreen background (Plate 66). This plate was later used to extract a matte for the C-123 model that could then be used for all the other passes. Because this bluescreen pass was designed only for the creation of a matte, the illumination on the plane could be tuned for this purpose; thus, the model's lighting was primarily designed to eliminate any extraneous blue spill.

As you can see from the background plate, the plane is supposedly sliding past a variety of different light sources. Rather than attempting to duplicate every single light source that is featured on the Las Vegas strip, the decision was made to shoot a variety of different lighting scenarios and then allow the manipulation and balance of these lights to occur within the composite itself. To this end, over a dozen additional motion-control passes of this same shot were photographed. An evenly illuminated "hero pass" was created, which featured basic ambient lighting without any of the specific colored lights in the scene. This element is shown in Plate 67. Additional passes were photographed that provided various highlights striking the plane from different directions. A pass was created that featured only the running lights on the plane's wingtips, and a general "fill pass" was done that illuminated the detail that would normally be lost in the shadows.

Once all these different photographic elements were selected and scanned into the system, the actual digital compositing work could begin. Before any of the layering was started, the background plate needed to be prepared. A number of objects that were in the scene needed to be modified; this manipulation included the removal of many power lines, as well as the repositioning of several traffic lights. Most of this work was accomplished via a combination of digital painting and compositing techniques. Many ground reflections were also removed, since they were coming from car headlights that would be obscured by the plane once it was placed into the scene. Many of these differences are visible if you compare Plate 65 (the final scene) with Plate 68 (the original background).

Now the plane itself could be placed into the scene. After pulling a key from the bluescreen plate, the basic lighting pass was layered over the background. Although the motion-controlled pass had theoretically been shot with the plane appropriately aligned to the Las Vegas plate, additional examination of the composited scene prompted a decision to slightly reposition the plane and increase its scale to give it a more dramatic presence. Then, while noting the various light sources that the plane was passing, a complex script was put together that selectively mixed in a number of the different lighting passes at various times during the shot. This allowed, for instance, the underside of the plane to be appropriately illuminated whenever a car's headlights pointed in that direction. To complete the lighting integration, several of the more noticeable neon signs along the street were duplicated, repositioned, and warped to follow the contours of the plane's body—adding them to the plane so that they appeared as reflections of the original signs.

A shadow was manually rotoscoped for the plane and used to darken the street underneath the plane, giving it a much better sense of actually being on the ground. Since the street itself was wet, a computer-generated stream of mist and spray was created for each of the plane's three tires, as well as a fourth overall mist that was used to give a better sense of atmosphere over the lower portion of the plane. Finally, additional mattes were hand-drawn for a couple of the vehicles in the foreground that would pass in front of the plane at some point during the length of the shot. These articulate mattes would allow a foreground car to pass in front of the plane, yet still leave the plane visible through the car's windows.

BUDWEISER LIZARDS COMMERCIAL

Although most of the shots discussed in this chapter are taken from feature-film composites, digital compositing is obviously used in a number of other situations as well. Television commercials are filled with digital effects, some of which can easily rival motion picture work in terms of quality and complexity. The two images shown in Plates 69 and 70 are from a Budweiser commercial. Plate 69 is the final composite that was created for one shot in the commercial, and Plate 70 is one of the elements used to create this composite. At first glance, this example might seem to be a very simple composite, requiring only a basic bluescreen extraction and a standard layering of the two elements together. But in reality there is far more to this shot.

The lizards that are sitting on the branch in the foreground are actually small puppets. You can see the control rods that were used to animate the creatures by manipulating the movement of the various appendages. These rods obviously needed to be removed from the scene, and a combination of techniques was used to accomplish this. Since the rods would often pass over another portion of the lizard or the branch, there was more to the process than simply painting out the rod itself. Depending on the situation, the portion of the image that was covered by the rod was recreated either by grabbing a portion of a clean plate or by using image data from the same plate, but from a different point in time when the rod was not obscuring the area in question. Even though the camera was locked down for most of these shots, the rod would often cover a portion of the lizard that was also moving, making clean plates useless. In these cases, the motion of the moving area was determined with automated tracking techniques, and the "clean" area was pasted into the scene by using this tracking data to duplicate the proper move.

A great deal of the animation, or at least the timing of the animation, was also dealt with in the composite. Multiple **takes** of each scene were usually shot, each with slightly different animation and timing. Since all the puppetry was done by hand, it was common for different takes to be slightly different. When it came time to create the final composite, the artist was able to choose from several of these different takes to determine which one was most appropriate for the scene in question. In fact, the artist was not limited to choosing a single take for a given scene. Instead, different pieces from the various takes were pasted together to create the final element. For instance, the "performance" of the lizard on the left might have been better in one take, while the movement of the lizard on the right was less than satisfactory for that same take. The artist was able to pick the version that worked best for either lizard and then use a simple split-screen to bring the best version of both lizards into the same final scene. This process of mixing and matching different takes was actually done on an even more minute level. Using a combination of soft-edged garbage mattes and careful tracking, different body parts from the various takes could also be combined. Thus, the moving lips from a certain take might be combined with the tail motion from another. If you look carefully at the final element (Plate 69), you will notice that both lizards have appendages in different positions than they were in the specific bluescreen element that is shown in Plate 70.

Once the final action for the foreground lizards was complete, additional integration was necessary to tie the scene together. Some basic color correction was applied, as well as many very specific manipulations that were designed to change the quality of the lighting. Using a series of animated garbage mattes once more, certain areas of each lizard were treated to increase the brightness of the highlights or to attenuate areas that should be in deeper shadow. Again, comparing the original bluescreen with the final image should show an obvious change in much of the lighting.

The background element was also heavily modified from the original scene. Since this scene is only one of a number of similar scenes from a number of different Budweiser commercials, there were opportunities to reuse certain plates instead of shooting a new element. This scenario was taken advantage of as often as possible since it greatly reduced the time and expense of each new commercial.

In this case, the production had already shot a plate of a similar background, only with a Budweiser sign that was hanging crookedly. In order to reuse this plate, the artist simply extracted the crooked sign using a soft-edged matte and then rotated it to the appropriate orientation. Once repositioned, a bit of manual painting was required to touch up the area around the sign and hide the modifications. Once this was done, a single new frame of the background was ready. Since the background is unmoving in this scene, the single frame could be extended to last for the duration of the shot. The original background plate had been photographed in sharp focus, but this scene required the background to be slightly defocused. Executing this defocus produced an element without any noticeable grain, so a final step to recreate moving grain was performed before the foreground was placed over this new background.

INDEPENDENCE DAY

Spaceships and flying saucers have been a staple of visual effects work for almost as long as the craft has been in existence. For the film *Independence Day,* the challenge was to make these saucers appear to be more massive than anything previously depicted.

Plate 71 shows a finished frame from the film. The alien "Destroyer" spaceship is approaching the city of New York, and the size of the ship alone is enough to cause dramatic atmospheric disturbances.

Several different visual cues are used in this scene to convey the sense of the ship's scale. The fact that the ship fills the frame is one of these cues, but we will also discuss a number of others.

As is typical, the first step on the way to creating this shot was to capture a suitable background plate. Plate 72 shows a view of the New York City skyline from beneath the Manhattan Bridge. The inclusion of this massive bridge in the foreground was no accident, but rather a conscious decision designed to establish the sense of scale. Had the shot been framed so that there was no noticeable foreground object, the impact of the image would have been far less dramatic. Instead, it immediately becomes evident that the Destroyer is quite a bit larger than the bridge.

A couple of factors made it fairly straightforward to produce the matte for the bridge. First, the sky is significantly different from the bridge, both in terms of color and brightness. In this situation, the compositor extracted a basic matte for the bridge, primarily by keying on luminance. The second factor that helped with generating this detailed matte is that the sequence was photographed with a locked-down camera. In this case it was a standard 35mm motion-picture camera, shooting full aperture. The static camera meant that it was necessary to create only a single frame of this matte. Any problem areas that weren't addressed by the procedural matte pull could be touched up by hand, using a digital paint system. The work would need to be done only on a single frame which would then be used throughout the entire shot.

Before this matte could be used to hold out the bridge for the sequence a stabilization pass was applied in order to remove a slight jitter that was in the original footage. This jitter appeared primarily as a random vertical offset in each frame of the sequence. Although minor, it would have been enough to cause a misregistration between the image and the matte on many frames. The unwanted motion was analyzed and each frame was repositioned to compensate, resulting in an extremely steady plate that would match exactly with the single-frame matte.

The final depth cue that should be noted is the atmosphere in the scene. In this situation the atmosphere is more than just a tool to convey a sense of distance—it is actually part of the effect. The roiling clouds were created from two separate elements. The first element, shown in Plate 73, consists of the model spaceship mounted on a motion-control rig. The Destroyer moves slowly toward the camera as the shot progresses, revealing itself from within the clouds. The model of the ship was shot on a stage, with a smoke generator providing the first layer of clouds. A second layer of clouds was shot in a **cloud tank,** a large water-filled glass enclosure. These "clouds" are actually produced by injecting a white, opaque liquid into the water in a controlled fashion. Underwater lights in the tank help to define the clouds, producing a more dramatic look. The result can be seen in Plate 74. Note that there is also an object in this plate that serves as a stand-in for the spaceship. Designed to mimic the basic contours of the more detailed model, the shape allows the clouds to move in an appropriate fashion and appear as if they are interacting with the ship.

To combine these two cloud elements into a single shot, a number of soft-edged mattes were hand-painted. These mattes allowed the compositor to selectively reveal portions of the two plates, and to control the amount of mix between them. Once the two layers were married together, they could be placed into the original background plate. In this case, some additional color correction was done to modify certain portions of the clouds. Several areas were tinted red, and the contrast was modified around the perimeter of the element. The leading edge of the cloud effect required specific attention.

If you examine Plate 74 closely, you will notice that there is a well-defined edge for the bottom of the clouds. The top of the clouds, however, does not feature such a clean edge. In fact, the surface of the water, seen from below, is acting like a mirror, and the top of the clouds are overlapping with their own reflection. This presented a problem, as the scene required the boundaries of the effect to be visible at the beginning of the shot. In order to create an appropriate edge for the top of the cloud-bank, the compositing artist simply used the bottom edge of the clouds and flipped the image. The timing of the footage was altered—a different range of frames was used—and this became the top edge of the clouds. Since the top and bottom edge came from different points in time, it was not obvious that they had originally been part of the same element. A soft-edged matte was used to place this edge back into the scene.

As mentioned, the original background plate was photographed "full aperture." In fact, all photography for the film was done in the Super 35 format, where a frame with a 2.35 aspect ratio is extracted from the original negative and used to create the final widescreen print. (Chapter 10 discusses this procedure in greater detail.) As you can see when you examine Plate 72, a great deal of image information at the top and bottom of the frame is discarded when the final frame is produced. Using the same technique that was discussed with the shot from *Speed*, the location of the 2.35 extraction was animated over the course of the shot, producing a slight camera move in the final scene.

X-FILES: FIGHT THE FUTURE

For the feature-film version of the popular *X-Files* television show, a number of very large and dramatic events were simulated. In one of these sequences the two main characters, Mulder and Scully, flee across a sheet of ice in the Arctic as a gaping hole opens in the ground behind them. Plate 75 shows a still from this shot, with the two characters appearing as small figures in the upper-right portion of the frame.

The basic ice sheet shown in Plate 76 was a miniature element created on a sound stage and consisting of nearly two thousand carved styrofoam blocks that were fit together like a jigsaw puzzle. The blocks were designed to fall apart on cue by withdrawing the support structure underneath the chunks. This element was photographed at speeds ranging from 96 to 120 frames per second, a trick that is often used to give miniature elements a more appropriate sense of scale. This miniature glacier was the primary element; all the additional layers were created to integrate with it.

Although in the original plan the geysers of steam were also intended to be photographed as part of this primary background plate, the interaction of the geysers with the miniature proved to be unconvincing. The decision was made to shoot the geysers as separate elements instead, photographed variously in front of black and greenscreens. An example is shown in Plate 77. A matte was pulled for each element, allowing it to be added to the scene wherever appropriate. Ultimately, this method ended up giving far more control over these geysers than the originally planned shot, since their timing and position could be easily adjusted to fit the action of the ice crumbling and to match with other shots in the sequence.

To further the complexity and sense of scale for the crumbling ice, a number of computer-generated layers were also created for the scene. The most prominent of these, the long cracks that form in the ice around Mulder and Scully as they are running, is shown in Plate 78. These cracks were created as 3D elements that originated from hand-painted designs. A procedural animation control system was applied to the cracks, allowing them to grow and expand in a convincing way. This technique also allowed the background ice plate to be modified so that the surface appeared to be pushed up around the areas of crack formation. Although barely noticeable on film, particle system animation was employed to cause bits of snow and ice to fall into the cracks. Other computer-generated elements (as many as five or six different layers) were also used to supplement the existing snow and to add to the snow and blocks of ice as they fell into the large central chasm.

The final element to be added to the scene was the plate that contained the characters of Mulder and Scully. As shown in Plate 79, doubles for the actors were photographed from an appropriate camera angle as they ran across an expanse of bluescreen material. Shooting this element outdoors, rather than on an enclosed stage, made the lighting feel much more appropriate for the scene into which the characters would be integrated. To light this same expanse of bluescreen with studio lighting would have required a huge number of lights to get an even illumination, and there would still be a significant problem with multiple shadows being cast from the different lights. The outdoor setting also allowed for the use of a large crane to place the camera in the proper position—a position that was determined by converting the camera information that was recorded for the miniature shoot into the equivalent location for a full-size element. Once the actors were extracted from this bluescreen element, they were tracked to match with the camera move on the background element.

Mountains and ominous dark clouds loom in the distance. These features were created with a combination of still photographs and matte paintings.

The final color-correction step was done not only to integrate all the elements appropriately, but also to ensure that certain critical details were visible in the nearly uniform expanse of glacial ice. These manipulations included careful adjustment of both contrast and brightness for each of the elements that were added to the scene.

T-REX: BACK TO THE CRETACEOUS

The images shown in Plates 80 through 82 give an excellent example of a large-format composite. Created for the Imax Corporation, the imagery is from the IMAX 3D production of *T-Rex: Back to the Cretaceous*. This film presents a combination of live-action plates and photorealistically rendered computer-generated dinosaurs. It was a particularly challenging project not only because of the large data requirements inherent with the standard IMAX process (as discussed in Chapter 10 and Appendix D), but also because it is a **stereoscopic** film. All of the imagery had to be produced twice, once for each eye. Although similar, each eye's view is different enough that essentially every element needed to be created, manipulated, and combined twice.

Consider the final result, shown in Plate 80a and 80b. These are, respectively, the left- and right-eye versions of the final composite.[1] Normally, when viewing this footage at an IMAX 3D theater, the audience would be wearing special polarized glasses. The two images would be projected simultaneously onto the viewing screen, but the light used to project the scene would be polarized differently for either image. The polarizing glasses would then restrict the visible image so that each eye would only see the image that was intended for it. If you look closely at the two images, you can see slight, subtle differences. The difference is most noticeable for objects that should be closer to the camera, so that the dinosaurs, for instance, can be seen to have a slightly different perspective in the two plates.

To create this illusion, the first step involved shooting the primary background plate. Shot on location in the Olympia rain forest region of upper Washington state, the filming was done with a camera that was specifically designed to capture this type of imagery. It features a pair of lenses that are mounted about three inches apart (which approximates the interocular distance of the average human) in order to capture the scene from both eyes' point of view. Although most stereo cameras are built so that the two eye-views are exposed on different strips of film, this particular camera actually captures both views simultaneously on the *same* strip, placing them side-by-side on the negative. Since this was an IMAX project, the film used was 65mm, and each frame covered 15 perforations. The two views are separated onto different strips of film as part of the postproduction process. For this particular shot, the entire length of negative was digitized and the separation was done by the compositor putting together the shot.

The frames were digitized at a very high resolution (in this case at about 4000 pixels across) to produce uncompressed digital files that are about 75 megabytes per frame. If you take into account the fact that each frame actually needs two of these images for each eye, the data requirement for just the background plate is more than three and a half *gigabytes* for every second of footage.

---

[1] Many people are able to "free fuse" two such images merely by holding the page about six inches away from their eyes and attempting to focus in the distance. The images will appear to converge and give the illusion of viewing a true 3D scene.

All the other elements that were added to the scene were computer generated and also needed to be rendered from two different camera views for each frame, at an equivalently high resolution.

These elements include the dinosaurs themselves, which were illuminated to match the lighting that was present in the original plate. Not only are the dinosaurs synthetic, so is the pool of water from which they are drinking. Plate 81 shows what the original background of this scene looks like. The water that was added is a fully computer-generated object that includes not only the water's surface but also the rocky bottom of the pool. The dinosaurs' reflections were generated with the 3D rendering as well. These CG elements are shown in Plate 82. Ground shadows were rendered for the dinosaurs and were used to darken the original plate appropriately, and a hovering layer of mist was added over the scene once the rest of the composite had been put together.

A shot like this would be challenging even without the added complexity that the stereoscopic process introduced. At first, it might seem that the addition of a second view wouldn't necessarily require all that much additional effort. After all, the second scene is almost identical to the first, and most of the work would be extremely similar. Unfortunately, this would prove not to be the case. Generating and compositing stereoscopic imagery can often be *more* than twice the work of a single-camera shot. We will look at some of the reasons for these difficulties.

One of the most significant challenges has to do with the recreation of the scene and the stereo camera in a 3D database, so that the CG dinosaurs and water could be rendered properly. This particular background plate includes a camera move; throughout the length of the shot the camera (attached to a track-mounted dolly) is moving forward. The track can be seen at the bottom of frame in Plate 81. This same camera move would need to be duplicated within the computer. Even without a camera move, it would still be necessary to determine the proper lens and camera location for such a shot, so that the 3D rendering software could create two views with the correct parallax differences.

An initial attempt was made to derive the camera position using 3D tracking tools. As described in Chapter 15, this process involves an analysis of a set of two-dimensional tracking data for multiple points in the scene to determine the type of lens that was used and the movement of the camera throughout the shot. This step was done for both eyes, which would theoretically produce two camera moves that were identical other than a three-inch offset. Unfortunately, when the reconstructed camera data was examined, it was found to differ significantly between the two eyes. Since the two lenses that originally photographed the scene were housed in the same physical enclosure, obviously the problem was with the data reconstruction. The 3D tracking software had been used very successfully and accurately on many past projects, so it was unlikely to be the cause of the problem. After a bit of research, it was discovered that the two lens assemblies that filmed the original scene were slightly different. Different enough to cause the images to be distorted on the original negative. This distortion was enough to compromise the accuracy of the 3D scene reconstruction software. After analyzing the amount of distortion that each lens introduced, additional software was developed that could correct these distortions in the footage. The plates from both camera views were warped subtly in order to remove the distortions, producing a new set of plates that could be tracked accurately. As an added benefit, these new plates were also more visually correct, meaning that a human observer would feel a greater sense of depth when viewing them.

By using this 3D tracking data to create a virtual camera, the image pairs that were rendered for each frame were now theoretically accurate. However, as is often the case with visual effects, the final test is always a visual one. Recreating any scene can never be done perfectly, and even if it could, there will always be times that aesthetic considerations will outweigh technical accuracy. Ultimately, the final tuning for any shot should be done by eye.

In many situations, the exact placement of the object in both frames wouldn't always be immediately obvious. Just as one would do when wedging some other variable such as color, a series of nearly identical images were prepared, each featuring incrementally different positional offsets for the element in question. This side-by-side comparison would allow the compositor and his or her supervisor to quickly view the apparent depth produced by each step and choose appropriate values.

Although this process would eventually give the proper results, it was time-consuming, since these iterative tests could span the course of several days as they were filmed-out, processed, and screened. Unfortunately, at least at the outset of the project, the only reliable method for viewing the shots in stereo was to screen them on film with the special glasses.

For this reason, the facility doing the visual effects work eventually developed some additional optical tools to give the artists a more exact method of viewing the spatial relationships between the two views. A simple proprietary system, these tools were actually a combination of software and optics that allowed the artist to interactively tune the apparent depth-placement while viewing the stereo pair at the full resolution of the workstation's monitor. Not only did these customized tools eliminate the need for costly and time-consuming tests on film, they actually proved to be *more* accurate than viewing the scenes in a screening room.

The heavily procedural nature of stereoscopic compositing dictated that the work be done in a system with strong batch-processing tools. As mentioned, multiple iterations of each shot were often generated in order to study the effect of slight changes in an object's position. Of course, many compositing jobs will involve steps that aren't done procedurally. For instance, when dealing with nonstereoscopic images a common, almost universal step is to manually retouch certain areas in the image. A skilled paint artist is able to paint frame by frame over the course of a short sequence in order to remove an undesirable artifact. This process is complicated immensely, however, when the problem area needs to be dealt with in a stereoscopic pair of sequences. It is often next to impossible to manually paint exactly the same information into both plates, and even the slightest discrepancies between the two eyes would become very obvious when viewed in stereo. Because of this, nearly all of the touch-up work in *T-Rex* was accomplished with the aid of a **procedural paint** solution. This paint system would record the brush-strokes that were used to do the modification on the first eye's frame, and then would apply the same strokes (usually offset slightly) to the other frame.

As it turns out, even processes that are very procedural in nature (such as bluescreen matte extractions) would often require the work to be done explicitly for both eyes. Although this particular scene does not feature any live-action foreground elements shot on bluescreen, there are a number of other shots in the film that do. And for these shots the compositing artist would almost always end up doing a distinct matte pull for each eye. This was primarily due to the slight color and brightness differences that show up in a bluescreen when viewed from a different angle.

THE PRINCE OF EGYPT

As we saw with the imagery from *James and the Giant Peach*, compositing techniques are certainly not limited to live-action elements. In fact, digital compositing is now being used extensively in the creation of traditional **cel animation** as well. A scene from the Dreamworks film *The Prince of Egypt* will be discussed as an example, concentrating on the completed frame shown in Plate 83.

Before the existence of computers, cel animation consisted of drawing and painting individual elements that were to make up a scene directly onto a piece of transparent cellulose acetate. (This is where the term "cel" comes from). These elements would all be placed together in a stack, layered so that the most distant elements were at the bottom. This group of elements was then photographed as a whole, creating a single frame of the sequence. This process was done repeatedly for subsequent frames, substituting different cells of animation and repositioning background layers as necessary.

In most contemporary animation, the final photographic step has been replaced with digital methods. Each scenic element is digitized on a flatbed scanner, and these separate images are then combined as digital images. They are, in fact, composited together.

The use of computers has certainly simplified the process of combining layers, but it has also allowed the animation artists to create scenes with many more layers than would have been previously practical. Historically, shots with many layers were problematic for a number of reasons. First, keeping track of the movement that would need to occur on each layer could prove to be rather arduous. Each cel could require a separate move, and each move would need to be slightly different, depending on the theoretical depth of the element in question. There were also problems that could occur when too many cels were layered on top of each other. Because the material that a cel is made from isn't perfectly transparent, multiple layers of this material could start to show a noticeable color build-up. The bottommost layers would be affected by the color of the cels above it. For this reason, the person painting the cel would need to be aware of that cel's eventual position in the layered stack. He or she might even decide to use brighter paints for the lower levels, choosing colors that would compensate for the slight attenuation and yellow shift that the cels would introduce.

All of the elements that are shown in Plates 84 through 91 (with the exception of Plate 90), originated as hand-drawn images. The scenic backgrounds originated as cel paintings before they were scanned to become digital elements. This process is also changing, gradually, as more and more of the traditional scenic artists are learning to use digital paint systems instead. For *The Prince of Egypt*, probably 99% of the scenic backgrounds were still created by artists working with traditional brushes and paints. But the studio's next production will feature a much more even mix of traditional and digitally painted backgrounds.

The animated characters in this scene were created in a slightly different fashion. They originated as line art that was drawn a frame at a time on individual sheets of paper. Each frame was then digitized, producing a series of black-and-white line drawings. A digital "ink and paint" system was then used to complete the process. Such a system is capable of converting these pencil sketches into strong outlines that mimic the look of a hand-painted cel. These outlines can then be filled with the appropriate colors. This process is hardly automatic—the artist will need to explicitly indicate many of the outlines, and will specify the colors that need to appear within these boundaries. But the software can often simplify some of this work. It can, for instance, automatically fill the same area over a sequence of frames, instead of requiring the paint artist to do this for each individual frame. Once the procedural work is completed, manual retouching will often be used to complete specific areas.

Multiple layers are used in traditional animation for a number of reasons, but primarily to save a great deal of time and effort. Backgrounds that do not change need only be drawn or painted a single time, while the more labor-intensive process of frame-by-frame animation will be limited to only those elements that need to change. But multiple layers can also be used to introduce a sense of depth in a scene through the simulation of parallax effects. This sort of **multiplaning** is created by moving the elements that are theoretically farther from the camera by a lesser amount than the elements that are near to the camera.

Plate 92 shows the scene composed within a proprietary scene composition package. This view allows us to see not only the ordering of the layers, but also the distance between the elements in our imaginary three-dimensional space. This information will be used to determine the appropriate multiplane effect for the scene. Thus the yellow, sun-filled sky is noticeably farther from camera than the other foreground elements, and will consequently show very little perspective shift as the camera moves. This same sort of tool can also be used to determine the proper placement of any 3D elements that will be added to the scene. Mixing CG with cel animation is becomingly increasingly more common, and it is only natural that the artist would want to work with both types of data within the same tool.

Within this composite, a number of things were done to better integrate the separate layers into the scene. The layer that features Moses standing on the hilltop (Plate 85) was modified so that the edges of the character were slightly shrunk wherever they passed in front of the sun. This made it appear as if the light was actually wrapping around the element a bit, as it would if a live-action actor were to stand in front of an intense back-light. Another subtle effect was applied to some of the shadows in the scene. The shadows that the characters from Plate 89 are casting can be seen in Plate 88. These shadows were hand-drawn, but were not specifically designed to match with the contours of the background shown in Plate 87. To help with this interaction, an additional distortion was applied to these shadows to help them fall on the surface in a more realistic fashion. The distortion was based on the luminance of the ground—brighter areas would warp the shadows by a greater amount, darker areas would warp the shadows less. This slight distortion was enough to make it feel as if the shadows were falling onto a three-dimensional surface, instead of a flat piece of painted artwork.

A few different atmospheric layers were also added to the scene. One of these is shown in Plate 90. It features a couple of small clouds that will surround some of the characters in the foreground. These clouds were generated with a procedural texture that could be controlled via a number of parameters within the composite.

Each sequence in the film was designed to feature a specific, limited color palette. This was not a decision based on a desire to limit the amount of data necessary to represent an image. Rather, it was an aesthetic decision that was made to help with the story telling. In fact, the images were usually represented with 16 bits per channel of color depth. This would prevent any quantization artifacts from appearing—a particular problem when one is attempting to display broad areas of similar colors.

A number of additional digital tools may be used to improve the quality of the final composite. One such tool modifies the images to introduce a pseudo motion-blur to certain areas of the image. Using a sophisticated (and proprietary) algorithm to analyze the motion of objects over a series of frames, this tool can selectively blur the portion of the image that is moving significantly between frames. Since the original hand-drawn elements will typically have no motion blur, this technique can produce images with a much smoother feel to their animation.

The shot being discussed is a very quick scene in the final film. Consisting of only 64 frames, it would be visible for less than three seconds. Unlike traditional visual effects work, where one often produces several additional frames of handle at the beginning and end of the shot, cel animation is almost always done exactly to length. Many of the shots in a major animated feature can easily cost more than $1000 per frame to produce, making any extra work a prohibitively expensive proposition. This same reasoning also drives certain shortcuts in other areas. For instance, hand-animated figures are not always created with 24 discrete frames for every second of animation. Instead, the artist will animate "on two's," producing only 12 distinct frames for each second. Each frame is then typically displayed twice in a row—a process that is now usually dealt with in the compositing stage. This double-frame animation is not the problem it might be with live-action footage. First of all, the animator will choose which elements are appropriate for this treatment, usually confining it to slower-moving characters or objects. Additionally, this sort of timing has been used for nearly as long as cel animation has been in existence, and can be considered a part of the stylized look of this medium.

TITANIC

The shot from the film *Titanic* that is featured in Plates 93 through 100 is probably the most complex one that we examine in this book. The image shown in Plate 93 is one of the final frames from the sequence, but the shot actually begins with a completely different view—a close-up on the actress who plays the elderly Rose, one of the main characters in the film. The camera pans past her to reveal a video monitor that is displaying the present-day *Titanic*—a hulking wreckage on the sea floor. This view expands to fill the frame, and the camera continues to move around the ship's bow, giving us a view of the rust-encrusted railing. Subtly the scene transitions to the day in 1912 when the ship was new and ready for launch. Hundreds of people are at the dock in Southampton, waiting to board, and others are waving from the lofty decks.

Literally hundreds of elements were used to create this scene, only a few of them shown in our color plates. We will concentrate primarily on the process that was used for the creation of this final portion of the shot, since the compositing, tracking, and morphing that went into the beginning of the shot would be difficult to describe without the benefit of several more pages of illustrations. We'll start with the ship itself. Although the film made use of everything from full-sized set pieces to completely computer-generated models, the *Titanic* that is shown in Plate 95 is a 1/20th scale miniature. After photographing the miniature on a stage in front of a black background, a matte was extracted for the ship with a combination of luminance-keying and garbage mattes. This element was shot with a motion-control camera, applying the same camera move that was used to capture the beginning elements in the scene.

The passengers and crew that are seen standing on the ship are all computer-generated characters. Created as carefully detailed digital models, these elements were rendered with integrated matte channels. The positional data that was used to drive the motion-control camera for the miniature shoot was also translated into a format that could drive the virtual camera, resulting in a perfect match with the miniature plate.

The sky behind the ship (Plate 96) is a matte painting, given life by the addition of a slight movement to the clouds and some animated smoke elements coming from the factories' chimneys. The foreground water in this same plate is a completely synthetic, computer-generated element. It was partially attenuated in certain areas to account for the shadow of the ship, and was also rendered with the appropriate camera move.

The dock on the right side of the frame (as well as all the people standing on it) was originally intended to be photographed as another element with the same camera move. A full-scale dock set had already been created for a number of other scenes in the film, and theoretically a matching camera movement would allow this final element to be easily integrated with the other pieces of the scene. This scenario became problematic, however, when the sweeping camera movement that the director was looking for proved impossible to capture with the equipment that was available. Instead, the decision was made to replace the dock with a digitally created reconstruction.

The primary architecture of the dock consists of several CG buildings, all created in the computer to match the live-action set that is seen in the surrounding shots in this sequence. Rather than render the entire dock as a single image, a number of smaller elements were rendered separately in order to give more flexibility to the compositing artist. One such element is shown in Plate 97. This strategy allowed the compositor to control the matting, atmosphere, and animation of these individual elements more explicitly. These elements ranged from buildings and gangways to crates and luggage. A few synthetic seagulls can also be seen circling the area.

The characters populating the dock are a combination of live and computer-generated actors. Most of the actors that are closer to camera, and thus larger in the frame, are real. They were shot on a stage, standing on a greenscreen surface. Although the camera is moving throughout the shot, the actors were filmed with a locked-down camera and then tracked into the plate. Since they are fairly far away, the shift in perspective is essentially unnoticeable. Rather than shoot a single plate with a huge number of extras, a smaller cast was chosen and photographed in a variety of different configurations that were designed to fit with the location on the dock where they would be placed. Approximately fifteen different clumps of foreground actors were used in this scene. Since these individual groups would all be fairly small relative to the full frame, the film footage was transferred directly to video using a telecine. This step saved both time and money, yet preserved more than enough resolution for this particular situation.

The shadows for all these elements were handled and manipulated separately from the characters themselves. The shadows were first extracted from the greenscreen plates with a combination of automated and manual techniques. This gave the compositor the ability to color correct and process the shadows in a different fashion from the actual actors. It also allowed all the shadows to be combined into a single shadow pass that could be used to darken the dock in the appropriate places all at once. This eliminated any overlap problems that would have come about if the shadows had been applied individually.

Since the dock was primarily a CG model, a basic Z-depth image was easily generated, providing a tool to aid with certain depth cues. This image is shown in Plate 98. It was used to reduce the contrast of the objects in the distance, adding atmosphere and an appropriate sense of distance to objects farther from the camera. A similar depth pass was generated for the *Titanic* itself, although in this case it was hand-painted. Notice how even the darkest objects become a more neutral gray as they recede in the distance.

The compositing script that was used to produce this shot is shown in Plate 93. The software that the artists used for this work is a proprietary package developed by the effects facility that did the work for their in-house use, and it features an extremely procedural, script-based compositing methodology. For a shot such as this one, the ability to build a script that could be modified at any stage of the composite was critical. With over 300 different layers, the limits of a nonscripted online system would have severely compromised the ability to modify elements throughout the compositing process. Additionally, the ability to distribute the processing of the script over dozens of different computers allowed this complex script to be processed in a reasonable amount of time.

Digital Compositing Software: Tools and Features

The purpose of the list given in this appendix is twofold. First, if you are already working with compositing software, it may help you to identify and understand tools within that package with which you were unfamiliar. We have tried to list features that are common to a variety of different packages, and to give a brief description of each. A more detailed description of certain features and operators can be found throughout the body of this book.

Second, this list can be used as a guide for evaluating and comparing software that you have never used but possibly intend to purchase or recommend. Given the wide and expanding variety of digital compositing tools that are available, it can be difficult to make a reasonable comparison without having a common baseline to reference. Of course, not all compositing packages will have all the features listed here. Many packages may have additional features that are *not* listed here. Please understand that the presence or absence of certain features does not necessarily determine whether the package will be useful. Only by evaluating your specific needs can you determine whether a particular package is suitable to the task. You may even find that a combination of several different tools will be needed to cover all the possible scenarios that you need to address. In general, you shouldn't hesitate to pass over a poorly designed "all in one" package in favor of a group of well-designed packages that can be used in conjunction with one another effectively.

This appendix will try not only to list a number of different potential features, but also to give an idea about what a reasonably good implementation of that feature might include. Don't use this as a "yes or no" checklist, but instead try to examine the features of the package in question to understand how complete the implementation might be.

Finally, remember the importance of the overall design of the package's user interface. This is probably the most difficult component of a package to evaluate, since it requires spending time with the product to understand the particular paradigm. It is something that cannot be dealt with in a simple features list, but absolutely should not be ignored. Chapters 8 and 9 go into greater detail about certain features and methodologies that are relevant to this topic.

The categorization of the features in this list is rather arbitrary, as is the naming of the tools themselves. Some of the features described below are named fairly consistently throughout the industry. For instance, "Brightness" almost universally refers to a tool that multiplies all three channels of an image by a constant value. In situations such as this, we'll give that name for the feature before we describe it. But many features can be referred to by completely different terminology depending on the software you are using. If you are using this list to help evaluate the functionality of a particular piece of software, you may need to explore a little bit before you can accurately determine whether, and to what extent, the software in question supports a specific feature. Remember too that many operators can be built as a combination of other operators. The list here consists primarily of tools that either cannot be built from other tools or are common enough to warrant inclusion.

COLOR CORRECTION

Although we will describe many of these tools in terms of the operations they perform on each *pixel*, in practice most of these tools should also be able to perform individually distinct operations on each *channel* of an image as well.

Add: Add a constant value to each pixel in an image.

Brightness: Multiply the RGB channels by an equal, specific amount.

Clamp: Clamp the value of each pixel in an image to be between a specific range. Values outside of this range will be forced to the limits of the new range.

Color-Space Conversions: The ability to convert images between various color spaces. These include RGB, HSV, HLS, CMY, CMYK, as well as a number of custom color spaces (such as the Cineon color space commonly used in film work).

Compress: Compress the value of each pixel in an image to be between a specific range. The entire gamut of values between 0 and 1 is scaled to fit within this new range.

Contrast: Modify the range/ratio of brightness values in an image. The midpoint of this contrast should be something that the user can control.

Divide: Divide the value of each pixel in an image by a constant value.

Expand: Choose a specific range of pixel values and expand them to fall in the range of 0 to 1. Values that were originally outside the range chosen will be pushed to 0 and 1 as well.

Expression Language: A robust language that can be used to modify the colors in an image based on arbitrary mathematical expressions. Ideally, this language will be capable of using information from more than one source image.

Fade: Multiply the RGBA values of a four-channel image by an equal, specific amount.

Gamma: Modify the apparent brightness of an image by raising or lowering the midrange values of the image.

Histogram Equalization: Stretch the range of values in an image to fit as completely as possible between 0 and 1.

HSV Modification: Modify an image based on its hue, saturation, and value.

Invert: Invert the value of each pixel in an image, producing a negative of the image.

Look-up Table: Apply a user-defined table that specifies a particular mapping of input pixel values to output values.

Matte Divide: Divide the RGB channels of an image by its alpha channel.

Matte Multiply: Multiply the RGB channels of an image by its alpha channel.

Multiply: Multiply the value of each pixel in an image by a constant value.

Reorder: Shuffle the order of the channels in an image.

Saturation: Modify the saturation of an image.

Set: Set any channel or set of channels to a specific constant value.

SPATIAL FILTERING

Blur: Apply some type of blurring algorithm. The user should be able to choose different horizontal and vertical blur values.

Convolve: Convolve an image with an arbitrary filter. The size of the kernel should be user-definable as well.

Dilate: Increase the coverage of bright areas in the image, while decreasing the dark areas.

Emboss: Modify an image to give it the sense of additional depth. Usually based on the luminance values in the source image.

Erode: Decrease the coverage of bright areas in the image, while increasing the dark areas.

Median: Replace the value of each pixel in an image by the median value of the neighboring pixels.

Sharpen: Apply some type of sharpening algorithm. The user should be able to choose different horizontal and vertical sharpening values.

GEOMETRIC TRANSFORMATION

For geometric transformations, you should be able to control whether each event occurs within a given resolution or whether it produces an image with a new resolution. For instance, a rotation applied to a specific image could either crop any piece of the image that rotates outside the original frame size, or it could cause the output resolution to be increased to prevent any such cropping. Portions of an image that are moved out of frame by a geometric transformation should not be *permanently* cropped. Instead, the data should be available for use by subsequent transformations. Optionally, you should also be able to specify whether you wish any portion of the image that moves out of frame to wrap around and reenter the frame on the opposite side.

The user should be able to choose the type of filtering that is used for most transformations. There are times when one may wish to choose different filtering along the vertical and horizontal axes.

Finally, for any animated geometric transformation, you should be able to choose whether or not the result is rendered with motion blur, and be able to control the extent of the motion blur that is applied.

Crop: Remove a portion of an image that lies outside a specific boundary, either by specifying two corners that define a rectangular region or by specifying a single point and the resolution of the desired result.

Fit: Scale an image to fit within a given resolution, usually with the option of maintaining the aspect ratio of the original image.

Lens: Create or undo the distortion caused by a camera's lens.

Pan: Reposition an image within a given frame.

Pin: Distort an image by moving four arbitrary points within the image to four new positions.

Resize: Change an image's size by specifying a new resolution.

Rotate: Rotate an image by specifying the center of rotation and the amount of rotation.

Scale: Scale an image by giving a multiplier for the X and Y axes.

Shear: Shear an image around a given point, specifying shear amounts for both the X and Y axes.

Twirl: Distort an image by twirling it around a certain point. You should be able to control the fall-off on the twirl as a function of distance from the center point.

Warp: Warp an image based on a control grid or a set of control splines.

Expression Language: A robust language that can be used to warp an image based on arbitrary mathematical expressions. Ideally, this language will be capable of using information from more than one source image.

Flip: Mirror the image around the X axis.

Flop: Mirror the image around the Y axis.

MISCELLANEOUS

Grain: Add simulated film grain to an image. You should either be able to specify a variety of parameters that describe grain characteristics (such as grain size, density, luminance and chrominance variance, etc.) or to choose from a list of different film stocks that you wish to emulate.

Radial Blur: Blur or smear an image radially about a certain point. You should be able to control the fall-off on the smear as a function of distance from the center point.

Smear: Smear an image in a certain direction by a certain amount. Often used to simulate motion blur.

IMAGE COMBINATION

The image-combination tools are described using the same conventions that were discussed in Chapter 4. Thus, A and B are considered the two source images. If there is a need to specify certain channels in an image explicitly, they will be indicated with subscripts; otherwise it is assumed that the operation will be performed on all four channels of an image equally. All images are assumed to be four-channel premultiplied images.

Add: Add two images together on a pixel-by-pixel basis (A + B).

Mix: Combine two images by using a weighted pixel average. (MV $\times$ A) + [(1 − MV) $\times$ B], where MV is the mixing value.

Atop: Place the foreground over the background, but only inside the background alpha. Thus, A atop B is really the same as (A in B_A) over B.

Reorder: Move specific channels between two different images.

Displace: Warp an image by using a second image to control the amount of warp at any given location.

In: Retain the foreground only within the background's matte. Thus, A in B is the same as $A \times B_A$.

Luminosity: A tool to modify the matte channel of a four-channel premultiplied image. Decreasing the matte channel gives the image a luminous look when it is placed over a background. Also known as the Opacity operator.

Max: Use the maximum value of the equivalent pixel location in the two images.

Min: Use the minimum value of the equivalent pixel location in the two images.

Multiply: Multiply one image by another image ($A \times B$).

Out: Retain the foreground only outside of the background's matte. Thus, A out B (or "A held out by B") is the same as $A \times (1 - B_A)$.

Opacity: See **Luminosity.**

Over: Place the foreground over the background using the foreground alpha. A over B is the same as $A + [B \times (1 - A_A)]$.

Screen: Invert both images, multiply them together, and then invert the result. $1-[(1 - A) \times (1 - B)]$.

Subtract: Subtract one image from another image ($A - B$). You should be able to choose whether the value of the resulting pixel is clipped to 0 if the result is a negative number or if the value of the resulting pixel becomes the absolute value of the result.

Under: Place the background under the foreground using the foreground alpha. Thus, A under B is the same as B over A.

Xor: Retain both source images only where their mattes do *not* overlap. $A \times (1 - B_A) + B \times (1 - A_A)$.

Z Compose: Choose the resulting pixel from either source image by comparing the Z-depth values for each image.

CONTROL

You should be able to control and limit how a given tool is applied. Various control methods include:

- The ability to restrict the operation so that it only occurs on specific channels of the image.
- The ability to restrict the operation so that it only occurs on the even-numbered or the odd-numbered scan lines of the image.

- The ability to specify a rectangular region of interest (ROI) outside of which the effect will not be applied.
- The ability to control the amount of the effect that will be applied, based on the grayscale values in an additional (separate or integrated) matte/mask image.
- The ability to limit the effect so that it will only be applied if it changes a given pixel by a user-specified threshold.

You should also be able to have some control over how the software uses the resources of the system on which it is running. This includes the ability to limit the amount of memory that the software will use, as well as having control over what disk space is used for any temporary image storage.

FIELD CONTROLS

Interlace: Merge two images into a new image by choosing alternating lines from each image.

Deinterlace: Separate a single image into two new images, one containing only the even-numbered lines from the original image and one containing only the odd-numbered lines.

Swapfields: Switch the even- and odd-numbered lines in an image.

MATTE GENERATION

Lumakey: Create a matte based on the luminance values in an image.

Chromakey: Create a matte based on a specific thresholded color in an image.

Difference Matting: Create a matte based on the differences between two images.

Specialized Tools: Any of a number of proprietary tools for creating a matte for an object. These tools may rely on the fact that the object was shot in front of a uniformly colored background or may use other techniques, such as motion analysis, to determine the matte's location and transparency.

TIMING/DURATION

Append: Append one image sequence to another to create a new, longer sequence.

Drop Frames: Remove frames from a sequence at regular intervals, either by specifying which frames to keep or which frames to drop.

Duplicate Frames: Duplicate certain frames in a sequence at regular intervals.

Hold Frame: Convert a single frame into a sequence of identical frames.

Pulldown: Perform the standard conversion between 24-fps film and 30-fps NTSC video.

Pullup: Perform the standard conversion between 30-fps NTSC video and 24-fps film.

Reverse: Reverse the order of the frames in a sequence.

Time Compress/Expand: A tool for shortening or lengthening a sequence of images, either by selectively averaging the frames in a sequence together (usually with some kind of weighted mix) or via the use of certain specialized motion analysis algorithms.

IMAGE GENERATION

Constant: Create a constant-color image.

Gradient: Create an image that contains a horizontal, vertical, or radial gradient between different colors.

Paint Tools: A broad category of possible features. An ideal group of paint tools would allow for procedural painting that can be applied to a sequence of images instead of just the one in question.

Shape Drawing: Create an image that contains user-defined shapes created via curves or polygons. The user should be able to control the color and transparency of the shapes and the softness of the edges.

Text: Create text with a user-specified font, color, size, orientation, and placement.

TRACKING

There are a number of features that would be considered to be related to tracking. The following lists a few specific items, and Chapter 7 provides much more detailed information.

Subpixel Accuracy: The ability to accurately track features at greater than whole-pixel resolutions.

Multiple Point: The ability to track several points at the same time.

Integration: Tracking information should be easily applicable to most geometric transformation tools, including Pan, Rotate, Scale, Pin, and Warp.

Stabilization: Choose a specific point and stabilize the plate based on the assumption that the point in question is unmoving.

OTHER

Finally, there are a number of additional features that most compositing packages should support. These include the following:

Resolution Independence: The ability to translate compositing parameters that have been created to work on a sequence of images at a certain resolution to work with a sequence at a different resolution.

File Format Independence: Support for reading and writing a wide variety of image file formats, such as those listed in Appendix C.

Platform Independence: The ability of a given piece of software to run on a variety of different hardware platforms, often from different manufacturers.

Extensibility: The ability to add functionality to the package via the use of macros, plug-ins, and so forth.

Optimization: Automated tools that can analyze and optimize complex compositing scripts.

Batch Processing: The ability to create complex scripts that define large hierarchical compositing processes.

Internal Accuracy: The ability to process data at different bit depths. Common depths include 8 and 16 bits per channel, as well as support for a floating-point mode, which would maintain pixel values that are pushed beyond the range of 0 to 1.

Proxy Support: The ability to use low-resolution stand-ins for the image/sequence in question, and the ability to prototype effects or scripts based on these proxies.

Digital Compositing Software: Manufacturers

The following is a list of companies that provide software tools for the creation and manipulation of digital images. While we have concentrated on companies that produce digital compositing software, most of these vendors also provide a variety of other tools, including 3D animation and rendering packages, digital editing systems, morphing software, and digital paint programs. Please consult the individual companies' Web sites for further details about the specific markets that they address.

In any list of this sort, there will inevitably be inaccuracies and exclusions, but at the time this book was written, the list was a reasonable overview of the major providers in the industry. Obviously, both specific products and the companies that provide them can change names or disappear entirely, and given the volatile nature of the software business, this list may actually be changing more rapidly than the technology itself.

Adobe Systems, Inc.	www.adobe.com
Advanced Digital Imaging, Inc.	www.adii.com
Alias | Wavefront	www.aw.sgi.com
Avid Technology, Inc.	www.avid.com
Chyron Corporation	www.chyron.com
Composite Components Company	www.digitalgreenscreen.com

da Vinci Systems, Inc.	www.davsys.com
Discreet Logic	www.discreet.com
Eastman Kodak Company	www.kodak.com
Equilibrium	www.equilibrium.com
eyeon Software, Inc.	www.eyeonline.com
The Foundry	www.thefoundry.co.uk
Hammerhead Productions	www.hammerhead.com
Interactive Effects	www.ifx.com
NewTek	www.newtek.com
Nothing Real	www.nothingreal.com
Photron	www.photron.com
Puffin Designs	www.puffindesigns.com
Quantel	www.quantel.com
Science.D.Visions	www.sci-d-vis.com
Silicon Grail	www.sgrail.com
Softimage	www.softimage.com
Ultimatte Corporation	www.ultimatte.com
Xaos Tools	www.xaostools.com
Zbig Vision, Ltd.	www.zbigvision.com

Digital Image File Formats

COMMON FILE FORMATS

The following list is an overview of some of the more common image file formats that a digital compositing artist may encounter. It should not be considered a comprehensive list, because there are dozens of other formats, and more are constantly being defined. For each format, information about typical file extensions, bit depth, channel support, and compression schemes is provided. Generally, the *maximum* bit depth for the format is given—many formats are able to store images at lower bit depths as well. The implementation standards for most of these formats are often poorly (or contradictorally) defined, and consequently you may see implementations that differ from our description. Vendors will often choose to disregard existing standards if it proves convenient; therefore, the best we can hope to do is to describe the most common implementations.

Name	Abekas/Quantel
Extensions	.yuv, .qnt, .qtl, .pal
Bit Depth	8 bits/channel.
Channels	Usually RGB only. There is no well-defined standard for matte or Z-depth channels for this format.
Compression	No.
Other Notes	There are a number of variations on this format, hence the different extensions listed. Most implementations actually hard-wire the image to be a certain resolution: 720 × 486 for NTSC or 720 × 576 for PAL.

Name	Alias
Extension	None, or .als
Bit Depth	8 bits/channel.
Channels	Typically RGB only. Matte channels and Z-depth information are usually stored as separate files.
Compression	Yes, lossless.
Other Notes	This file format is usually only generated by the Alias renderer. It is becoming less and less common as Alias is supplanted by the Maya 3D system.

Name	Avid OMF
Extension	.omf
Bit Depth	8 bits/channel.
Channels	RGB.
Compression	Yes, lossy.
Other Notes	The OMF file format was created for the Avid nonlinear editing systems. It is actually a collection of format specifications that includes the ability to store images at certain fixed quality levels (usually via JPEG encoding) and also has support for imbedded audio information.

Name	Bitmap (OS/2 and Microsoft)
Extension	.bmp
Bit Depth	8 bits/channel.
Channels	RGB or RGBA, although four-channel .bmp files are fairly rare.
Compression	Yes, lossless, although .bmp files are often stored uncompressed.
Other Notes	This format is the native format for all the Microsoft Windows operating systems, as well as the OS/2 system. There are a large number of slight variations on this format, since it is not terribly well defined.

Name	Cineon
Extension	.cin
Bit Depth	10 bits/channel.
Channels	Usually RGB only, without support for alpha or Z-depth information.
Compression	No.
Other Notes	See the section at the end of this appendix for a much more detailed discussion of this format.

Name	DPX
Extension	.dpx
Bit Depth	10 bits/channel.
Channels	Usually RGB only.
Compression	No.
Other Notes	The DPX file format is an extension of the Cineon format. The primary difference between the two is the ability to store some additional information in the DPX file's header.

Name	GIF
Extension	.gif
Bit Depth	Indexed color, 1 to 8 bits total.
Channels	No support for Z-depth, and transparency is done via indexing (see Notes).
Compression	Yes, "lossless" from the compression itself, but obviously lossy in terms of having a severely limited color palette
Other Notes	The GIF format does not support an integrated matte channel, but does allow for a single color in the image (usually black) to be defined as "transparent." This format is rarely acceptable for any kind of high-end work, since there are no intermediate levels of partial transparency.

Name	IFF
Extension	.iff
Bit Depth	Up to 32 bits/channel.
Channels	The specification supports an arbitrary number of channels, but most applications can only deal with RGBA and Z.
Compression	Yes, lossless.
Other Notes	The IFF file format is really a general-purpose data storage format that has been extended to fit a variety of needs. There are *many* variations of this format, including an older format supported on the Amiga platform, the format supported by Alias|Wavefront and Nothing Real in their various products, and the standard AIFF audio format.

Name	JPEG
Extension	.jpeg, .jpg, .jfif
Bit Depth	8 bits/channel.
Channels	No support for alpha or Z-depth information.
Compression	Yes, lossy.
Other Notes	The term "JPEG" is typically used to describe both the file format and the compression scheme that is used with the format.

Name	Pixar
Extension	.pic
Bit Depth	8 bits/channel.
Channels	RGBA and Z.
Compression	Yes, lossless.
Other Notes	This file format is usually only generated by the RenderMan renderer.

Name	RLA
Extension	.rla
Bit Depth	8 or 16 bits/channel.
Channels	RGBA and Z-depth.
Compression	Yes, lossless.
Other Notes	Originally the format created for the Wavefront renderer, it has become more universal over time.

Name	SGI
Extension	.sgi, .rgb
Bit Depth	8 or 16 bits/channel.
Channels	Originally the format only supported RGB information, but the latest specification includes support for an integrated matte channel. No support for Z-depth.
Compression	Yes, lossless.
Other Notes	Proprietary format created by Silicon Graphics Inc. as a standard part of their IRIX operating system.

Name	Softimage
Extension	.pic
Bit Depth	8 bits/channel.
Channels	Support for integrated matte channel.
Compression	Yes, lossless.
Other Notes	This file format is usually only generated by the Softimage renderer.

Name	Sun bitmap
Extension	.sun, .bmp, .ras
Bit Depth	8 bits/channel.
Channels	Generally just RGB.
Compression	Yes, lossless.
Other Notes	This file format is usually only generated by the Softimage renderer.

Name	Targa
Extension	.tga, .tpic, .vst
Bit Depth	8 bits/channel.
Channels	Most implementations support RGB with an integrated alpha channel, but no Z-depth capabilities.
Compression	Yes, lossless.

Name	TIFF
Extension	.tiff, .tif
Bit Depth	8 bits/channel usually, although the newest specifications allow for higher bit depths.
Channels	Usually implemented with RGB and alpha, although the specification allows for an arbitrary number of images(and consequently channels) within any given file.
Compression	Yes, lossless.
Other Notes	A very flexible, common format that has a huge number of implementation variations, depending on the software in question.

THE CINEON FILE FORMAT

This section has been included in order to describe the Cineon file format in a more in-depth fashion than the other formats listed in this chapter. There are a couple of reasons why this was considered necessary. First of all, this file format is by far the most common method used to represent and store images that were captured from an original film source. Images from most other sources can be placed into a variety of different file formats without any problem, but to usefully represent the large dynamic range of a film image requires some additional features. The Cineon file format was developed by Kodak specifically to address these needs, and consequently it has become the *de facto* standard for storing film data. However, unlike most other file formats, the person who is manipulating Cineon images should have at least a rudimentary understanding of the format's basic principles in order to use it effectively. Therefore, we will take the time to look at this format's characteristics, and particularly the way that it encodes data, in greater detail.

While theoretically the Cineon format can support a variety of different configurations in terms of channels and bit depth, by far the most common use is as a three-channel RGB image with 10 bits of data used for each channel. The choice of 10 bits per channel was not arbitrary, but is tied closely to an analysis of how film works. To reduce the file size, as well as to fit into the 8-bit chunks that computers prefer, these three 10-bit channels are stored into a 32-bit structure. Since this is the only compression scheme that is used (other than the nonlinear color space that will be discussed in a moment), the file size of a Cineon image is predictable and based only on the resolution of the image itself. To compute the amount of disk space a Cineon image will consume, use the following formula:

$$\frac{(X \text{ Resolution}) \times (Y \text{ Resolution})}{250,000} = \text{File Size (in megabytes)}$$

For example, an image that is 1828 by 1556 will require about 11.377 megabytes on disk. There may be minor deviations from this formula, depending on the amount of information that is kept in the header of the file you are creating, but any major discrepancies will indicate that your image is probably not truly stored in the standard three-channel, 10 bits-per-channel Cineon format.

Before we go any further into the specifics of the Cineon format itself, there is a common misconception about it that should be addressed. Although discussions of this format usually focus on the specialized way the data is stored, in fact the structure of the Cineon file format is really not much different from most other image file formats. However, when Kodak first published the specifications for this format, it was as a part of their entry into the business of providing film scanning and recording services. Consequently, not only did they need to describe the Cineon file format itself, they also created and documented a specialized color space that would be used to encode the scanned images stored in this format.

This color space mimics the way that a film negative responds to light, in terms of the density of the developed negative compared with the light that reaches it. Thus, the nonlinear color space that the Cineon file format uses is sometimes referred to as a **density space**. This response is logarithmic in nature, and so it is also (more commonly) referred to as a "logarithmic space," or simply **log space.** The characteristics of this color space were assumed to be a part of the Cineon format itself, and consequently the two became somewhat synonymous. But it is important to understand the distinction since (as we mentioned when we originally discussed nonlinear encoding in Chapter 15) there is effectively no way to *force* a file to store a particular type of data. Thus, although an image that is stored in the Cineon format is *probably* represented in log space, there is no guarantee that this is the case. Many software packages will automatically perform the encoding when they write a Cineon file, but many packages will not. The same thing is true when *reading* a Cineon file—many software packages will automatically linearize the image, many will not. Ultimately, it is up to the compositing artist to understand exactly how the data that they are using is represented; otherwise, significant problems could result. For the rest of this discussion, we will operate under the assumption that the term "Cineon image" refers to an image that is also not only saved in the Cineon file format, but whose data is encoded using the Kodak-specified logarithmic color space.

Whenever we wish to digitize an image that was shot on film, we typically scan the original negative itself. There are really two reasons for using the negative instead of scanning a **print** from this negative. The first is in order to have as sharp and grain-free an image as possible. Obviously a print that is made from the original negative would be slightly inferior to the original, and thus less desirable. But more important, we scan the negative because it contains a great deal more information than even a first-generation print. As we discussed in Chapter 15, a piece of film negative can actually hold a much greater range of values than a piece of print film. We want to bring all this information into the digital realm, and thus we must scan the negative, not a print.

At first glance, it may seem somewhat pointless to capture and keep all this additional data if the print that we will eventually be making is unable to display it. While it is true that the print itself may not be able to use the data, much of the intermediate digital compositing work may find it to be crucial. Therefore, the encoding method that is used to generate a Cineon image was designed to keep as much of the data in the original negative as possible, while still storing this data efficiently. For this reason, a Cineon file is often referred to as a "digital negative." This term occasionally generates some confusion, since a Cineon image doesn't *look* like a negative image when viewed. In reality, the final step that is performed on a scanned image before it is saved in the Cineon format is a simple digital inversion. Whites become blacks, colors become their complements, and, although no data is lost, the image is now much more comfortable and intuitive to work with.[1]

The contrast range of a piece of film negative is about 1000 to 1. In other words, the brightest areas of the negative where tonal variations can still occur are actually 1000 times brighter than the darkest areas where the negative can capture these variations. This is a very large range of brightness levels, and to capture this range digitally requires a fairly high bit depth. If the images are being captured in linear space, it takes about 14 bits per channel to represent enough color variations so that quantizing artifacts or banding will not be visible. However, if the nonlinear log-space encoding is applied, only 10 bits per channel are necessary—the standard bit depth for the Cineon format.

As we've said, even though the negative is able to capture a wide range of brightness values, the final print that will be produced from such a negative will not have nearly as great a range. In particular, much of the detail in the brightest areas of the image will simply register as "white" when transferred from the negative to a positive print. The same thing is true, to a lesser extent, for the blacks of the image. Theoretically, these thresholds can be considered to be the white point and the black point of the image, which means that we may be able to discard some of this data as unnecessary. More on this in a moment.

You may occasionally see documentation that attempts to provide numerical values for what the black point or white point would be for a "standard" Cineon file. Typically, the numbers that are given place the black point at about 90 and the white point at about 685.[2] But it is very dangerous to blindly assume that these numbers are always appropriate. They are based on the assumption that the film was exposed "normally," a nebulous concept at best. Cinematographers will often over- or under expose a negative in order to achieve a specific effect, and thus there really is no such thing as a normal exposure. What's more, there may be steps performed when printing the negative onto a positive that also shift the brightness range. Thus, any default numbers for the white and black points

---

[1] Incidentally, most scanning systems will give you the option of whether or not to compensate for the fact that the base color of a negative has an orange cast. This is done by determining the color of an unexposed area of the developed negative and then subtracting this characteristic color from the digital values that are produced when scanned. If this base correction is not applied, the scan will have a noticeable cyan tint—the orange becomes cyan when the values are digitally inverted. This is generally not a problem, since presumably you will be color correcting the image to match a reference clip anyway, and as long as you are still working with the original bit depth, you have more than enough room for such a correction.

[2] These numbers are usually given in the 10-bit range of 0 to 1023, as is the standard practice when discussing Cineon images. If you want to convert them to floating-point numbers in the range of 0 to 1, you will need to divide by 1023.

should only be considered a starting point. The only way to truly determine what values will eventually be white or black on the print is to visually compare the digital image with an accurate sample, that is, a piece of film that has been developed and printed to properly represent the brightness and color balance that the director and the cinematographer desire for the shot. The white point and the black point, as well as any necessary color changes, can be applied to the digital data in order to duplicate this reference clip as closely as possible.

There are very good reasons for wanting to know, before the compositing process begins, the white and black points. These reasons have to do with some choices that can be made to reduce the amount of data that is dealt with. The most accurate way to work with 10-bit log-space images is to keep them as standard Cineon files while they are stored on disk, and then linearize them into a 16-bit representation whenever any compositing operations need to be performed.[3] This practice will obviously require a good deal of disk space and processing horsepower, but it is the best way to ensure that the quality of the original negative is preserved. It also allows for a great deal of flexibility, since the extra headroom will mean that the brightness of the image can be adjusted significantly without revealing any artifacts. For instance, the brightness of the image could be decreased by 10% and there would still be plenty of detail that can drop down from above the white point to prevent white areas from becoming clipped.

You may find that the quality and flexibility of such a scenario is not worth the amount of disk space and CPU that it requires, however. In this situation, it is not uncommon to reduce the data, truncating it to a more convenient size. For instance, if you are reasonably certain that you will not need to digitally "print down" the brightness of the image, much of the high-end detail will never be used. Therefore, it is common to discard most of this headroom (and occasionally a bit of the low-end information also) in order to reduce the space requirements. This procedure is usually done by remapping values in the range of about 90 to 700 into the range of 0 to 255, which will result in an image that can be stored as an 8-bit file. Although this step reduces the precision, it is not nearly as severe a reduction as if we had mapped the full range of 0 to 1023 into our 8-bit space. Usually there will be no visible artifacts that result from working with such images unless, as we mentioned, the need arises to decrease the brightness of the images by a great amount. If this is attempted, the truncated high end will become noticeable, and bright areas will appear clipped and artificial. The only recourse at this point would be to return to the original 10-bit image and perform the

---

[3] Even though we have said that 14 bits per channel is enough, most compositing systems prefer to store data in 8-bit chunks, meaning that 14 bits or 16 bits will both be saved in the same fashion.

brightness adjustment *before* truncating the data to 8 bits. This may or may not be a tremendous burden, depending on the situation.

Note that the conversion from 10 bits into 8 bits that we have just described is a direct mapping from one range into another. However, we did *not* specify any linearization in this step. The 8-bit images that were produced are still considered to be stored in log space. These images should still be linearized before most compositing operations are performed on them. If you are truly more concerned with saving disk space and increasing speed than you are with protecting yourself from banding artifacts, you can even convert your 10-bit log-space image into an 8-bit linear image. Usually this involves the same range reduction that we just discussed, mapping the black and white points to 0 and 255 and then linearizing the result. For many situations this process may produce an image that is perfectly acceptable and indistinguishable from the original when it is sent back to film. But unfortunately, the only way to be sure of this is by actually producing your final image and looking at it. Again, if problems are noticeable, you will probably need to return to the original 10-bit image and redo the composite at a higher bit depth.

Viewing a Cineon image directly will require your image-viewing program (or your monitor) to have a custom look-up table loaded. This LUT will map the log-space data into a linear viewing space, as well as mapping the user-specified white and black points to the monitor's range limits. Some vendors actually offer fully calibrated systems that include both software *and* hardware tuning in order to properly display Cineon images. This type of system will give the most accurate representation, since the monitor can be adjusted to display a greater contrast ratio than it would normally be capable of. However, a very close approximation can be accomplished via purely software means as well. Attaining this approximation may require a bit of calibration, including a comparison with images that were taken all the way through the film-out and printing process.

Common Film and Video Formats

This appendix is provided as an additional source of information about some of the film and video formats that the typical compositor might encounter in the course of his or her daily work. It builds on the topics and discussions that were covered in Chapter 10, and you should read that chapter before attempting to decipher some of the information given here. Please note that, although sample resolutions are given for a number of the formats discussed, these should be considered examples rather than standards. There are many ways to digitize any given format, and thus there is no guarantee that a specific digitization method will produce an image that is identical to what we have described.

FILM

Although there have been a myriad of film formats developed over the years, some clear standards have emerged that can help to narrow our focus. Within this section, we give the basic dimensions for a range of formats, as well as a comparison of their relative sizes. For the 35mm formats, this includes several of the more prevalent framings. In addition, we give some examples of what the resolution and file size might be like for these framings and formats.

Figure D.1 diagrams the sizes for the major 35mm film formats. These formats are shown to scale, with the precise measurements given in Table D.1. If you take the time to examine the measurements that are given in this table, you may find that certain scanning resolutions do not have exactly the same aspect ratio as the negative that is used to capture that format. These minor discrepancies are related to the way the scanner is constructed, and can mostly be ignored.

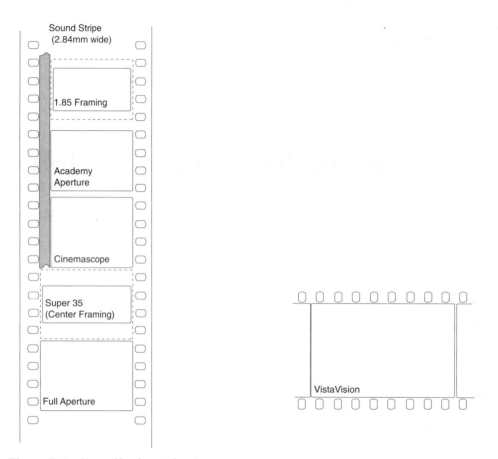

Figure D.1   *35mm film format framing.*

Keep in mind that the aspect ratio for any given format will not necessarily be preserved when the image is projected. For instance, the Cinemascope negative (after taking into account the anamorphic squeeze) has an aspect ratio of 2.36:1, but is always projected with a mask that produces a 2.35:1 image.

Figure D.2 and Table D.2 compare the relative areas of the negatives used to capture the listed formats. For instance, an IMAX negative is approximately 10.55 times larger than the size of the negative used for standard Academy framing.

Scanning Resolutions and File Sizes

As mentioned in Chapter 10, a film scanner can be built to work at any resolution, and since the negative is an analog medium, there is no bias to sample it at any particular resolution. Theoretically, any correlation between the resolution of the

Table D.1 *Common Film Formats*

Format	Width	Height	Area	Aspect ratio
16mm	0.404″	0.295″	0.119″	1.37
	10.26 mm	7.49 mm	76.86 mm	
Super 16	0.493″	0.292″	0.144″	1.69
	12.52 mm	7.42 mm	92.84 mm	
Academy aperture	0.864″	0.630″	0.544″	1.37
	21.94 mm	16.00 mm	351.04 mm	
Full aperture	0.980″	0.735″	0.720″	1.33
	24.89 mm	18.67 mm	464.53 mm	
1.85 framing	0.825″	0.446″	0.368″	1.85
	20.95 mm	11.33 mm	237.29 mm	
Super 35*	0.945″	0.394″	0.372″	2.35
	24.00 mm	10.01 mm	240.12 mm	
Cinemascope	0.864″	0.732″	0.632″	2.35
	21.94 mm	18.59 mm	407.87 mm	
VistaVision (8-perf)	1.485″	0.991″	1.472″	1.5
	37.71 mm	25.17 mm	949.07 mm	
65mm (5-perf)	2.066″	0.906″	1.872″	2.28
	52.47 mm	23.01 mm	1207.13 mm	
IMAX	2.772″	2.072″	5.744″	1.33
	70.39 mm	52.62 mm	3704.07 mm	

*These figures describe Super 35 as composed for 2.35 projection, the most common use of this format.

digital image and the original negative is more or less arbitrary. In practice, however, certain standards have emerged, largely because Kodak Cineon scanners are becoming more and more common. Other vendors provide excellent alternatives, but most of them are very similar in terms of the resolutions that they will produce when scanning a given piece of film. Therefore, the examples we give in Table D.3 are all based on Kodak's specifications.

The "full" mode reflects the image that is produced when the scanner is run at its maximum resolution (scanning at about 167 pixels per millimeter, or 4233 pixels per inch). Most people choose to work with resolutions that are less heavy—often exactly half of the full resolution of which the scanner is capable. Thus, a "half" resolution is also given.

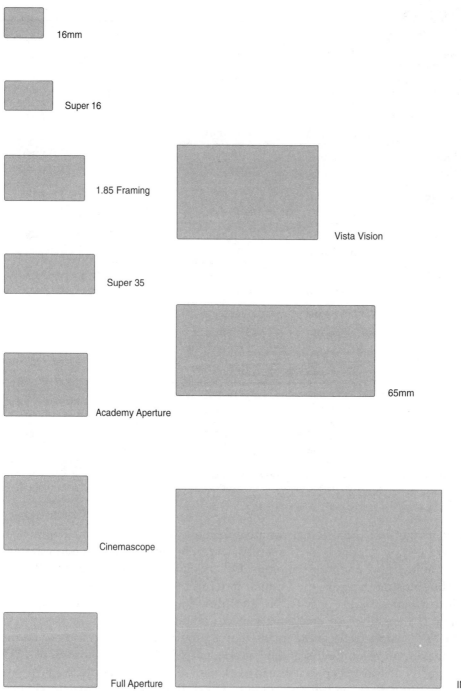

Figure D.2   *Common film formats.*

Table D.2 *Relative Negative Sizes*

	16mm	Super 16	1.85	Super 35	Academy	Cinemascope	Full aperture	VistaVision	65mm	IMAX
16mm	1.00	0.83	0.32	0.32	0.22	0.19	0.17	0.08	0.06	0.02
Super 16	1.21	1.00	0.39	0.39	0.26	0.23	0.20	0.10	0.08	0.03
1.85	3.09	2.56	1.00	0.99	0.68	0.58	0.51	0.25	0.20	0.06
Super 35	3.12	2.59	1.01	1.00	0.68	0.59	0.52	0.25	0.20	0.06
Academy	4.57	3.78	1.48	1.46	1.00	0.86	0.76	0.37	0.29	0.09
Cinemascope	5.31	4.39	1.72	1.70	1.16	1.00	0.88	0.43	0.34	0.11
Full aperture	6.04	5.00	1.96	1.93	1.32	1.14	1.00	0.49	0.38	0.13
VistaVision	12.35	10.22	4.00	3.95	2.70	2.33	2.04	1.00	0.79	0.26
65mm	15.71	13.00	5.09	5.03	3.44	2.96	2.60	1.27	1.00	0.33
IMAX	48.19	39.90	15.61	15.43	10.55	9.08	7.97	3.90	3.07	1.00

Table D.3 *Typical Scanning Resolution and File Sizes*

Format		Horizontal resolution	Vertical resolution	File size (MB) (Cineon format)
Full aperture	Full	4096	3112	51
	Half	2048	1556	13
Academy aperture	Full	3656	2664	39
	Half	1828	1332	10
Cinemascope	Full	3656	3112	45
	Half	1828	1556	11
VistaVision	Full	6144	4096	101
	Half	3072	2048	25

Since the Cineon format is such a predictable, as well as common, method for storing film images, we have also given an approximate file size for these scanned images if they are stored as Cineon files. As mentioned in Appendix C, these estimates will only be accurate for 10-bit, three-channel Cineon files.

VIDEO

Video is, in many ways, an even more poorly defined format than film. This is particularly true for any definition of how a video image should be represented as a digital bitmap. There are a number of different standards for this, but unfortunately many (most) of these standards conflict with each other! Certainly part of the problem is that an analog video signal can be sampled at any arbitrary resolution, and thus there is no "correct" number of samples for the horizontal resolution of a video signal. But there are a number of different ways that have been developed to represent video digitally as well, and even within this digital realm there are a number of discrepancies. Different digital video formats, such as DVD, MPEG-1 and MPEG-2, D1 Video, ATV (Advanced TV, the new standard for digital television transmission in the United States), VideoCD, DTV, SDTV, and even HDTV, can all theoretically represent the type of video image that is displayable on a television monitor. Some of these standards are in agreement with each other in certain aspects, but ultimately they do not all agree on a specific resolution for either NTSC or PAL.[1] Consequently, it will be impossible for us to give any sort of definitive definition for the pixel resolution of a video image. Instead, we will try to give a few more pieces of information that may be useful, and will encourage you to do as much research as possible into the specific hardware that you will be using for your work.

The most commonly referenced "standard" for digital video is the specification usually referred to as "CCIR-601".[2] This was the specification that was used when developing the D1 Video system, the standard for most broadcast graphics. One of the most significant things that CCIR-601 defined was the horizontal resolution of both the NTSC and the PAL formats. It dictated that the horizontal resolution for *both* these formats would be 720 pixels wide. This has helped somewhat to narrow the range of possible resolutions that can be used to represent a video frame, but still has not brought complete consensus to the industry.

As we mentioned in Chapter 10, although both NTSC and PAL have a well-defined number of scan lines, these lines do not all contain visual information. Other data such as time code, blanking, and even closed captioning are also part of the lines that are contained with each video frame. Usually we are interested only in the lines that contain picture information, which are referred to as the "active lines." Unfortunately, the specifications do not really provide the exact dimensions for the active lines in either format.

It is probably tempting to assume that, since we know that the horizontal resolution is defined to be 720 and the aspect ratio is defined to be 4:3, we can

---

[1] Although, strictly speaking, the terms NTSC and PAL refer to the analog formats, we will follow the industry convention of using these two terms as synonyms for their digital equivalents as well.
[2] A more current version of this specification is contained in the ITU-R BT.601-5 document, but virtually nobody bothers to reference this document in daily use, nor do they believe that it will be the last word on the subject, Therefore, when people discuss digital video they still use the term CCIR-601.

easily compute the vertical resolution. Unfortunately, this is not the case. First of all, NTSC and PAL have a different number of scan lines, so obviously there is more to the equation—namely, the pixel aspect ratio for these formats. As we mentioned in Chapter 10, the industry standard for NTSC is considered to be a pixel aspect ratio of 10:11. The pixels are slightly taller than they are wide. The pixel aspect ratio for PAL is a slightly squat 59:54.[3] Factoring all this information together yields the following resolutions:

$$\text{NTSC: } 720 \times (3/4) \times (10/11) = 490$$
$$\text{PAL: } \ \ \ 720 \times (3/4) \times (59/54) = 590$$

Thus, theoretically at least, NTSC should have a digital resolution of 720×490 and PAL should be 720×590.

Well, unfortunately, neither of these numbers is commonly used. For a number of different reasons, the exact values that are chosen for NTSC and PAL are usually a bit different. Part of the reason is that home television sets are essentially incapable of displaying the full width and height of the video signal that is sent to them: Information will be cut off along the edges. Therefore, the numbers were massaged a bit. Currently, the most common digital representations for NTSC and PAL are as follows:

$$\text{NTSC: } 720 \times 486$$
$$\text{PAL: } \ \ \ 720 \times 576$$

These resolutions are as close to a standard as exists. They are the resolutions that most digital compositing artists will find themselves using, particularly if they are working on broadcast graphics. The fact that the numbers are slightly different from the values we computed based on the specification above indicates that the aspect ratio will be slightly wrong, but in practice most people ignore this, and the difference is so slight as to be unnoticeable.

HDTV

In the United States, the emerging standards for high-definition television (HDTV) include a number of different formats and are included as part of the ATSC (Advanced Television Systems Committee) specification for Advanced TV, or ATV. The ATV standard also includes a number of formats that are roughly equivalent

---

[3] In 1995, SMPTE released a document, RP 175, that defined the pixel aspect ratio for NTSC and PAL as 160/177 and 1132/1035, respectively. Not only do these numbers conflict with just about every piece of hardware in existence, they are far more cumbersome than the standards adopted by the industry. Consequently, most manufacturers seem to have decided to ignore this document and continue with the existing numbers.

to current video resolutions as well. Table D.4 details the different resolutions that fall within this specification. In addition, the specification includes a provision whereby each of these formats can be transmitted as an interlaced signal or progressive scan. It is likely that the primary HDTV resolution that will be used is 1920 × 1080.

Table D.4   *ATV Resolutions*

Horizontal resolution	Vertical resolution	Aspect ratio
1920	1080	16:9
1280	720	16:9
640	480	4:3

Bibliography

You've probably never read an introduction to a bibliography before. If you're like me, you hardly ever read the bibliography itself, dismissing it as nothing but a few pages of densely packed text at the back of the book that might be useful to a researcher somewhere but certainly is not something worth spending a lot of time on—which is part of the reason I wanted to write an introduction, so I can try to convince you to really make use of these pages. You'll notice that this isn't a terribly big bibliography. Instead of trying to impress you with the number of sources I consulted while writing this book, I thought I'd try to list those few books (and magazines) that I found to be really worthwhile. In effect, I weeded out all the crap so you don't have to. You can thank me later. If you really *want* a huge list of further references on all the various topics covered in this book, go to the library, or get some of the books I've listed below and read *their* bibliographies.

This list is not intended to be a recommendation of the "if you only own one book on this subject" sort. Far from it, since I can make absolutely no claims for having surveyed the literature nearly that broadly. If you find a better book on any of the subjects listed, let me know. In the meantime, be assured that the books that are listed are worth reading and owning.

Adams, Ansel. *The Camera*. Boston: Little, Brown & Co., 1980.
Adams, Ansel. *The Negative*. Boston: Little, Brown & Co., 1981.
Adams, Ansel. *The Print*. Boston: Little, Brown & Co., 1983.

There are so many books out there on photography and the camera that it would probably take a separate book to list them all. Some of them are excellent, many are not. But if you have to recommend a book on the subject, who can complain if you mention one written by Ansel Adams, quite possibly the most famous photographer ever. His book *The Camera,* as well as the companion volumes *The Negative* and *The Print,* is available as a reasonably priced, high-quality paperback and should be easily locatable. He discusses the science of the camera as well as the art. Buy these books to look at the pictures, if nothing else, but I hope you'll read them and then be inspired to actually go out and take some photos yourself.

American Cinematographer Manual, 7th ed. Hollywood: ASC Press, 1993.

This is the bible for cinematographers and camera operators. Discusses cameras, film, lenses, filters, and a number of special techniques, from underwater cinematography to ultraviolet photography to stereoscopic technologies. There is also a companion volume, the *American Cinematographer Video Manual*, that deals with many of the same issues from a video and television perspective.

Konigsberg, Ira. *The Complete Film Dictionary.* San Diego: Meridian, 1989.

If you work in the film business, or want to, or just like to know about the (often intentionally arcane) terminology that is used by film professionals, you must get a copy of Konigsberg's book. It has everything from specific technical details about camera equipment to comprehensive essays on various film genres. A great reference, and a lot of fun to just poke around in.

McAlister, Micheal J. *The Language of Visual Effects.* Los Angeles: Lone Eagle Publishing, 1993.

A thorough "dictionary" of terms related to visual effects (including miniatures, opticals, CGI, camera equipment, etc.) written by a veteran visual effects supervisor.

Murray, James D., and vanRyper, William. *The Encyclopedia of Graphics File Formats*, 2nd ed. Cambridge, MA: O'Reilly & Associates, 1996.

If you only own one book on the subject of graphics file formats, this should be the one. Not only does it list specific technical information on over 100 formats, it also spends time describing image formats in general and describes a variety of compression techniques.

Rock, Irvin. *Perception.* New York: Scientific American Books, 1984.

This book covers a huge range of issues relating to how the human eye and brain are able to perceive the world. It also gives a number of examples of how to fool the eye/brain into thinking that it sees something that it doesn't. This information is useful more often than you might think.

Williamson, Samuel J., and Cummins, Herman Z. *Light and Color in Nature and Art.* New York: John Wiley & Sons, 1983.

Like the title says, the book looks at light and color not from a purely theoretical perspective, but rather as it relates to real-world phenomena. A huge number of diverse subjects are touched on, including standard stuff like photography and perception, but also topics such as firefly luminescence, paint manufacturing in the Middle Ages, desert mirages, and fata morgana.

Finally, there are a number of other references that are worth considering. The conference proceedings from the yearly SIGGRAPH conferences will usually have a number of technical papers that touch on digital compositing techniques. If you can track it down, the classic paper by Porter and Duff was presented for the 1984 session:

Porter, Thomas, and Duff, Tom. *"Compositing Digital Images."* *Computer Graphics* 18, no. 3 (July 1984): 253–259. Proceedings of SIGGRAPH '84..

There is also a fine magazine, *Cinefex,* that has been covering feature-film visual effects for over a decade now. Every issue will provide you with a number of discussions about how digital compositing techniques are being used in the real world. As a bonus, you'll also learn about model making, pyrotechnics, and make-up effects.

Cinefex, P.O. Box 20027, Riverside, CA 92516; (909) 781-1917.

Glossary

This glossary is intended to be a practical guide to words commonly used in the digital compositing field. It includes not only well-defined technical terms but also a number of colloquialisms that are often used within the industry. As mentioned in the introduction to this book, digital compositing is still a fairly new, volatile field. As such, any attempt to define the terminology that is in use within this discipline risks rapid obsolescence. What's more, many terms used in the digital compositing world can be rather ambiguous, or at least very context dependent. This is due in no small part to the fact that digital compositing is a mesh of so many different disciplines. Terms from the fields of traditional animation, computer animation, image processing, photography, computer science (both hardware and software), art, special effects, visual effects, electronics, optics, physics, film, television, video games, and multimedia have all become a part of the digital compositing lexicon. We have attempted to give some idea of how multiple-definition terms might be interpreted depending on the situation in which they are used.

If you regularly work with digital compositing software, you may find that there are a number of specific compositing operators that are not mentioned within this glossary. This omission is due to the extreme variability within the industry between different software vendors when choosing a name for a particular operation. Appendix A provides a list of typical features that are found in a compositing package, including a number of the common operators. Consequently, if you have come across a term in everyday use that is not found in this glossary, you may wish to check that appendix as well. Of course, your best bet is probably to check the manual for the particular software that is being discussed.

You will find that many entries will need to resort to the use of other digital compositing terms in their definitions. In most cases, if there is a word within a given definition that is also defined elsewhere in this glossary, that word is printed in bold. The exceptions to this rule are those words (such as "digital") that are used so often that it would be cumbersome to note their every occurrence.

A

Academy aperture: A specific 35mm film framing. See Appendix D for more details.

active region: The portion of the video signal that is used for actual image information, as opposed to blanking, closed-captioning, time code, etc.

affine: Any linear **geometric transformation** including pan, rotate, scale, and shear.

AIFF: Audio Interchange File Format. A standard **file format** for storing audio data.

algorithm: A procedure or set of instructions for solving a problem or accomplishing a particular goal.

aliasing: An artifact that is due to limited **resolution.**

alpha channel: The portion of a four-channel image that is used to store transparency information.

analog: Information/data that is continuously variable, without discrete steps or quantization. As opposed to **digital.**

anamorphic: Any distorted image that can be undistorted to restore it to its original format.

anamorphic format: A film format characterized by the fact that the image captured on the negative is horizontally squeezed by the use of a special lens. It is later unsqueezed at projection time by the appropriate amount. For most 35mm feature-film work, the standard anamorphic format produces a 2.35:1 aspect ratio when projected. See **Cinemascope, Panavision,** and Appendix D for more details.

anamorphic lens: A lens that changes the width-to-height relationship of the original image. The most common anamorphic camera lenses in film work compress the horizontal axis by 50%. See **Cinemascope.**

animated: Having characteristics that change over time.

animatic: A rough animation that gives some idea about the timing of a sequence. Essentially a moving **storyboard.**

animation: Moving imagery that is created on a frame-by-frame basis. This may be accomplished via the use of computers or with more traditional **cel animation** techniques.

animator: A person responsible for producing **animations.**

antialiasing: Techniques used to mitigate the artifacts caused by a lack of sufficient **resolution.**

aperture: (1) In a lens, the size of the opening that light passes through (usually given in terms of its **f-stop** or **t-stop**). (2) In a camera body, the mask opening that defines the area of film that will be exposed on each frame. (3) In a projector, the mask opening that defines the area of the frame that will be projected.

articulate matte: A **matte** whose shape changes over time and which is designed to accurately follow the contours of the object to which it corresponds.

artifact: A (usually undesirable) item in an image that is a side effect of the process used to generate or modify that image.

ASA rating: A standard numerical rating for specifying a film's sensitivity to light. "ASA" refers to the American Standards Association, now known as the American National Standards Institute, or ANSI. Many manufacturers now use their own specific **exposure index** instead. See also **DIN rating, ISO index.**

ASCII: Abbreviation for American Standard for Computer Information Interchange. A very common alphanumeric text interchange format. The term is used colloquially to refer to data that is stored in a text format that doesn't require a special program to decode and is usually somewhat comprehensible to a human reader.

aspect ratio: A single number that is the result of dividing the width of an image by its height. The units used to measure the width and height are irrelevant, since they will cancel when divided together to give a unitless result. See also **pixel aspect ratio.**

atmosphere: A **depth cue** that causes objects to decrease in contrast as they move into the distance.

B

background: In a composite, the bottom element over which all others are added. In general, the background makes up the majority of the image.

backing color: The color of the uniform background that is used when shooting an element for **traveling matte** extraction.

banding: An artifact that appears in areas of a color gradient where the lack of sufficient color resolution causes noticeable bands instead of a smooth transition. Also known as **contouring.** See also **Mach banding.**

base: The transparent material (usually cellulose acetate) on which emulsions are applied to make photographic film. Note that it is generally not completely transparent, but rather has a slight characteristic color that may need to be compensated for when scanning.

batch compositing: A method of compositing that entails the creation of a script or set of instructions that will be executed at a later time.

beauty pass: When using **motion control** to shoot multiple passes of an object, the beauty pass is the one that features the most significant information about the object, in contrast to other passes such as the lighting pass, shadow pass, or reflection pass.

BG: Abbreviation for **background.**

bicubic interpolation: A method of **interpolation** based on an average of the 16 nearest neighbors. See also **linear interpolation, bilinear interpolation.**

bilinear interpolation: A method of **interpolation** based on an average of the four nearest neighbors. See also **linear interpolation, bicubic interpolation.**

bit: The basic unit for representing data in a digital environment. A bit can have only two different values: 0 or 1.

bit depth: A way of specifying the **color resolution** in an image by measuring the number of bits devoted to each **component** of the pixels in the image.

bit-mapped image: An image that consists of a rectangular, two-dimensional array of **pixels.** The standard method for representing an image in a digital format.

black point: (1) On a piece of film, the measured density in the area of greatest opacity. (2) In a digital image, the numerical value that corresponds to the darkest area that will be represented when the image is eventually viewed in its final form.

bluescreen: (1) Commonly used as a generic term that refers to **bluescreen photography** or any similar process, which may use other colors as well as blue. (2) Literally, a screen of some sort of blue material that is suspended behind an object for which we wish to extract a **matte.** Ideally, the bluescreen appears to the camera as a completely uniform blue field.

bluescreen photography: The process of photographing an object in front of a bluescreen with the intention of extracting a **matte** for that object using various keying and/or color-difference techniques.

blue spill: Any contamination of the foreground subject by light reflected from the **bluescreen** in front of which it is placed. See also **spill, green spill.**

bounce light: Light that is reflected or "bounced" off other objects in a scene before it reaches the subject.

Box filter: A specific digital **filter** that is often used when **resampling** a digital image. The Box filter is fast, but fairly low quality.

burn-in: Photographic double exposure of an element over a previously exposed piece of film.

C

camera aperture: A specific 35mm film framing, also known as **full aperture.** See Appendix D for more details.

CCD: Abbreviation for charge-coupled device, a light-sensitive semiconductor that is often used in scanners and video cameras to capture an image.

cel animation: **Animation** that is the result of sequences of images drawn on individual clear acetate cels. Many aspects of traditional cel animation are now being supplemented by digital techniques.

CGI: See **computer-generated imagery.**

channel: For a given image, the subimage that is composed only of the values from a single **component** of each pixel.

characteristic curve: A curve that plots the relationship between light falling on a piece of film and the resulting density of the developed image.

chroma-keying: A **keying** technique that allows one to separate an object from its background based on colors that are unique to either the foreground or background.

chromatic resolution: Another term for **color resolution.**

chrominance: The color portion of a video signal, carrying the **hue** and **saturation** values. See also **luminance.**

Cinemascope: An **anamorphic** film format that produces an image with an aspect ratio of 2.35:1. Although Cinemascope (or CinemaScope) was originally a specific process developed by 20th Century Fox in the 1950s, it has become a generic term for the 2.35 anamorphic format. The most common lenses used for this purpose today are produced by **Panavision.** See Appendix D for more details.

Cineon: A specific image file format for film. See Appendix C.

circle of confusion: The size of the circle to which an idealized point will diverge when the lens is focused at different depths. Used as a way to measure the focus of a lens.

clip: A small piece of film, often "clipped" from a longer shot, that can be used as a reference for color, lighting, etc.

clipping: The process (intentional or otherwise) whereby data above or below a certain threshold is removed or lost. With digital images, this usually translates to colors outside a specific range.

cloud tank: A large water-filled glass enclosure that is used to create clouds and other atmospheric effects. The clouds are usually produced by injecting some opaque liquid (such as white paint) into the water.

CMY: Cyan, magenta, and yellow. The three complementary colors, or a method of specifying the colors in an image based on a mix of these three components.

color correction: Any process that alters the perceived color balance of an image.

color difference method: A compositing technique that utilizes the difference in color between the different channels of an image in order to extract a **matte.** The technique relies on the subject being photographed in front of a uniformly colored background, such as a **bluescreen.**

color resolution: The amount of data allocated for specifying the value of an individual color in an image. See also **bit depth.**

color space: Any method for representing the color in an image. Usually based on certain components such as RGB, HSV, etc.

color temperature: A method of specifying color based on an absolute temperature scale, degrees Kelvin (K). The color is equivalent to the color of light that would be emitted if a pure black object were heated to that temperature. Higher color temperatures are more blue, lower temperatures are more red.

color timer: A person who adjusts the scene-to-scene color **continuity** when preparing the final print of a film.

color timing: The color balance of a particular image or scene, or the process of color correcting and balancing that image or scene.

color wedge: A series of images that feature incremental alterations in the color of a certain element (or sometimes the entire frame) for the purpose of choosing a final value for the color of that element.

complementary color: The color that results when the primary color is subtracted from white.

complementary matte: The matte that results when the primary matte is inverted.

component: One of the elements that is used to define the color of a pixel. In most digital images, the pixel color is specified in terms of its red, green, and blue components.

component video: Video signal in which the luminance and chrominance elements are maintained separately.

composite video: Video signal in which the luminance and chrominance elements are combined (encoded) into a single signal.

compositing: The manipulated combination of at least two source images to produce an integrated result.

compositing engine: Within a package used for compositing, the code that is responsible for the actual image processing operations, in contrast to other code that may deal with the user interface, file input/output, etc.

compositor: A person who creates composites.

compression ratio: The ratio of the data sizes between the uncompressed element and the compressed equivalent.

computer-generated imagery: An image or images created or manipulated with the aid of a computer. Often used to refer specifically to 3D computer animation, although it is really a much broader term.

computer graphics: An image or images created or manipulated with the aid of a computer.

continuity: The smooth flow of action or events from one shot or scene to the next, without any indication that the different shots/scenes may have been photographed at different times or processed differently.

contouring: An **artifact** that results from not having enough **color resolution** to properly represent a color gradient. See also **Mach banding.**

contrast: The ratio of the brightest tones in an image to the darkest.

control points: The specific points that are interpreted to define the shape of a curve.

convolution filter: A matrix of numbers used to control the weighted averaging performed in a **convolve** operation. Sometimes also referred to as the **convolution mask.**

convolution kernel: The group of pixels that will be considered when performing a **convolve** operation. Generally we are only worried about the size of the kernel, which is usually a square matrix with an odd number of elements in each dimension. The most common kernel size is 3×3. Occasionally the term is used as a synonym for the **convolution filter.**

convolution mask: See **convolution filter.**

convolve: An image processing operation that involves the specialized averaging of a neighborhood of pixels using a **convolution filter.** Also known as a **spatial convolution.**

cool: A nonexact term that is used to describe an image that is biased toward the blue portion of the spectrum.

CPU: Abbreviation for central processing unit, the computational heart of a computer.

crawling: An undesirable **artifact** characterized by edges that do not remain stable over time.

cropping: The removal (intentionally or otherwise) of part of an image that is outside a specific boundary.

C-scope: Abbreviation for **Cinemascope.**

cukaloris: Panel with irregular holes cut in it to project patterned shadows onto a subject. Also known as a **kukaloris,** cuke, or cookie.

cursor: A graphical marker, usually controlled by a device such as a mouse or a tablet, that is used to point to a position or object on a computer's display.

D

D1 format: A digital **component video** format. D1 is considered to be a nearly lossless format.

D2 format: A digital **composite video** format. D2 is a lower quality than **D1,** but is also significantly less expensive.

D5 format: A digital **component video** format. D5 is considered to be of the same quality as **D1,** and also has provisions for storing **HDTV**-format imagery.

dailies: Imagery produced during the previous day's work, or a meeting to view this work.

decibel (dB): Unit of loudness measured on a logarithmic scale. The human ear can perceive a 1 dB change in loudness.

decimation: The process of throwing away unnecessary information when reducing the size of an image.

decoder: A device that separates a **composite video** signal into a **component video** signal.

deinterlace: The process of separating the two **fields** that make up a video image into two distinct images.

densitometer: Instrument used to measure the optical density of a piece of processed film.

density space: A **nonlinear color space** that is based on the density of a piece of developed negative relative to the amount of light that reached it.

depth channel: Another term for the **Z-channel.**

depth cue: Information that helps to determine the distance of an object from the camera.

depth of field: The depth of field of a specific lens is the range of acceptable focus in front of and behind the primary focus setting. It is a function not only of the specific lens used but also of the distance from the lens to the primary focal plane, and of the chosen aperture. Larger apertures will narrow the depth of field; smaller apertures will increase it.

depth of focus: A term that is often improperly used when one wishes to refer to the **depth of field.** Depth of focus is a specific term for the point *behind* the lens (inside the camera body) where a piece of film should be placed so that the image will be properly focused.

desaturation: A term to describe the removal or loss of color in an image. A completely desaturated image would consist only of shades of gray.

detail generator: An adjustment available on some video cameras that introduces additional **sharpening** into the captured image.

difference matte: A **matte** created by subtracting an image in which the subject *is* present from an otherwise identical image in which it is *not* present.

diffusion: An effect, caused by **atmosphere** or special **filters** placed on the lens, that is characterized by a scattering of light, elevated dark areas, and an overall softer look.

digital: A method of representing data via discrete, well-defined samples. As opposed to **analog.**

digital compositing: The digitally manipulated combination of at least two source images to produce an integrated result.

digitization: The process of sampling any analog subject to produce a digital representation. Within the field of digital compositing, usually refers to the process of converting a video or film source to digital information.

dilation: An image processing technique that results in brighter areas of the image increasing in size and darker areas decreasing. See also **erosion.**

DIN rating: A standard numerical rating for specifying a film's sensitivity to light. "DIN" is an abbreviation for Deutsche Industrie Norm (German Industry Standard). Many manufacturers now use their own specific **exposure index** instead. See also **ASA rating, ISO index.**

Dirac filter: Another name for the **impulse filter.**

director: The person with the primary responsibility for overseeing the creative aspects of a project or production.

dissolve: A specific **transition effect** in which one scene gradually fades out at the same time that a second scene fades in. Halfway through a linear dissolve the image will be a 50% mix of both scenes.

dither: A method for representing more colors than would normally be available with a given **palette.** Dithering uses combinations of colored pixels and relies on the fact that the human eye will average them together and interpret the result as a new intermediate color.

D-max: See **maximum density.**

D-min: See **minimum density.**

DOD: Abbreviation for **domain of definition.**

DOF: Abbreviation for **depth of field.**

domain of definition: A (usually rectangular) region that defines the maximum boundaries of useful information in an image. Generally, everything outside of the DOD will have a value of 0 in all channels of the image. The DOD is usually determined automatically, as opposed to a **region of interest.**

dots per inch: A common method for measuring spatial resolution in the print industry. The horizontal and vertical scales are assumed to be equal, unless specified otherwise.

double exposure: In the optical world, a double exposure is accomplished by exposing two different images onto a single negative. The result is a mixture of the two images. In the digital world, this effect is accomplished by mathematically averaging the two images.

double framing: The process of duplicating and repeating every frame in an image sequence. The result is a new image sequence that appears to be moving at half the original speed. Also known as double printing.

DPI: Abbreviation for **dots per inch.**

drop frame: Video footage in which two frames are dropped every minute except the tenth. It is used to compensate for the fact that time code works at exactly 30 frames per second but NTSC video runs at only 29.97 **fps.**

dubbing: The process of making a copy of a video tape.

DVE: An abbreviation for digital video effect, this usually refers to any of a number of **geometric transformations** that are typically performed by specialized real-time video equipment. Examples of a DVE move include animated pans, rotations, or flips, as well as various hardware-specific effects such as page turns or customized wipes.

DX: Abbreviation for **double exposure.**

dynamic range: (1) The range of brightness values in a scene or an image, from brightest to darkest, often expressed as a ratio. (2) In a digital image, the total number of different colors in the image.

dynamic resolution: Another term for **color resolution.**

E

edge detection: An algorithm used to enhance or isolate transition areas, or "edges," in an image.

edge matte: A specialized **matte** that includes only the outlines or borders of an object.

edge numbers: Sequential numbers printed along the edge of a piece of film by the manufacturer to help identify particular frames.

editing: The process of assembling shots and scenes into a final product, making decisions about their length and ordering.

effects animation: A term that is usually used to refer to elements that were created via **cel animation** or digital **rotoscoping** techniques but are not character related. Common examples include sparks, lightning, or smoke.

effects filter: Any of a number of different optical **filters** that can introduce **diffusion, flares,** glows, etc. Dangerous when shooting **bluescreen** elements.

EI: Abbreviation for **exposure index.**

eight-perf: A nickname for the **VistaVision** film format that comes from the fact that each VistaVision frame has eight **perforations** along each edge.

element: A discrete image or sequence of images that will be added to a composite.

emulsion: The light-sensitive material that is applied to a transparent **base** to create photographic film.

encoder: (1) A piece of video equipment that combines a **component video** signal into a **composite video** signal. (2) A generalized term used to refer to a number of different data capture devices, usually ones that convert measurements into digital data.

erosion: An image processing technique that results in darker areas of the image increasing in size and brighter areas decreasing. See also **dilation.**

E-split: See **exposure split.**

exposure index: A standardized, but manufacturer-specific, numerical rating system for specifying a film's sensitivity to light. There are also several industry-standard systems in use, including the **ASA rating,** the **ISO index,** and the **DIN rating.** To make it even more interesting, many manufacturers will specify a rating for both daylight lighting and tungsten lighting.

exposure latitude: Amount of over- or underexposure a given type of film can tolerate and still produce acceptable results.

exposure split: A simple **split-screen** shot in which multiple exposures of a given scene are combined in order to bring areas of widely divergent brightness into the same shot. Also known as an **E-split.**

exposure wedge: A series of images that feature incremental alterations in the exposure (brightness) of a certain element (or sometimes the entire frame) for the purpose of choosing a final value for the exposure of that element.

F

fade: Decreasing the brightness of an image over time, eventually resulting in a black image.

fast Fourier transform: An algorithm for converting an image so that it is represented in terms of the magnitude and phase of the various frequencies that make up the image. Yes, there *is* a regular Fourier transform, but nobody uses it because it's not . . . fast.

FFT: Abbreviation for **fast Fourier transform.**

FG: Abbreviation for **foreground.**

field: (1) An image composed of either the even or odd scan lines of a video image. Two fields played sequentially will make up a video frame. (2) A unit of measure on a **field chart.**

field chart: A method of dividing an image into a grid so that certain areas of the frame can be specified by grid coordinates.

field dominance: The order in which the fields in an interlaced image are displayed. Essentially, whether the even or the odd field is displayed first for any given frame.

field of view: The range of a scene that will be captured by a specific camera. FOV is usually measured as the number of horizontal degrees (out of 360), although a vertical field of view is also a valid measurement.

file format: A standardized description of how a piece of data (such as an image) is to be stored.

film gauge: The width of a particular film stock, i.e., 16mm, 35mm, etc.

film recorder: A device that is capable of transferring digital images to a piece of film negative.

film recording: The process of transferring digital images to a piece of film negative via the use of a **film recorder.**

film speed: A very context-dependent term that may refer to (1) the rate that film is moving through a camera or a projector (24 frames per second in normal feature-film work) or to (2) the light sensitivity of the film itself. Slow-speed film is less light sensitive; high-speed film is more sensitive.

film weave: Irregular horizontal movement (generally undesirable) of a piece of film as it moves through a camera or projector.

filter: (1) A translucent material that is placed in front of a light or camera to modify the color that is transmitted. Certain of these optical filters may also be designed to introduce specific artifacts, such as **diffusion, flares,** etc. (2) Any of a number of algorithms used within the computer for sampling an image. Different filters can be used when transforming an image, and can result in differing amounts of sharpness or artifacts. (3) The process of using either of the aforementioned types of filters.

final: The term given to a composite shot once it is considered complete and has been approved by the appropriate decision makers.

fixed matte: As opposed to a **traveling matte,** a fixed matte will not change position or shape during the shot.

flare: Any of a number of effects that will show up on an image as the result of a light source shining directly into the lens of a camera.

flashing: Flashing is an optical process whereby unprocessed negative is exposed to a small amount of light for the purpose of reducing the contrast or saturation of the scene that will eventually be photographed with that film. In the digital realm, flashing is the application of any number of nonspecific techniques to produce similar results. An image that appears to suffer from some of these characteristics is often referred to as appearing "flashed."

flat: Another term for low **contrast**.

flat lens: Another term for a **spherical lens.** Sometimes also used as a relative term for measuring the distortion and exposure variance of any lens.

flip: A simple geometric transform in which an image is mirrored about the X-axis so that it is now upside-down. This process is different from merely rotating the image 180 degrees.

flop: A simple geometric transform in which an image is mirrored about the Y-axis.

focal length: A measure of the magnification power of a given lens, based on the distance from the center of the lens to the film. Also known as simply the "length" of a lens. A longer focal length will produce greater magnification than a shorter length.

focus: (1) To adjust a lens so that the image it produces is as sharp as possible. (2) The point in space behind a lens where this sharpness occurs.

folding: The process of consolidating discrete mathematical operations into a single function.

foreground: Usually the primary element to be added to a composite and placed over the **background.** Often, there may be several foreground elements in a composite.

format: (1) The size, resolution, aspect ratio, etc. for a given image. (2) The **file format** for a given image. (3) The physical medium (such as film, video, etc.) used to capture or display an image sequence. (4) A multitude of additional variations and subcategories of the first three definitions.

four-perf: A nickname for the standard 35mm film format that refers to the fact that each frame spans four pairs of **perforations**.

FOV: Abbreviation for **field of view.**

fps: Abbreviation for **frames per second.** See **frame rate**.

fractal compression: A **lossy** image-compression algorithm that is based on repeated use of scaled and rotated pixel patterns.

frame: A single image that is usually part of a group designed to be viewed as a moving sequence.

frame rate: The rate at which sequences of images are captured or displayed. The frame rate is usually measured in frames per second, or **fps.**

freeze: The process of stopping the action. In digital compositing, this is usually accomplished by repeating the same frame for a duration of time.

freeze frame: A single frame that is held for a duration of time.

fringing: An **artifact** of the matting process in which a foreground element has a noticeable (usually bright) outline.

f-stop: A measurement of the **aperture** of a lens.

full aperture: A specific 35mm film framing, also known as **camera aperture.** See Appendix D for more details.

G

gamma: (1) In film, a measure of the contrast of an image or emulsion, based on the slope of the straight-line portion of the **characteristic curve.** (2) An adjustment applied to a video monitor to compensate for its nonlinear response to a signal. (3) A digital effect used to modify the apparent brightness of an image.

gamut: The range of colors that any given device or format is able to display or represent.

garbage matte: A rough, simple **matte** that isolates unwanted elements from the primary element in an image.

gauge: See **film gauge.**

Gaussian blur: A specific method for blurring an image based on a **Gaussian filter.**

Gaussian filter: A specific digital **filter** that is often used when resampling an image.

gel: Abbreviation for gelatin filter, a flexible colored optical **filter.**

generation loss: The loss of quality of an image due to repeated duplication. Generation loss is significantly reduced and in some cases completely eliminated when dealing with digital images.

geometric transformation: An effect that causes some or all of the pixels in a given image to change their current location. Such effects include **translation, rotation, scaling, warping,** and various specialized distortion effects.

GIF: Graphics Interchange Format, a specific image file format. See Appendix C.

G-matte: Abbreviation for **garbage matte.**

grading: Another term for **color timing,** used primarily in Great Britain.

grain: The individual particles of silver halide in a piece of film that capture an image when exposed to light. Because the distribution and sensitivity of these particles are not uniform, they are perceived (particularly when projected) as causing a noticeable graininess. Different film stocks will have different visual grain characteristics.

graphical user interface: A **user interface** that utilizes images and other graphical elements to simplify the process of interacting with the software. Also known as the "look and feel" of the software.

gray card: A card (gray) usually designed to reflect about 18% of the light that strikes it; used as a reference for measuring exposure.

grayscale image: A completely **desaturated** image, with no color, only shades of gray.

greenscreen: Identical in use and concept to a **bluescreen** (only it's green).

green spill: Any contamination of the foreground subject by light reflected from the **greenscreen** in front of which it is placed. See also **spill, blue spill.**

GUI: Abbreviation for **graphical user interface.**

H

handles: Extra frames at the beginning and end of a shot that are not intended for use in the final shot but are included in the composite in case the shot's length changes slightly.

HDTV: High-definition television. A proposed new television standard with significantly greater spatial resolution than standard **NTSC, PAL,** or **SECAM.**

Hermite curve: A specific type of **spline curve** that allows for explicit control over the curve's tangent at every **control point.**

high-pass filter: A **spatial filter** that enhances high-frequency detail. It is used as a method for **sharpening** an image.

histogram: A graphical representation of the distribution (usually frequency of occurrence) of a particular characteristic of the pixels in an image.

histogram equalization: An **image processing** technique that adjusts the contrast in an image so that it fits into a certain range.

histogram sliding: Equivalent to adding a certain number to the values of every pixel in an image.

histogram stretching: Equivalent to multiplying the values of every pixel in an image by a certain amount.

HLS: Hue, luminance, and **saturation.** A method of specifying the colors in an image based on a mix of these three components.

hold: To stop the action by using the same frame repeatedly.

hold-out matte: A **matte** used to prevent a foreground element from completely obscuring an object in the background plate.

hot: A nonexact term for describing an image that is too bright. Completely unrelated to the terms **warm** and **cool.**

HSB: **Hue, saturation,** and brightness. A method of specifying the colors in an image based on a mix of these three components.

HSL: **Hue, saturation**, and lightness. A method of specifying the colors in an image based on a mix of these three components.

HSV: **hue, saturation,** and **value.** A method of specifying the colors in an image based on a mix of these three components.

hue: A specific color from the color spectrum, disregarding its **saturation** or **value.**

Huffman coding: A **lossless** image-compression scheme. See also **run-length encoding, JPEG, MPEG.**

I

ILM: See **Industrial Light and Magic.**

image processing: The use of various tools and algorithms to modify digital images within a computer.

IMAX: A proprietary film capture/projection process that uses an extremely large-format negative.

impulse filter: A specific digital **filter** that is often used when **resampling** a digital image. It is considered to be the lowest-quality, highest-speed filter in common use. Also known as the **Dirac filter** or the **nearest-neighbor filter.**

in-betweening: The process of **interpolating** between the **keyframes** of an animation sequence.

in-camera effects: **Visual effects** that are accomplished solely during principle photography, involving no additional postproduction.

indexed color: A method of storing image data, in which the value of the pixel refers to an entry in a table of available colors instead of a numerical specification of the color itself.

Industrial Light and Magic: A pioneering visual effects company that was the first to widely use digital compositing in feature-film work.

interframe coding: The process used in **MPEG** encoding whereby intermediate images in a sequence are defined by their deviation from specific keyframes.

interlacing: The technique used to produce video images whereby two alternating **field** images are displayed in rapid sequence so that they appear to produce a complete **frame.**

interocular distance: The spacing b etween the eyes, usually referring to the human average of about 2½inches; an important factor for the production of **stereoscopic imagery.**

interpolation: The process of using certain rules or formulas to derive new data based on a set of existing data. See also **bicubic interpolation, bilinear interpolation, linear interpolation.**

ISO index: A standard numerical rating for specifying a film's sensitivity to light. "ISO" refers to the International Standards Organization. The **ISO Index** actually incorporates both the American **ASA rating** and the European **DIN rating.** Many manufacturers now use their own specific **exposure index** instead. See also **ASA rating, DIN rating.**

J

JPEG: A (typically **lossy**) compression technique, or a specific image format that utilizes this technique. "JPEG" is an abbreviation for the Joint Photographic Experts Group.

K

kernel: The group of pixels that will be considered when performing some kind of spatial filtering. See also **convolution kernel.**

key: Another term for a **matte.**

keying: The process of algorithmically extracting an object from its background and combining it with a different background.

keyframe: Any frame in which a particular aspect of an item (its size, location, color, etc.) is specifically defined. The non-keyframe frames will then contain **interpolated** values.

keyframe animation: The process of creating animation using **keyframes.**

keyframing: Another term for **keyframe animation.**

keystoning, keystone distortion: A geometric distortion resulting when a rectangular plane is projected or photographed at an angle not perpendicular to the axis of the lens. The result is that the rectangle becomes trapezoidal.

kukaloris: See **cukaloris.**

L

lens flare: An **artifact** of a bright light shining directly into the lens assembly of a camera.

letterboxing: A method for displaying images that preserves the **aspect ratio** of the film as it was originally shot, using black to specify areas outside of the original frame.

lighting reference: A **stand-in** object that can be used to judge the lighting in a scene.

linear color space: A **color space** in which the relationship between a pixel's digital value and its visual brightness remains constant (linear) across the full **gamut** of black to white.

linear interpolation: A method of **interpolation** that is based on the average of the two nearest neighbors. See also **bicubic interpolation, bilinear interpolation.**

linear space: See **linear color space.**

locked-off camera: A camera whose position and lens settings do not change over the duration of the shot.

log space: An abbreviation for **logarithmic color space,** a **nonlinear color space** whose conversion function is similar to the curve produced by the logarithmic equation.

long lens: A relative term, in contrast to a **short lens.** Also known as a **telephoto lens.**

look-up table: A method of mapping input colors to output colors. Instead of using an algorithm to define the color modification, a table of values is created so that every possible input color will have an output value defined.

lossless compression: A method of compressing and storing a digital image in such a fashion that the original image can be completely reconstructed without any data loss.

lossy compression: A method of compressing and storing a digital image in such a fashion that it is impossible to perfectly reconstruct the original image.

low-pass filter: A **spatial filter** that removes high-frequency detail. It is used as a method for blurring an image.

luminance: In common usage, synonymous with brightness. In the **HSL** color space, luminance is the weighted average of the red, green, and blue components.

luma-keying: A matte-extraction technique that uses the **luminance** values in the image.

LUT: Abbreviation for **look-up table.**

LZW compression: A **lossless** compression method that finds repeated patterns in blocks of pixels in an image. Variations of LZW compression are used in a number of image file formats, including **GIF** and **TIFF.** "LZW" stands for Lempel-Ziv-Welch.

M

Mach banding: An optical illusion (named after the physicist Ernst Mach) in which the eye perceives emphasized edges in areas of color transition. This illusion causes the eye to be more sensitive to **contouring** artifacts.

macro: (1) In the digital world, a combination of functions or effects that are grouped together to create a new effect. (2) A specialized lens that is capable of focusing at an extremely close distance to the subject.

mask: An image used to selectively restrict or modify certain image processing operations on another image.

matte: An image used to define or control the transparency of another image. See also **articulate matte, complementary matte, difference matte, edge matte, fixed matte, garbage matte, G-matte, hold-out matte, rotoscoped matte, static matte, traveling matte.**

matte channel: Another name for the **alpha channel** in a four-channel image.

matte line: An artifact of the matting process wherein a foreground element has a noticeable outline.

matte painting: A hand-painted image, usually intended to be photorealistic, that is combined with live-action footage.

maximum density: The point of exposure at which additional light (on the negative) will no longer affect the resulting image. The definitions of maximum and **minimum density** would be reversed if you were speaking of print (reversal) film instead of negative. Also known as **D-max.**

median filter: A specialized **spatial filter** that removes pixel anomalies by determining the median value in a group of neighboring pixels.

minimum density: The point of exposure just below the amount needed (on the negative) to start affecting the resulting image. The definitions of minimum and **maximum density** would be reversed if you were speaking of print (reversal) film instead of negative. Also known as **D-min.**

Mitchell filter: A specific digital **filter** that is often used when **resampling** a digital image. The Mitchell filter is particularly well suited to **transforming** images into a higher resolution than they were originally.

moco: Abbreviation for **motion control.**

monochrome: An image that contains only a single hue, and the only variation is in the luminance of that hue. Typically, a monochrome image consists only of shades of gray.

morphing: A process in which two image sequences are **warped** so that key features align as closely as possible and then a selective **dissolve** is applied to transition from the first sequence to the second. The result should be a seamless transformation between the two sequences.

motion blur: An artifact caused by the fact that a camera's shutter is open for a finite duration as it captures an image. Any object that is moving during that time will appear blurred along the path that it was traveling.

motion control: A method of using computer-controlled mechanisms to drive an object's movement so that it is continuously repeatable.

motion-control camera: A camera whose position, orientation, and lens settings are **motion controlled.**

MPEG: A (typically **lossy**) compression technique specifically designed to deal with sequences of images, or the format of the images produced by this technique. "MPEG" is an abbreviation for the Moving Pictures Experts Group.

multimedia: A broad categorization that generally refers to some method of displaying information using sound and imagery simultaneously.

multiplaning: A technique that simulates a moving camera by translating the different layers in a composite by an amount that is appropriate to their intended distance from this camera. Layers that are intended to appear farther away are moved by a smaller amount than layers that are intended to be nearer, producing a simulated **parallax** effect.

N

ND filter: See **neutral density filter.**

nearest-neighbor filter: Another term for the **impulse filter.**

neutral density filter: An optical **filter** that is designed to reduce the intensity of the light passing through it without affecting the color of the light.

Newton's rings: An artifact, usually seen in optical printing, characterized by circular moiré patterns that appear in the image.

NG: Abbreviation for "no good."

nonlinear color space: A **color space** in which the relationship between a pixel's digital value and its visual brightness does not remain constant (linear) across the full **gamut** of black to white.

nonlinear editing: Editing that does not require that the sequence be worked on sequentially.

nonsquare pixel: A pixel whose width is not the same size as its height. The ratio of width to height is measured in terms of a **pixel aspect ratio.**

NTSC: National Television Systems Committee. Refers not only to the committee itself, but also to the standard that they established for color television in the United States and other countries. It carries 525 lines of information, played back at a rate of approximately 30 frames per second (actually 29.97). Due to its unreliable color reproduction ability, the initials are often said to stand for "Never The Same Color" or "Never Twice the Same Color."

O

off-line compositing: Another term for **batch compositing.**

Omnimax: A proprietary film capture/projection process that uses the same large-format negative as the **IMAX** process but is designed for projection on the interior of a dome-shaped screen.

on-line compositing: A method of compositing that uses a highly interactive hardware/software combination to quickly provide the results of every compositing operation. Distinguished from an **off-line** or **batch compositing** system.

opaque: The characteristic of an image that causes it to fully obscure any image that is behind it. Opaque is the opposite of **transparent.**

optical compositing: The process of using an optical printer to produce composite imagery.

optical flow analysis: A method for procedurally determining the movement of objects in an image by examining the full sequence from which the image was extracted.

optical printer: A device used to combine one or more different film elements and rephotograph them onto a new piece of film.

overcranked: Footage shot at a faster-than-normal rate is said to have been shot overcranked.

oversampling: Sampling data at a higher-than-normal resolution in order to mitigate sampling errors or inaccuracies from uncharacteristic data.

P

paintbox: Usually used in the video postproduction world as a generic term for a variety of paint and compositing devices.

paint software: A program that allows the artist to "paint" directly onto an image in the computer using a device such as a **tablet** or a mouse.

PAL: Phase alternation by line. A standard for color television found in many European, African, and Asian countries. It carries 625 lines of resolution, played back at a rate of 25 frames per second.

palette: The range of colors available for use in any particular application. A system that uses eight bits per channel would have a palette of over 16 million colors.

pan and scan: A technique that is used to convert images shot with a **widescreen** film process to a less expansive video format. It generally involves selectively cropping the image to fit into the new frame, arbitrarily choosing what portions of the image are unnecessary.

Panavision: (1) A manufacturer of motion picture lenses and cameras. (2) The trade name for a specific wide screen process and lenses developed by the Panavision company. It is an anamorphic format that produces an image with a 2.35:1 aspect ratio. See also **anamorphic format, Cinemascope.**

parallax: The perceptual difference in an object's location or spatial relationship when seen from different vantage points.

particle system: A 3D computer graphics technique that is used to create a large number of objects that obey well-defined behavioral rules. Useful not only for controlling multitudes of discrete objects such as asteroids or flocks of birds, but also as a tool for creating natural phenomena such as fire or smoke.

perf: Abbreviation for **perforation.**

perforation: One of the sprocket holes that runs along the edges of a piece of film. They are used to guide the film reliably through the camera.

persistence of vision: The characteristic of the human eye that allows it to continue to perceive an image for a fraction of a second after it disappears.

perspective: A term relating to the size and depth relationships of the objects in a scene.

perspective compensation: The use of a two-dimensional **geometric transformation** to correct a 3D discrepancy.

picture element: See **pixel.**

pipeline: A well-defined set of processes for achieving a certain result.

pixel: Originally an abbreviation for "picture element," although the term "pixel" is generally considered to be a true word nowadays. A digital image is composed of a rectangular array of individual colored points. Each one of these points is referred to as a pixel.

pixel aspect ratio: The width of a given pixel divided by its height. A number of image representation methods do not use pixels that have an equivalent width and height. The pixel aspect ratio is independent of a particular image's **aspect ratio.** See also **nonsquare pixels.**

plate: A piece of original photography that is intended to be used as an **element** in a composite.

playback speed: The rate (usually measured in frames per second) at which a sequence of images is displayed.

posterization: An effect applied to an image that intentionally causes **banding.**

postproduction: Work done once principle photography has been completed.

practical effects: Effects that are accomplished "live," without any postproduction. Practical effects include explosions, artificial rain, smoke, etc.

precomp: Abbreviation for **preliminary composite.**

preliminary composite: (1) Any intermediate imagery that is produced during the digital compositing process that can be saved and used as a new source element. (2) A quickly assembled composite that is designed to show the relationship of various photographic elements to determine if any of these elements needs to be reshot.

premultiplied image: An image whose red, green, and blue **channels** have been multiplied by a **matte.** Usually this matte is stored as the **alpha channel** of this image.

preproduction: Any planning, testing, or initial design that is done before actual production begins.

Primatte: A proprietary **chroma-keying** tool that can be used to extract a **matte** from an image shot in front of a uniform backing.

print: A positive image that is suitable for viewing directly or for projection. Generally produced from an original negative.

procedural paint: A specialized form of **paint software** that can actually apply brush strokes and other paint processes over a sequence of images instead of just a single frame. Parameters for these painting effects can usually be animated as well.

processing: (1) The time spent by the computer as it computes any instructions that it has been given. (2) At a photo laboratory, the process of developing and printing a piece of film.

producer: Administrative head of a project. Responsible for budget, schedule, etc.

production sense: The near-mythical ability of an experienced digital artist to decide on the proper course of action when creating a visual effects shot.

progressive scan: A method of displaying an image that does not rely on **interlacing.**

projection speed: The **playback speed** for projected imagery.

proxy: A scaled-down image that is used as a stand-in for a higher-resolution original.

pull a matte: The process of creating a **matte** for an object, usually through **keying** techniques.

Q

quantization :   The process of assigning discrete digital values to samples taken from a continuous analog data set.

quantization artifact: A term generally used to refer to a visually noticeable artifact of the **quantization** process.

quantizing: Colloquial term for a **quantization artifact.**

R

raw stock: Unexposed, unprocessed film.

real-time: (1) Displaying a sequence of images at the same speed as they will be viewed in their final form. (2) Computational processing that appears to be nearly instantaneous.

rear projection: A compositing process in which the previously photographed background scene is projected onto a large translucent screen from behind while the foreground action takes place. The composite is thus considered an **in-camera effect.**

record: One of the red, green, or blue color-sensitive layers in a piece of film. Thus, the "blue record" is equivalent to a digital image's blue **channel.**

region of interest: A (usually rectangular) region that is determined by the user in order to limit certain calculations. See also **domain of definition.**

release print: A print of a movie that will be sent to theaters for display. A release print is several generations removed from the original negative.

render: The process of creating a synthetic image from a 3D database.

RenderMan: Specialized **rendering** software offered by Pixar, Inc.

repo: See **reposition.**

reposition: The process of adjusting the placement of an **element** within the frame.

resampling: The process of reading previously **sampled** data for the purpose of converting or modifying it.

resolution: The amount of data that is used to capture an image. The term is typically used to refer specifically to the **spatial resolution** of a digital image. See also **color resolution, temporal resolution.**

resolution independence: The characteristic of a software package that allows the user to easily work with and move between an arbitrary number of different **resolutions.**

RGB: Red, green, and blue. The three primary colors, or a method of specifying the colors in an image based on a mix of these three components.

ride film: A location-based entertainment that features a film whose camera movements are synchronized with some sort of moving seat or platform.

ringing: A visual **artifact,** often caused by excessive **sharpening,** that is characterized by overemphasized transitions between bright and dark areas in an image.

RLA: A specific image file format. See Appendix C.

ROI: Abbreviation for **region of interest.** Also used in the financial world as an abbreviation for Return On Investment, something your employer is probably worrying about right now.

rotation: A **geometric transformation** that changes the orientation of an image relative to a certain axis.

rotoscope: Originally the name of a device patented in 1917 by Max Fleischer to aid in **cel animation.** Now used as a general term for the process of creating imagery or mattes on a frame-by-frame basis by hand.

rotoscoped matte: A **matte** created via **rotoscoping** techniques.

RP: Abbreviation for **rear projection.**

RTFM: Abbreviation for "read the manual" (sort of), a suggestion that is often given when someone asks a question instead of taking the time to look it up themselves.

run-length encoding: A **lossless** compression scheme that consolidates sequences of identical pixels into a single data representation.

rushes: Another term for **dailies,** used primarily in Great Britain.

S

sampling: (1) The process of reading a signal at specific time increments. see also **digitization.** (2) The process of reading the color value from a pixel or a group of pixels.

saturation: The brilliance or purity of a given color. The difference between a pastel and a pure color is the amount of saturation.

scaling: A **geometric transformation** that changes the size of an image, usually without changing its location or orientation.

scan line: A single horizontal row of pixels in a digital image.

scanner: A device for **digitizing** film, print material, etc.

scene: (1) The image captured by a camera. (2) A collection of shots that share a common setting or theme.

Scope: Abbreviation for **Cinemascope.**

screen resolution: The number of horizontal and vertical pixels that a given display device is capable of showing. This should be independent of the resolution that the system is capable of processing.

SECAM: Officially this is an acronym for *séquentiel couleur à mémoire,* but most English speakers use the translation "sequential color and memory." A standard for color television used in France and a few African and Eastern European nations. It carries 625 lines of resolution, played back at a rate of 25 frames per second.

sequence: (1) A collection of images designed to be played sequentially. (2) A group of related **scenes** in a film, usually set in the same time and/or location.

server: A computer that is shared over a network by several users.

SFX: Often used as an abbreviation for **special effects,** although sound effects people will dispute this usage.

sharpening: The process of applying an algorithm that emphasizes the edges in an image. The result is an image that appears to have increased **sharpness.**

sharpness: The visual sense of the abruptness of an edge.

short lens: A relative term, in contrast to a **long lens.** Also known as a **wide-angle lens.**

shot: An unbroken continuous image **sequence.**

Showscan: A proprietary film capture/projection process that is characterized by a large-format negative and a playback speed of 60 frames per second.

shutter angle: The part of a motion picture camera that determines how long a given area of film will be exposed to a scene. Most cameras have the ability to adjust their shutter angle. A larger shutter angle will result in increased **motion blur** on moving objects.

shutter speed: The amount of time that a camera will spend capturing an individual image.

SIGGRAPH: The Special Interest Group for Graphics, a subgroup under the Association for Computing Machinery; and the major organization for graphics professionals. Also, the annual conference sponsored by this group, which features a large number of courses, seminars, and really big parties.

sinc filter: A specific digital **filter** that is often used when **resampling** a digital image. The sinc filter is particularly well suited to **transforming** images into a lower resolution than they were originally.

skip frames: A method of speeding up the motion of a sequence of images by removing selected (usually regularly spaced) frames. Also known as skip printing.

slate: Information about a particular shot that is placed at the head of the shot, before the actual image begins.

slop comp, slap comp: A very rough initial composite that is usually used to test or visualize basic element relationships.

slow-mo: Abbreviation for **slow motion.**

slow motion: Imagery that was filmed at a faster speed than it is to be projected. The result is a sequence that appears to be moving slower than normal.

SMPTE: Society of Motion Picture and Television Engineers.

solarization: An effect that is produced when a range of brightness within an image is inverted. Can be used to mimic an optical effect that occurs with extreme overexposure.

spatial aliasing: An **artifact** that is due to limited **spatial resolution.**

spatial convolution: See **convolve.**

spatial filter: A method of sampling and modifying the data in an image by looking at pixel groups.

spatial resolution: A measurement of the amount of data used to capture an image. In a digital image, spatial resolution is usually specified by giving the X and Y dimensions of the image as measured in **pixels.**

special effects: A term used to encompass both **practical effects** and **visual effects.**

special visual effects: See **visual effects.**

spherical lens: A lens that does not change the apparent width-to-height relationship of the scene being photographed. This is in contrast to an **anamorphic lens.**

spill: Any light in a scene that strikes an object it was not intended to illuminate. See also **blue spill, green spill.**

spline curve: A continuous smooth curve defined by a certain number of **control points.**

split-screen: A basic composite in which two elements are combined using a simple matte with little or no articulation.

square pixel: A **pixel** with equal *X* and *Y* dimensions.

squeezed image: An image that has been **anamorphically** compressed.

stabilization: The process of removing bounce or jitter from a sequence of images.

staircasing: A **spatial aliasing artifact** in which a line or edge appears jagged, like the profile of a staircase, instead of smooth.

stand-in: A reference object photographed in a particular scene that can later be used to help match the color and lighting of any new elements that will be added to that scene.

static matte: Another term for a **fixed matte.**

steadiness: An image sequence in which the individual frames are stable relative to each other and do not suffer from any frame-to-frame jitter or bounce.

steady test: A test to determine if a camera or the imagery shot with that camera is steady.

stereoscopic imagery: Imagery that is designed to send a different image to each observer's left and right eyes, thereby producing a sense of depth.

stochastic sampling: A random or semirandom sampling of a data set. Used for **antialiasing, motion blur,** etc.

stock: General term for motion picture film, or the specific manufacturer, manufacturer's product code, or rating of that film.

stop: A way of measuring exposure that traces back to the different **f-stop** settings available on any given lens. F-stops on a lens are calibrated so that each successive stop will give twice the exposure. Thus, "increase the brightness by one stop" means to double the brightness; "decrease by two stops" would result in one-fourth the original brightness.

stop-motion animation: An animation technique that involves photographing miniature objects or characters a frame at a time, changing the pose or position of the object between each frame. The result, when played back at normal speed, is of a continuously animating object.

storyboard: A sequence of drawings that shows the intended action in a scene. Used as a visualization tool before the scene is shot.

strobing: A rhythmic flicker in a moving image.

subpixel: Any technique that works at a resolution of greater than a single pixel, usually accomplished by making slight weighted corrections to several surrounding pixels.

super: Abbreviation for **superimpose.**

superblack: Any brightness level that drops below the normal representation of black for a given image or device. In video, superblack levels may be used for keying.

superimpose: To place one image on top of another, usually with some transparency involved.

super 35:   A specific 35mm film format. See Appendix D for more details.

superwhite: Any brightness level that rises above the normal representation of white for a given image or device.

T

tablet: A user-input device that provides a greater amount of control than the traditional computer mouse. Generally used in conjunction with a special pen.

tail slate: **Slate** information that is recorded at the end of the shot instead of the beginning. Generally only used in live-action photography; the slate information is filmed upside-down, to distinguish it from a normal slate.

take: When a particular shot is photographed multiple times in order to achieve a desired result, each time is referred to as a "take." This concept extends to digital compositing, where each test that is sent to film or video is usually kept track of by a "take number."

TARGA: A specific image file format. See Appendix C.

telecine: A device for rapidly converting motion picture film into a video format. Some newer telecine devices will convert to **HDTV** resolutions as well. A telecine device is much faster than a film **scanner,** but will produce lower-quality results.

telephoto lens: Any lens that has a longer-than-normal **focal length.** For a 35mm camera, a focal length of 50mm is considered normal, since it reasonably duplicates the magnification of a human eye.

temp comp: See **temporary composite.**

temporal: relating somehow to time or something that changes over time.

temporal aliasing: An **artifact** that is due to limited **temporal resolution.**

temporal resolution: A measurement of the amount of data used to capture a sequence of images. Temporal resolution is usually specified by giving the number of frames per second used to capture the sequence.

temporary composite: A rough composite produced for a number of different reasons, usually to better judge the spatial and color relationships of the elements in a scene so that they can be modified to produce a **final** composite.

TGA: See **TARGA.**

3D graphics: **Computer graphics** that involves the creation of three-dimensional models within the computer.

3:2 pulldown: Usually synonymous with **2:3 pulldown.**

3:2 pullup: Usually synonymous with **2:3 pullup.**

TIFF: Tagged Image File Format, a specific image file format. See Appendix C.

time code: An electronic indexing method used with video tapes. Time code is measured in hours, minutes, seconds, and frames.

timeline graph: A graph that represents the temporal relationships between objects or data.

timing: (1) A general term referring to how a particular event or object moves or evolves over a period of time. (2) See **color timing.**

tracking: The process of selecting a particular region of an image and determining that region's movement over time.

transformation: Usually refers to a **geometric transformation.**

transition effect: A method for moving from one **scene** to the next. See also **wipe, dissolve.**

translation: A **geometric transformation** that refers only to a change in position, without a change in scale or rotation.

translucent: A term that refers to something that is partially **transparent**; usually implies some additional image distortion, such as blurring.

transparent: The characteristic of an image that allows other images that are behind it to still be partially visible. Transparent is the opposite of **opaque.**

traveling matte: Any **matte** that changes over time, as opposed to a **static matte.**

t-stop: A measurement of the **aperture** of a lens that also takes into account the amount of light lost when passing through the lens elements themselves.

2D graphics: **Computer graphics** that does not use any **3D** techniques and thus involves no explicit depth information.

2:3 pulldown: A method for converting 24-fps film to 30-fps video.

2:3 pullup: A method for converting 30-fps video to 24-fps film.

U

Ultimatte: A proprietary tool based on the **color difference method** that can be used to extract a matte from an image shot in front of a uniform backing.

UNIX: A powerful operating system developed in the 1960s. It is most popular on high-end workstations, although an excellent variant, LINUX, is available for a number of platforms, including PCs.

unsharp masking: A particular technique used to **sharpen** an image that involves subtracting a slightly blurred image from the original. Used not only in the digital realm but also as a photographic technique.

unsteadiness: Not possessing the characteristic of **steadiness.**

user interface: The portion of a computer program that deals specifically with how the user interacts with the software. See also **graphical user interface.**

V

value: In the **HSV** color space, the value equals the maximum of the red, green, and blue components.

vaporware: A product that does not yet exist, but is nevertheless being promised for delivery.

VFX: Abbreviation for **visual effects.**

VHS: A video recording format that carries a pathetic 240 lines of resolution.

vignetting: A camera or lens artifact characterized by a darkening of the image in the corners of the frame.

VistaVision (or **Vistavision**): A specialized 35mm film format that runs the film through the camera horizontally instead of vertically and is able to capture more than twice the resolution of a standard 35mm frame. Generally only used for **visual effects** work nowadays. See Appendix D for more details. Also known as **eight-perf.**

visual effects: A broad term that refers to just about anything that cannot be captured using standard photographic techniques. Visual effects can be accomplished **in-camera** or via a number of different **optical** or digital **post-production** processes. Visual effects are a subcategory of **special effects.**

visual effects producer: The individual responsible for the administrative side of visual effects production.

visual effects supervisor: The individual responsible for the creative and technical side of visual effects production.

W

warm: A nonexact term used to describe an image that is biased toward the red portion of the spectrum.

warping: A geometric, per-pixel distortion of an image, often based on some kind of spline- or grid-based control.

warping engine: Within a package used for compositing, the code that is responsible for any **geometric transformations.**

weave: See **film weave.**

wedge: See **color wedge, exposure wedge.**

white point: (1) On a piece of film, the measured density in the area of least opacity. (2) In a digital image, the numerical value that corresponds to the brightest area that will be represented when the image is eventually viewed in its final form.

wide-angle lens: Any lens that has a smaller-than-normal **focal length.** For a 35mm camera, a focal length of 50mm is considered normal, since it reasonably duplicates the magnification of a human eye.

widescreen: A generic term that usually refers to any image with an **aspect ratio** greater than 1.33:1.

wipe: A specific **transition effect** in which one scene is horizontally or vertically revealed to replace another scene.

wire removal: A generic term for the process of using digital painting or compositing techniques to remove undesirable wires, rigs, or harnesses that were needed to aid certain stunts or **practical effects.**

witness points: Specific objects placed into a scene that can later be analyzed to determine the movement and configuration of the camera that photographed the shot.

working resolution: The resolution of the images that will be produced by any given compositing process.

X

x: An abbreviation used to denote a **frame.** "24x" denotes 24 frames.

X-*axis*:   Generally the horizontal axis.

Y

Y-*axis*:   Generally the vertical axis.

YIQ: A color space used for **NTSC** television, in which the brightness (Y), orange-cyan (I), and green-magenta (Q) components are encoded together.

Z

Z-*axis*:   The axis perpendicular to the **X-axis** and the **Y-axis,** and consequently the axis that is used to represent depth.

Z-buffer: Another term for a **Z-depth image.**

Z-channel: A **Z-depth image** that is integrated with a color image as an additional **channel.**

Z-depth compositing: Compositing images together with the use of a **Z-buffer** to determine their relative depths, or distances from the camera.

Z-depth image: A specialized image that uses the brightness of each pixel to specify the relative depth for each pixel in the corresponding RGB image. This depth may be measured relative to some arbitrary fixed point in space or relative to the virtual camera that is being used to capture the scene.

zoom: (1) In a real camera, to increase the **focal length** of the camera's lens, magnifying a portion of the scene. (2) With digital images, to increase the scale of a portion of an image in order to duplicate the effect of a camera zoom.

Index

Plate 53 *A scene with two light sources of different intensity. (a) Both bulbs seem to have the same intensity.*

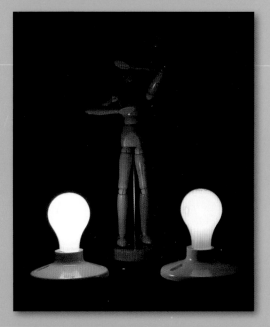

Plate 53 *(b) Reduced exposure reveals the difference between the two light sources.*

Plate 53 *(c) The image in Plate 53a after attempting to digitally decrease the brightness.*

Plate 54 *An image represented with nonlinear Cineon encoding.*

Plate 55 *Color correction in linear color space (left) versus nonlinear space (right).*

Plate 56 *Warping of the two elements involved in the morph. (a) The skull element warped to match the smiley face.*

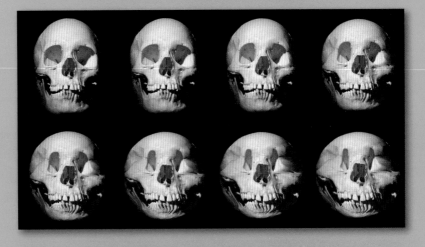

Plate 56 *(b) The smiley face element warped to match the skull.*

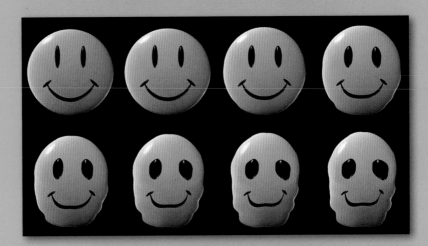

Plate 57 *The final morph transition between the two elements.*

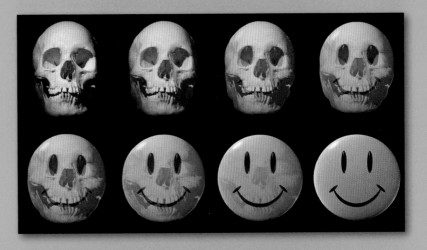

Plate 58   *A composite image created for the film* Speed.

Plate 59   *The original plate for this scene.*

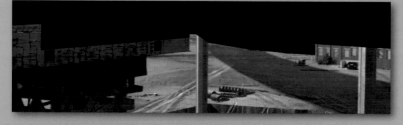

Plate 60   *A digital matte painting created for this shot.*

Plates 61–63
Three final frames from the film Star Trek: Insurrection.

Plates 61–63 from *Star Trek: Insurrection*™ & © 1998 Paramount Pictures.

Plate 64 *The original plate for the scene. This frame corresponds to Plate 61.*

Plate 65 *A composite image created for the film* Con Air.

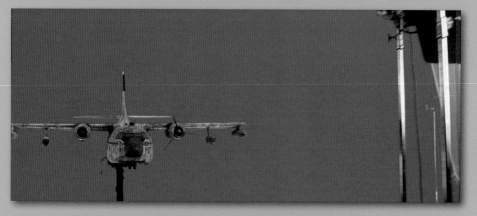

Plate 66 *A bluescreen element of the plane miniature.*

Plate 67 *The original background plate.*

Plate 68 *One of the lighting passes for the plane.*

Plates 66–68 from *Con Air* © Touchstone Pictures and Jerry Bruckheimer.

Plate 69 *A composite image created for one of the Budweiser "Lizards" commercials.*

Plate 70 *One of the bluescreen elements used to create the shot.*

Plate 71 *A composite image created for the film* Independence Day.

Plate 72 *The original background plate.*

Plate 73 *An element for the scene that features a miniature spaceship and a smoke effect.*

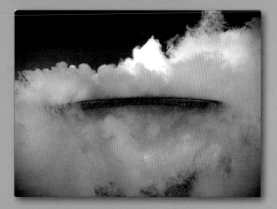

Plate 74 *An element for the scene that was shot in a cloud tank. Note the stand-in object that is used for the spacecraft.*

Plate 75   *A composite image created for the film* X-Files: Fight the Future.

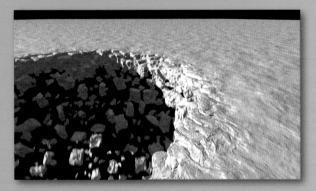

Plate 76   *A miniature element that provides the main ice sheet.*

Plate 77   *A geyser element shot in front of a greenscreen.*

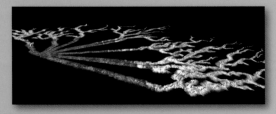

Plate 78   *A CG element that provides the cracks in the ice.*

Plate 79   *The human figures in the scene, photographed on a bluescreen surface.*

Plate 80 *A set of composite images created for the IMAX film* T-Rex: Back to the Cretaceous. *(a) The left eye's view.*

Plate 80 *(b) The right eye's view.*

Plate 81 *The original background plate.*

Plate 82 *Computer-generated dinosaurs and water.*

Plates 80–82 from *T-Rex: Back to the Cretaceous* © 1998 by the IMAX Corporation.

Plate 83 *A composite image created for the film* The Prince of Egypt.

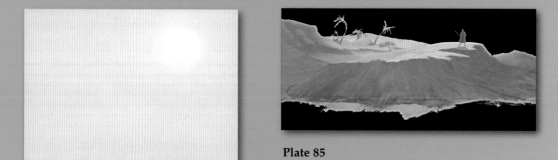

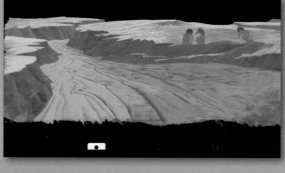

Plate 84

Plate 85

Plate 86

Plates 83–86 Photos from the motion picture *The Prince of Egypt*™ & © 1998 DreamWorks L.L.C., reprinted with permission of DreamWorks Animation.

Plate 88

Plate 87

Plate 89

Plate 90   *Computer-generated dust element.*

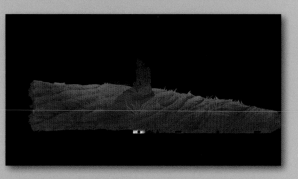

Plate 91

Plate 92   *A layout of the scene, showing the depth relationships between the various elements.*

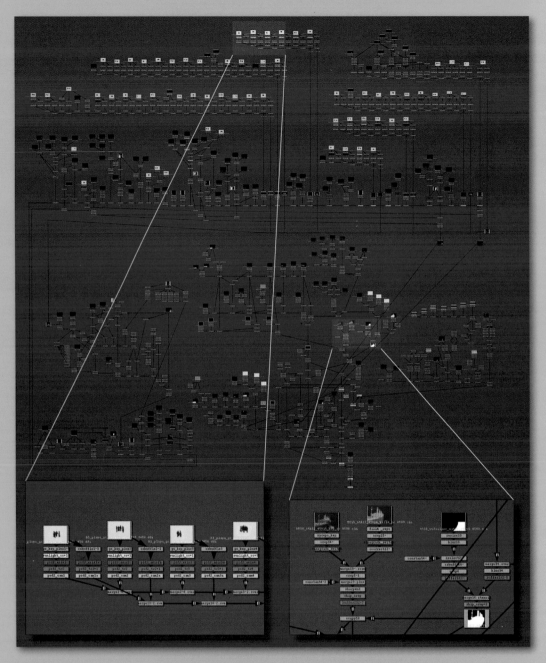

Plate 93 *The script used to create the image shown in Plate 94. Sections are magnified to show detail.*

Plate 94 *A composite image created for the film* Titanic.

Plate 95 *An element that features a miniature of the ship.*

Plate 96 *An intermediate element that contains computer-generated water and an animated sky.*

Plate 97 *A computer-generated dock element.*

Plate 98 *An element used to control the atmosphere on the dock.*

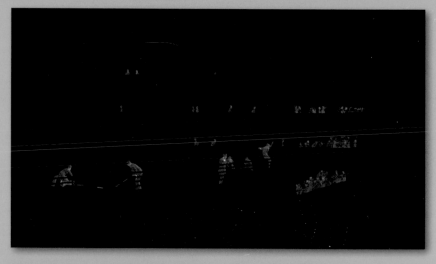

Plate 99 *An element featuring people that were on the ship.*

Plate 100 *An element featuring a group of people on the dock.*